The first eight pages of this book are printed
on treefree® paper hemp paper made by
John Hanson of Lyme Regis.

This work has been published by Whitaker Publishing.
Unit F03, Acton Business Centre, School Road,
London, NW10 6TD, United Kingdom

email address: info@whitakerpublishing.com

Whitaker Publishing

First published in 2006

Printed by POLPRINT 63 Jeddo Road, London W12 9EE
Bound by MARBA BOOK BINDING

Hemp for Victory

History and qualities of the world's most useful plant

Editors and senior authors:
Kenyon Gibson,
Nick Mackintosh and Cindy Mackintosh

Foreword by Woody Harrelson

Contributing authors:
John Quincy Adams, Paul Benhaim, J.P. Darien,
Yves de Saussure, Mina Hegaard,
Samuel C.H. Heslop and Mikhail Lubin

Earliest known depiction of hemp.
Jomon period (ca. 5500 B.C.)
Kyushu Island, Japan.
Courtesy of the Dave Olson collection.
www.taima.org

FOREWORD

In 1994, soon after my involvement with a campaign to stop a senate bill allowing the deforestation of six million acres of U.S. National Forest in Montana, I wanted to further my knowledge about alternative industries that didn't require destruction of ancient trees. It became a personal mission to find a sustainable alternative to the wood-based paper industry. I happened upon a revolutionary book titled, *The Emperor Wears No Clothes*, by Jack Herer. At the time, it was the leading resource and historical guide about hemp. It was easy to become an avid spokesperson for hemp as I discovered its wide range of uses, including food, medicine, paper, plastics and fuel.

I am the first to say that I've done a lot of stupid things in my life; a lot of friends think my advocacy for hemp has been hurtful to my career and certainly I have gathered more media flack for hemp than anything else (except promoting peace). But I think in the long run I care less about being smart than being right. And I believe this economy, with the various industries (petrochemicals, pharmaceuticals, paper, mining, etc.) that comprise the many arms and legs of the 'BEAST', (as I affectionately call it), is strangling the life and soul out of our planet. We need to become sustainable and hemp, with its '25,000 uses', could be the slingshot that fells the beast, because in the macro sense, the beast is the modern Goliath, threatening a Mother Earth David.

What you hold in your hands now is the next generation of information about the undeniable value of the hemp plant. *Hemp for Victory* is perhaps the most comprehensive history and collection of information about hemp to date. I have no doubt that the emperor of the hemp movement himself, Jack Herer, would be proud of *Hemp for Victory*. In this day and age when educating ourselves is crucial for a paradigm shift, this book is a must read.

Woody Harrelson,
London, 2006

INTRODUCTION

There should be no necessity for an apology or an excuse for preparing a work upon hemp culture at this time. The hemp plant is the most widely diversified and, commercially and industrially, the most important plant in cultivation in Europe. It was among the first introduced into America, and one of the most extensive in cultivation among the colonists; and there is no good reason existing why it should not, but every reason why it should, today be among the first as the basis of another great and grand national industry, employing hundreds of millions of capital and hundreds of thousands of work-people.

These words, penned by Samuel Boyce, served well in 1900, for which reason they have been chosen as the opening lines in this present work. Not without irony, as the nation in which Boyce lived and wrote was a major proponent of hemp. One of its presidents chose to make notes on the cultivation of hemp and his work is reprinted here, after having been first published as part of government record. This was John Quincy Adams, who, after a glorious career as an ambassador, or minister as they were called in his day, became the sixth President of the United States. Previous presidents were also supportive of hemp.

The current situation does not reflect their attitudes, but rather ignores scientific and economic advice. Hemp, with all its benefits, is hard to suppress. Those who do are often fantasists, and the sensible must contend with their extreme views as they restore a profitable industry with its plethora of benefits.

At this moment in history we are inundated with the word 'patriotism', used to exhort any range of actions, sensible or otherwise. Thomas Jefferson encouraged Americans to grow hemp for such a reason, calling for them to do so for economic stability and military might. One might use such an argument today, not just in the US, but in any country where hemp may be grown.

For those familiar with the current hemp laws, the thought of Jefferson talking about hemp conjures up an irony, as he would be arrested for growing hemp, since certain interests have affected the laws of the country which he worked so hard to build.

Early Americans were not the only advocates of hemp. This is a plant which man has used for millennia; wearing it, hunting with it, sailing by force of its fibres, catching the daily meal with hempen nets, and preparing those meals with hemp seeds and their oil. Many places on the earth are named after hemp, such as Hempstead, Southampton, Hempville, or Bangladesh; Cana, the town in which Christ performed his first miracle, may well have been the Hebrew word for 'Hemptown' in his day, and the disciples most likely used its fibres, superior as they were, for their nets and ropes. Mention of hemp in the Bible exists prior to their time, as hemp oil was used for anointing. Hemp was esteemed for its strength as well as for a certain spiritual essence.

Archaeological record places hemp at 10,000 B.C., from which date consistent use is made of hemp in textiles, cordage, energy, oil, paper, medicine and countless other ways. That history is traced in the first part of this book, which is divided into geographical regions.

The second part examines the different applications, and is written by authors who have a practical knowledge of the hemp industry from first hand involvement in existing businesses, such as Mina Hegaard (of Minawear Hemp Clothing) and Paul Benhaim, (author of *H.E.M.P.* and a consultant to the British government). There is surrounding hemp a great controversy, mostly concerning its medicinal uses, which are covered in this part. THC occurs in the flowers and leaves of all strains of hemp, although the small amount present in most varieties is not enough to consider smoking, or, on the other hand, worrying about. It is much a matter of convenience for certain parties to exploit that fact when trying to prohibit all types of cannabis. If we take a look at the products made from cannabis, we see the reason in the argument for hemp, and question the motives of those opposed, no matter how much they try to appear as guardians of public morality.

The 'how of hemp' is examined in the third part; botany, cultivation, processing, and machinery. Much of this is written for those actually working with hemp, and compares notes from hundreds of years of growers and processors. G.A. Berti's *La Coltivazione della Canape* (ca. 1657) and Robert Wissett's *On the Cultivation and Preparation of Hemp* (1804) are compared to later works, including the very recent *Advances in Hemp Research* by Paulo Ranalli and *The Cultivation of Hemp* by Dr. Ivan Bócsa and Michael Karus. Comparison of older methods with newer techniques is presented for the purpose of providing a full range of views into the growing and processing of hemp. In some instances, modern methods have not been redeveloped, and it is well worth studying what was before our time; in many details, especially in that of retting, those older works will be essential to anyone working with hemp.

Part Four, 'The Many Fields of Hemp', looks at the topic from different angles, examining its place in art, commerce, language, the environment, literature, etc. Hemp's place in commerce, for instance, is looked at with notes on businesses that exist today, from Minawear in California to publicly traded businesses. Technical chapters are also included, explaining cellulose, dioxin and 'other' hemps; a final chapter on etymology shows both a linguistic and a historical progression.

As this has been written by many authors, and as the English language is not standardised in all regards world-wide, there will be differences in spelling and style between them, which have been left in on purpose, to allow each their own voice. In addition, there are numerous quotes from ealier sources and these also have been left in their original form, including punctuation and measurements.

In the appendices one will find a nineteenth century medical essay on hemp, a select bibliography and a resource guide listing businesses that sell hemp.

Seven years a-growing, this book is intended as an interesting read for all, hopefully encouraging many who have not heard of hemp to get involved. Some parts of it are technical, they may be more for those who work with hemp. There is a great wealth of information regarding hemp, but as it has passed into obscurity, some of this material is only re-emerging for the first time in centuries between these covers. The hemp industry needs to catch up in this highly advanced world, and the more knowledge available to those who are perfecting it the faster it will once again be a part of our lives.

Some people at this time will no doubt continue their opposition to hemp, whether out of malice or simply from folly, so that there is a struggle going on with this issue. Thus, a history of hemp brings us into the present, with laws being changed back-and-forth. As hemp once posed a threat to some investors, so it does again today; for which reason, some would rather leave the issue alone and allow the few to exercise power over the many. As storms destroy whole cities and ocean currents are changing their ways, we may not be able to allow these 'chosen' few to remain in power. Ill-begotten wealth often breeds contempt, afflicting the public with malicious fools who will stay in power as long as they can, using any trick they can conjure up, from war to religious sentiment to keep knowledge from others. Hosea, speaking in ancient Israel, warned of the fate of those from who chose to be ignorant: "Without knowledge, the people perish."

Conversely, it can be said that with knowledge people prosper, and it is in this hope that I have taken the effort to write on hemp. With such a commodity, many postive changes can be put in place from which we can all benefit. I also write to entertain, as the history of hemp is an amusing study, and only takes on the tone of a polemic when discussing the dishonesty involved in its suppression. The history of hemp is much a history of the human race, as hemp was ubiquitous.

For the historical record alone, a book on hemp is worth writing, and I hope the reader will enjoy this tome and also join in the struggle to revive this crop, the Phoenix of the vegetable kindom.

Kenyon Gibson
Chiswick, 2006

DEDICATION AND ACKNOWLEDGEMENTS

This book is dedicated to William Kingsland and William Rodriguez. The former helped with the production from the very beginning by proofreading and researching. Sadly, he passed away at his home in Manhattan just a month before publication. He will be missed greatly by myself and other authors of this book, as well as by his neighbours, with whom he shared a passion for architectural history and landmarks conservation. The latter has provided much inspiration, as he has himself been in a process of bringing facts to light which some have tried to suppress. Rodriguez was the last man out alive from the North Tower on 9/11, after having stayed in to save the lives of many others, acts for which he has received a Congressional Medal of Honour. I hope that this book helps to shed light on the forces which suppressed his testimony, as they are much the same that worked to create a disinformation campaign about hemp.

In addition to these two, I owe a word of thanks to many others. First among those are the Mackintoshes, Nick and Cindy, who shared the senior authorship of this work and caused this project to take form. The title was chosen by them in August of 2001, and it has now proven most appropriate. Other authors, John Quincy Adams (a posthumous contributor), Paul Benhaim, J. P. Darien, Yves de Saussure, Mina Hegaard, Samuel C.H. Heslop and Mikhail Lubin have all added much to this. The first on that list is well known as having been the sixth President of the United States. Paul Benhaim is also well known, especially in the hemp world, as he is the author of previous books and a tireless campaigner for hemp. J.P. Darien is a botanist whose specialty is neo-tropical cryptogams. Yves de Saussure also writes on hemp, his own book having appeared in 2002. Mina Hegaard is the founder of Minawear Hemp Clothing and is the person who originally inspired this book to be written. Samuel C.H. Heslop is a hemp campaigner who is currently working on hemp paper production and distribution in Europe. Mikhail Lubin is a student of Slavic languages.

In the rare book trade Chris Baron, Joel Block, Don Conner, Steve Feldman, Mike and Sue Lowell, Rudiger Mach, Raymond Sutton and Tony Swann supplied valuable material from which to source. Larry Chase of Largo Stamps in New York City provided stamps.

However much effort went into the writing, formatting and publishing, there is the prior work of earlier sources, without which this book would not have been. Anyone familiar with the modern hemp movement must have heard of *The Emperor Wears no Clothes*, by Jack Herer. It was this author who tracked down a wealth of information in the 1980s, even finding 'missing' material in the Library of Congress.

A decade later, John C. Lupien wrote his master's thesis on the 'demonization' of hemp; a work that explores in detail the history behind the legislation against cannabis, it is his research that has shed much light on the anti-hemp movement.

Further, Gerard Colby Zilg provided a wealth of information in his 1974 exposé of Du Pont. While not about hemp, it describes the indescribable. It is now a scarce book, due in part to the efforts of his subject, whom he took to court for suppressing his freedom of speech. In 1984 he reprinted his book, with yet more of the sordid history of this corporation. These authors and dozens of others have all contributed to this present historical monograph.

It was in California that research for the book first began, getting off to a good start with the help of a British ex-pat, Alison Corke. Others in the US who gave assistance and encouragement include: Dana Beal, Denis Cicero, Chris Conrad, Deborah Daly, Justin Dennis, John Dvorak, Dr. Sezar Fesjian, Jimmy Fitzpatrick, John Kaminski, Harley Kelley, Dave Olson, Gene and Christine Philcox, Rich Ray, Diane Reifer, John Roulac, John Shannon, Eddie and Ausra Silkaitis, Nick Swerdlow, Michael Stranger and Peter Vroutos.

From the sunny coasts of California to the banks of the Thames the staff at a number of libraries have helped this along, anonymous individuals but not forgotten for their part in this undertaking. The University of California system, the New York Public Library, the Library of Congress, Trinity College Library Dublin, the University of Edinburgh Library, the Scottish Library, and finally, the British Library, were all institutions in which a great store of writings relating to hemp were to be found, along with a friendly and professional staff.

Hemp for Victory was mostly written in the UK, where assistance and encouragement was received from: Juliette Atkinson, Derek Bielby, Jane and Tania Blonder, Nick Chow, George Davies, Paul Dean, Osborne Douglas, Andria Efthimiou, Alex Frowen, Leah Georgiades, Woody Harrelson, Stephen Haude, John Humphrys, Dr. Nick Kollerstrom, Laura Louie, Karen McGeachen, Annie Machon, Paul Morgan, Keith Mothersson, Steve Pank, Gary Pearce, Colin Preece, Bobby Pugh, Sue Riddlestone, Chris Sanders, David Shayler, Tony Taylor, Mark Upton and Matthew Wild.

From other lands assistance came from: Sirdar Mohamed Osman, Israel Shamir, Dr. Jevgeni Shergalin, Roger Snow and Dr. Hayo van der Werf.

Special mention belongs to Tony Gosling, for editing advice; John Hanson, for research; Diana Mackintosh, for help with a difficult Italian translation; and also to Martin Buchan, who in the last stages patiently created the final layout, sorting through the plethora of images, sidebars and tables to cogently present it as a whole piece, woven together with the text on the silver screen of his computer, the anvil on which the work was forged into shape.

CONTENTS

PART THREE: Methods

PART FOUR: The Many Fields of Hemp

APPENDICES

PART ONE

WORLD WIDE HISTORY

...whatever makes the past, the distant, or the future, predominate
over the present, advances us in the dignity of thinking beings.

Samuel Johnson
Journey to the Western Islands

I. Early Roots

KENYON GIBSON, NICK MACKINTOSH
AND CINDY MACKINTOSH

*T*he story of hemp begins in Asia, where this plant has been grown and used for millennia. Looking back, and imagining for a few moments an early scenario of a bygone era, we might conjure up an image of a dawn breaking gently over a river, the rising sun warming the water and sending a mist over the boats that line the river's banks, through which can be seen people who are starting to rise from their slumber; the sunlight grows brighter and then more lights, adding a touch of red, break through the haze as the river inhabitants kindle fires, over which they sling pots to brew their tea. A fog enshrouds all this, and then, as if by signal, disappears. The sun, now higher in the sky and more energetic, appears to direct the stage from its great celestial distance, as the last wisps of vapour disappear, like white smoke over the surface of the water, which is now taking on a mellow, golden hue.

Into these traces of fog, and over the reflection of sun and sky, go the boats that are the means of support for many of the villagers. They line this stretch of the village, tied with hempen lines to their posts, swaying gently in the tide at night, waiting to take their passengers to work during the day.

On a few of these vessels can be seen bamboo palanquins on which teams of cormorants wake and start to preen, oiling themselves in anticipation of the day which they will spend diving for their meals and that of their keepers. Sleek creatures of the river, at first stark black, then bronze and green in colour, they are graceful in their task, a form of fishing which has been practiced both from necessity and for the pleasure of seeing them perform, an aquatic form of the sport of falcony. Other boats carry fishermen who will secure their catch by simpler means, as they will cast upon the surface of the water hemp seeds which will instantly attract fish, brought to the surface by this nutritious meal. Fishing by line is also practiced, and this again utilises the hemp plan, the stalks of which provide the twine. Nets are used as well, and these too are produced with fibres from the hemp plants.

As boats pass the last of the houses, the fields come into view where rice, beans, tea and hemp are growing, all staples of the region. This last mentioned crop towers above the others like masses of living emerald green, saturated with blazing sunlight, as the Kentucky author James Lane Allen so eloquently described hemp growing in his own part of the world. It is from these plants that the villagers will make clothes, nets, oil and other necessities. Noted for its strength and flexibility, the hunters and soldiers use it to string their bows.

The Orient has given to civilisation many of her treasures, including knowledge of medicines, spices, falconry and a plethora of products one takes for granted in the West. Of all these gifts, the most useful, and presently most controversial, is hemp. This is a fibre producing plant of the Cannabinaceae family, the roots of which go deeply into the culture of most Asian nations, whose inhabitants have utilised it for food, paper, cordage, textiles and medicine. Archaeological evidence from a relic found in Taiwan places such use as early as 10,000 BC[1]. Similar remains from Mainland China have been dated at 8,000 BC. Here hemp was widespread and commonly used, long before any Europeans were aware of it. In the *Lu Shi* of 500 AD (Sung Dynasty), mention is made of an emperor from 2,800 BC who taught people to use hemp cloth.[2] This work mentions its use in medicine as does a major section of the *Pen T'sao Kang Mu*, a Ming Dynasty pharmacopoeia. According to that work, hemp was of a 'superior' quality and had a calming influence on the physiology. It was said to aid the growth of the body's muscle fibre, bring an improvement to the hair on the head, increase the flow of mother's milk, and benefit the *Qi* (the vital force or life energy). Note is also made of hemp's culinary role, perhaps reinforced by the consensus that hemp imports fertility and strength, slowing down the ageing process and helping to attain the status of *Shen Xian* (Divine Genie).[3] The use of hemp continued into the twentieth century, as noted by anthropologist Berthold Laufer,[4] and Ralph Loziers, general counsel for the National Oil Seed Institute in 1937. Loziers informed the US House Ways and Means Committee: "Cannabis sativa L. is used in all of the Oriental nations. It is grown in their fields and used as oatmeal. Millions of people everyday are using hemp seed in the Orient as food. They have been doing that for many generations, especially in periods of famine."[5]

Perhaps the most famous use that the Chinese made of hemp was the production of paper. It is a popular explanation that Ts'ai Lun first used hemp for paper in 105 AD. In one version of this discovery, he also invented the first papermaking mould.[6] For centuries this craft remained a state secret. The Arabs managed to get a hold of this knowledge in the middle of the eighth century when they conquered Chinese craftsmen at Samarkand, and brought these skills to the Middle East and beyond. This account is widely accepted, though it may be only a popular tale; recent evidence shows that there had been paper in China prior to Ts'ai Lun.

With all these applications, hemp was continuously in demand in China and was grown throughout, with the possible exception of the extreme south, as the American agronomist Lyster Dewey noted in 1913. One variety, the *Ta-ma* (great hemp), which is cultivated chiefly in the provinces of Chekiang, Kiangsu and Fukien, grows up to fifteen feet. Kentucky growers sought this and similar varieties. It had dark seed; large leaves, and long slender branches, and did well as a rotation crop, alternating with rice in lowland soils.[7]

An eighteenth century historical note shows that Chinese hemp was cultivated to a great standard and that there was demand for it also in Britain, where Keane Fitzgerald grew a crop that attained a height of fourteen feet. He wrote: "as the culture of so valuable a kind of hemp as this promises to produce appears to be of consequence to a maritime and commercial kingdom, I have applied to the Directors of the East India Company, to give proper orders to their factors and super-cargoes in China, to procure some of the best seed that can be obtained."[8]

Christian missionaries were a key source of such exports, as they noted the qualities of the Chinese varieties. Vance seed was another favourite of the Kentucky farmer, named after an American who procured it from a connection he had in France.[9] In 1852 another variety, *So-Na*[10] was taken to Kentucky and Louisiana. Many types of hemp grow in China as the wide range of soil and climate favour the development of varietal differences.[11] Most have names containing the word *Ma*, which character depicts a male and female plant hung upside down to dry. *Ma* is the earliest known word for hemp, believed to be the origin of hemp in any language.

Recent records show that hemp continued to be cultivated in China into the twentieth century, diminishing during the instability of the 1940s and 1950s, but recovering steadily at the rate of one percent a year from 1954-1974, with Sansu, Qinghai, Ningxai, Inner Mongolia, Shanxi, and Yunnan as the leading production centres.[12] Yunnan especially has a rich history of hemp production, as it figures into the economy of the region, where it is used for ceremonial purpose, including the making of burial shrouds.[13] Professor Erik Mueggler describes this in detail in his 1998 article "The Poetics of Grief and the Price of Hemp in Southwest China," citing hemp production as "central to the domestic economy in Zhizuo and its surrounding mountain through most of the twentieth century."[14] The fact that hemp could be grown in areas that no other crop could be produced made it a very practical harvest, even though external forces caused great fluctuation in the cost of hemp during the last century.

In the 1980s hemp production increased in answer to world-wide demand, and aided by improvements made to the de-gumming process in Shangdong.[15] Much of China's hemp output is used for textiles, and exported to the West. In addition to the long heritage of hemp growing that is part of Chinese culture, several other factors work to China's advantage in this industry. One is growing consumer awareness, another is the prohibition of hemp in some countries, and a third is the lack of machinery in the West that can process hemp textiles. In 1997 China produced 36 percent of the world's hemp fibre, and 73 percent of the world's hemp grain.[16] Her imports go to over a dozen countries, some whose laws prohibit the growing of hemp. China is at present increasing its cultivation of this crop, which is much her birthright, a growing part of her manufacturing empire.

T 'ang-Ma (cold hemp), grown in the mountains of Central China, was used primarily for the production of seeds, with the stalks used for fuel.

Hsien-Ma, grown in Manchuria, which was used for fibre, attained a height of 8-9 feet, and matured in 150 days.

Shem-Ma, also grown in Manchuria, but used for oil seed, attained a height of 3-5 feet, and matured in 100 days. It has been noted that these last two varieties remain distinct without crossing or producing any intermediate forms.

Shane-Ma-tse, cultivated in the mountains and valleys of Shansi and Chihli, Northern China.

Hoa-Ma, the most important fibre plant of western China, grown in Szechwan and as a winter crop on the plains of Chengtu in that province.

Hsiao Ma is a name used in Northern China to distinguish hemp from the castor oil plant, which is also called *Ta-Ma*.

Huo-Ma is a word meaning 'fire hemp seed', commonly used by traditional Chinese pharmacists to denote the cleaned hemp seeds. These seeds are incorporated into local herbal stomach remedies.

Si-Ma and *Tsu-Ma* are words used to designate the staminate and pistillate forms, respectively. Other forms of the word *Ma*, such as *Ch'u-Ma*, may signify similar fibre plants.

Several other names using the word *Ma* are used for fibre plants, such as *Ch'ing-Ma, Huang Ma, Ch'u-Ma*, for abolition hemp, Indian jute and China grass respectively. In addition to *Da-Ma*, (great hemp), the Chinese vernacular terms for cannabis include *Xian-Ma*, (line hemp), and *Huang - Ma*, (yellow hemp). The fruits of cannabis are called *Ma-Zi*, (hemp seed). The female inflorescence is called *Ma Fen*, fragrant hemp branch. The terms *Ta-Ma, Xian-Ma* and *Huang-Ma* for the plants and their products and *Da-Ma Zi* or simply *Ma Zi* for the fruits are usually applied to the fibre and seed producing *C. sativa* cultivars and landraces.

JAPAN

Across the sea from China the Japanese were also using hemp, as early as 5500 BC during the Jomon period. An early cave painting from this period (which serves as the frontispiece to this book) was discovered on the southern island of Kyushu, which is Japan's closest island to the mainland. From other images painted alongside of it, there seems to be a connection with maritime trading, suggesting that hemp was brought to Japan by ship. Princess Shotoku sponsored the first recorded printing in the eighth century AD, and hemp fibres have been used for paper ever since in Japan.[18]

In the late nineteenth century Japanese hemp was exhibited at the World's Colombian Exposition. Noted for its fineness, it won critical acclaim as a highly prized commodity.[19] A 1913 article in the *USDA Yearbook* gives a description of Japanese hemp culture as follows:

> Hemp, called 'asa' in the Japanese language, is cultivated chiefly in the provinces or districts of Hiroshima, Tochigi, Shimane, Iwate, and Aidzu, and to a less extent in Hokushu (Hjokkaido) in the north and Kiushu in

the south. It is cultivated chiefly in the mountain valleys, or in the north on the interior plains, where it is too cool for cotton and rice and where it is drier than on the coastal plain. That grown in Hiroshima, in the south, is tall, with a rather coarse fiber; that in Tochigi, the principal hemp-producing province, is shorter, 5 to 7 feet high, with the best and finest fiber, and in Hokushu it is still shorter.[20]

The *Nōmin Seikatsushi*, an encyclopaedia of farming, relates the following:

Asa is a fibre plant that has been used since old times and used to be called *kingusa.* Before cotton it was the main source of material for clothes for people. Already in the Middle Ages it was a commercial product. The *Hokuriku* area was the major growing area. In modern days it was gradually overtaken by cotton, but since its fibre was very strong it continued to be used for nets, ropes, floor mats, mosquito nets and summer clothes. Major growing areas were Yamato, Omi and Echigo.[21]

The 1913 record gives further directions:

Seeds from Hiroshima, Shimane, Aidzu, Tochigi, and Iwate were experimented with by the United States Department of Agriculture in 1901-1902. The plants showed no marked varietal differences. They were all smaller than the best Kentucky hemp. The seeds varied from light grayish brown, 5mm (1/5") long, to dark gray, 4mm (1/6") long. The largest plants in every trial plot were from Hiroshima seeds, and these seeds were larger and lighter coloured than those of any other variety except Shimane, the seeds of which were slightly larger and the plants slightly smaller.[22]

Japanese religious ceremonies used hemp for driving away evil spirits, in marriage and to invoke spirits. Shinto priests wore special hempen clothes, as did the royal family because of hemp's traditional association with purity. This may account for the royal status conferred on hempen garments. But hemp's place was not restricted to ceremonial and religious rites. It was well known for its practical uses and the durability of the fibre, for which reason it was commonly used for rope. An old Japanese legend tells of a peasant girl who fastened the end of a ball of hemp to the garment of her lover when he bade her good-bye without telling her his name. The thread led to the temple of Miva, revealing the priestly origin of the stranger.[23]

In the twentieth century the artist Shimizu painted the celebrated work *Taima Shukaku*, meaning 'Hemp Harvest.' This work, which depicted a long-standing tradition in his country, was a finalist in a

Tourism promotional brochure from the town of Miasa in Nagana Prefecture, Central Honshu, Japan. The Kanji characters across the top depict *Mi* = Beautiful and *Asa* = Hemp. The *Asa* Kanji is drawn to represent hemp plants drying from the rafters of a shed. Other images of current hemp crops in Japan, woodcuts and paintings can be found at *www.giggling-piglet.com* and *www.taima.org* Courtesy of Dave Olson.

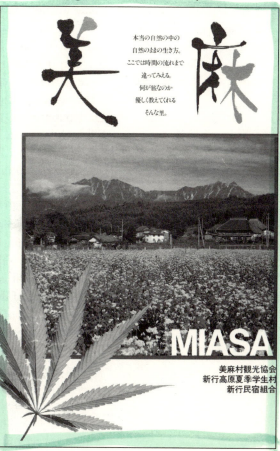

national competition.[24] Cultivation was greatly cut back, however, during the US occupation, but has resumed to a degree with the recent awareness of hemp's value to the economy. One modern use of it is in a traditional condiment called *shichimi*, where ground hemp seed, known as '*ono mi*', is added to a spice mix often served with ramen noodles.[25] Today, cultivation is under study for use especially in areas where organic farming principles decree natural forms of pesticide and proper crop rotation.

INDIA, NEPAL & THE HIMALAYAS

The word 'bhanga' occurs in the *Sanskrit Atharvaveda* (ca.1400 BC)[26] and the first known mention of hemp as a medicine occurs in the work of Suskota, from before the eighth century AD,[27] and is advised for use in veterinary medicine in a work written by Raja Rudradeva of Kumaon in the sixteenth century.[28] An earlier record includes a sample of hemp paper with Sanskit characters dated to the second or third century AD.[29] In 1563 Garcia Da Orta, the Portuguese writer, published his *Colloquies on the Simples and Drugs of India*.[30] Well-known to all who are interested in the botany and pharmacy of India, it became a standard reference work, containing the first mention of many important plants. While Da Orta's mention of cannabis is limited, it planted the seed in the minds of many Europeans that *Cannabis sativa* was to be found in India. Ultimately the British were to gain the most influence on the sub-continent, and they made further extensive study and use of this plant.

> Japanese hemp is of excellent quality, and appears in trade in the form of very thin ribbons, smooth and glossy, of a light straw colour, the frayed ends showing a fibre of great fineness.
> *Matthews' Textile Fibres,* **1938**

Towards the end of the eighteenth century the East India Company sent Dr. William Roxburgh, a botanist, to India to study fibre plants. Dr. Roxburgh wrote many articles on hemp and other fibre plants, which were gathered into one collection and published after his death. In 1855 J. Forbes Royle made further studies of these, adding his own observations. Dr. Roxburgh in the year 1800 thought Rohilcund and the neighbouring hills suited to the cultivation of hemp, noting:

> I have seen it in great abundance, in a wild state, in the Deyra Doon, and also in the Khadir land of the Saharunpore district, especially along the upper part of the Doab Canal, and where it was chiefly valued for its leaves; being made into bhang and subjee, and the stems, when dried up, being burnt for firewood.
>
> There would be little difficulty in cultivating this plant in low Khadir land, where it is wild; nor in converting it into merchantable Hemp. For the natives of the neighbourhood already make use of it, partially for the manufacture of ropes; and the inhabitants of Malabar are said by Dr. H. Scott to employ the Hemp for making their fishing nets. This fact, though not generally known, is mentioned by Kirkpatrick in his account of Nepal, and was ascertained by General Hardwick, in his visit to Srinuggur, as well as by myself, when travelling in the Himalayas…I also obtained specimens of the rope and cloth when travelling there, but which I regret I am unable now to find. The plant I have seen in a very luxuriant state at least ten or twelve feet high, in the Himalayas, at elevations of 6000 and 7000 feet,

especially in the neighbourhood of buffalo-sheds. In such situations and near villages it could no doubt be easily cultivated to a great extent, and yield a valuable and profitable product.

The hemp could likewise be cultivated in the plains at two seasons of the year; that is, during the rainy season, as is now the case, but likewise along with the cold-weather cultivation, which is so similar to that of the summer culture of European countries.[31]

Though hemp was widespread in India and Nepal, not all partook of its cultivation or use, as one British observer, a Mr. Bolten wrote in 1854: "Cultivators of this crop are chiefly of the caste of Kolee and Deyra Doons, the latter and other Doons, commonly of the same tribe which furnishes Agurees, or miners, are the only persons who can manufacture the Bhungela, or Hempen stuff."[32] A Mr. Strechley that same year recorded a negative saying uttered by Brahmins regarding hemp: "*Tera ghur bhung bono holo*" (May hemp be sown in your house).[33]

Hemp Imported from India, and Sold in England			
From: *The Fibrous Plants of India,* by J. Forbes Royle, 1855			
	Cwt*		Cwt
1803	4820	1807	4738
1804	833	1808	4023
1805	3399	1809	1543
1806	6421	1810	2555
*Note – cwt = 121 lbs/51 kls.			

In 1804, Robert Wissett, a clerk of the British East India Company, wrote a treatise concerning the cultivation and uses of hemp. Fibre cordage was important both to everyday living, and for the building of infrastructures. Of the forty or more plants used for cordage in India, true hemp (*Cannabis sativa*), was one of the most preferred.[34] Royle cites its use in the Himalayas: "...they make a course sack cloth...as well as the strongest ropes for crossing their broad and rapid rivers."[35] To the strength of this region's hemp Major Heber Drury also testifies in *The Useful Plants of India*: "...in point of strength and durability as evidence by the samples produced, there is no doubt that good Himalayan hemp is superior to Russian hemp; at any rate proof exists that it can be produced of a superior quality."[36] This was put to the test in 1853 by D.F. MacLead, Esq., comparing samples from Kote Kangra, in the Sikh Himalayas, with China-grass and Petersburg hemp. The China-grass was found to break with 320 lb., the Petersburg hemp at 160 lb., but the Kote Kangra hemp did not break even at 400 lb. of test weight; it "...appeared to all the practical men who have since then examined it, as the strongest fibre with which they were acquainted."[37] Royle includes other accounts, such as that of a Captain H. Hoddleston (1840):

The real Hemp, or cultivated kind, is grown chiefly on high lands, and principally on the northern faces of the mountains, in well prepared and abundantly manured soils close to villages, or in recently cleared lands by burning the primeval forests, the soil of which, from the accumulated decomposed vegetable matter of years, is rich enough to ensure the superior growth of the plant and an abundant crop without any manure for one season. No irrigation is ever resorted to, and very little is produced under an elevation of 3000 feet, the heat of the valleys being detrimental to its quality, and the plant appears to flourish best at elevations of from between 4000 to 7000 feet.

In India it is believed that by burying the hemp seed in the head of a snake, the plant will grow strong.

The middling district situated between the "Pindur" to the north and the "Nyar" or "Samee" rivers to the south, and centrically with regard to the province of Kumaon and Gurhwal, may be termed the chief Hemp-producing districts of British Burhwal. The fields nearest to villages, as being the easiest for manuring, and the culturable wastes with a rich soil of accumulated rotten vegetation, or recently cleared forest lands, being those in which the Hemp plant is alone cultivated to advantage with respect to its quality.

The culture of "Bhang" or Hemp, as practiced in this district, is as follows: After the ground has been well cleared and prepared, the seed is sown, towards the end of May, or early in June, at the rate of 20 or 25 pathas, equal to about 26 or 33 seers (from 52 lb. to 66 lb. Avoirdupois) per beesee, which latter is the common denomination now used in Gurhwal, and very near equal to an English acre. During the early growth of the plant the ground is kept free from all weeds, and the young plants are thinned, leaving a few inches between each, and until the crop has attained a good height, the ground is kept clean from all rank vegetation – after which it attains to the height of twelve and fourteen feet, and is cut in September and November.

Of this cultivated Bhang there are two kinds, the plant called Goolanga or Goolbhanga which produces seed (the female), and the one which only flowers, but has no seed; and this latter is called "Phoolbhang" (the male), from which the best sort of Hemp is prepared; the plants being cut a month or six weeks earlier, and producing a stronger and superior fibre to the other. On the stalks being cut green, they are dried for several days in the sun, by being piled against the walls of the terraced fields until they become quite brown.[38]

Quoting further sources, he adds: "Mr. Hodgson states, that the cultivation is peculiar to the Northern districts of Nepaul…The Northern districts (popularly called Cachar) are nevertheless the prime seats of culture, and there alone is the plant manufactured into rope or cloth; though the edible extracts are sometimes prepared nearer to and around Katmandhoo."[39] From an anonymous extract he then continues:

In the Himalayas the Hemp grows wild, and is, moreover, carefully cultivated both on account of its exhilarating secretions, and its strong and flexible fibre. With the properties of this the Hillmen are well acquainted, as they make with it both twine and rope, and a coarse cloth (bhangela) with which they clothe themselves, as well as make sacks and bags. Their hempen wrappers they wear much as a Highlander does his plaid, fixing it in front with a wooden skewer, instead of a brooch. The culture seems to be very well understood in most parts, though the best methods are not always practised either of planting, or of picking, or of preparing their Hemp. All along the Himalayas – that is in Nepaul, in Kemaon, in Gurhwal, and up to the newly acquired hills of the Punjab, at elevations of from 3,000 and 4,000 to 7,000 feet – Hemp is cultivated by the Hillmen, though chiefly for their own use, the plants growing to 8 or 10, some say 12 or 14, feet in height.[40]

In addition to fibre cultivation, the Indians grew hemp for medicinal purposes. In the nineteenth century Dr. William O'Shaughnessy wrote a treatise detailing the medical uses. At the time it drew attention to the properties of cannabis, with the pharmacists of the time following his ideas and producing extracts from this plant. The most famous of all writings on Indian hemp is J.M. Campbell's *The Indian Hemp Drugs Commission Report of 1893 to 1894*. In this he strongly cautions against restricting cannabis as people use this for "...a solace in discomfort, a cure in sickness."[41] Both Hindus and Moslems throughout all classes of society used hemp medicinally, as did Queen Victoria.

Hemp continued to be grown early in the twentieth century, with India exporting 11,000 tons in 1904[42] and producing 36,000 tons in 1919.[43] Nepalese hemp cultivation was under way at that time; the tradition of such cultivation was documented in the July 1916 issue of *Deutsche-Hanfbau Gesellschaft*, which shows photographs of this mountain crop growing up to twenty feet high. The Indians have a thriving pharmaceutical industry at present, although cannabis products are no longer employed. The same may be said of the fibre industry, which today is supplied mostly by jute. However, there is one use which survives to modern times in India, and that is the planting of cannabis around food crops as a natural pesticide.

Hemp is still grown vigorously in the Himalayas: the progeny of earlier mentioned harvests grows on according to age old method in this region, when today a traveller can buy hats, belts, paper, baskets, oils, and other products made from locally grown hemp. Anita Roddick, founder of The Body Shop, has encouraged a regional paper making industry, under her 'trade not aid' philosophy of creating jobs and supporting fair trade.

THE MIDDLE EAST & ASIA MINOR

Early records show hemp in Çatal Hüyük around 8,000 BC.[44] Phrygian hemp remains from 800 BC have been found in Gordion, near present day Ankara,[45] and mention is made in cuneiform tablets from 650 BC. Shortly after the time of Christ, Pliny recommended hemp from Alabanda, a city of Cairn, in Asia Minor as the best. A tenth century treatise on hunting by a Syrian, Sid Mohamed El Mangali, records its use as twine for nets, and insists that it be used for certain game which require strong netting to keep down.[46] This same work also mentioned hemp seeds, as they were used in making bird lime.[47]

Hemp was used as food, as lamp oil, as medicine, and for making paper. The availability of paper enabled a great period of enlightenment in the Arab world, with many a Koran printed on hemp paper. Cannabis grows readily throughout the Middle East, and is harvested for fibre in Turkey (Asia Minor), noted as a "producing country of moderate importance" in the 1950s.[48] Presently this country is investing in studies on cultivation of hemp, especially as entry into the European Union would enable farmers to legally grow and harvest this crop.

As early as 751, the Arabians had learned and appropriated this process from some Chinamen who lived in Samarcand. In 794, they established the first imperial paper-factory in Bagdad and propagated this new industry throughout their country. They became so expert that they were able to manufacture the most varied kinds of paper, from the largest and heaviest writing paper for records and archives, to the very thin sheets required by the carrier-pigeon-post, organised by the government of the Califate in Bagdad. The raw vegetable fibres were soon replaced by hemp fibres, obtained by crushing the waste of (textiles). For three centuries they were apparently the monopolists of this industry.

Friedrich Keinz,
The Earliest Water-Marks, **1904**

9

1. Robinson, Rowan. *The Great Book of Hemp.* Rochester, (Vt), Park Street Press, 1996. p. 103
2. Dewey, Lyster H. "Hemp", article in *USDA Yearbook* 1913. Washington, GPO, 1914
3. Jones, Kenneth. *Nutritional and Medicinal Guide to Hemp Seed.* Gibsons, BC, Rainforest Botanical Library, 1996. p. 16
4. Laufer, Berthold. "The Domestication of the Cormorant in China and Japan" published in *Field Museum Natural History Anthropological Series XIII.* Chicago, 1931
5. Herer, Jack. *The Emperor Wears no Clothes.* Van Nuys, AH HA Publishing, 1998. p. 52
6. Snow, Phoebe. *How a Book is Made.* London, RKP, 1960. p.4
7. Dewey
8. Keane, Fitzgerald. Experiments with Chinese Hemp Seed, (in a letter to Sir Joseph Banks), published in the *Transactions of the Philosophical Society of London,* read 17 Jan. 1782
9. Hopkins, James. *A History of the Hemp Industry in Kentucky.* Lexington, University of Kentucky Press, 1998. p. 107
10. *Ib.,* p. 105
11. Dewey
12. Kaplan, Frederick M., Julian Subin and Stephen Anders. *Encyclopedia of China Today.* London & Basingstoke, Eurasia Press, 1979. pp. 19-65
13. Mueggler, Erik. "The Poetics of Grief and the Price of Hemp in Southwestern China." Published in the *Jour. of Asiatic Studies,* 1998
14. *Ib.*
15. Conrad, Chris. *Hemp: Lifeline to the Future.* Los Angeles, Creative Xpressions, 1994. p. 129
16. Nova Scotia Dept. of Agriculture and Marketing. *A Maritime Industrial Hemp Product: Marketing Study.* Nova Scotia, 1998
17. Benhaim, Paul. *H.E.M.P.: Healthy Eating Made Possible.* London, Fusion Press, 2000
18. Hunter, Dard. *Papermaking: The History and Technique of an Ancient Craft.* NY, Knopf, 1947
19. Dodge, Richard. "Hemp Culture", published in *USDA Yearbook,* 1895. Washington, GPO, 1896
20. *Ib.*
21. *Nômin Seikatshusi*
22. Dewey
23. Schaefer, Gustav. "Hemp" published in *CIBA Review 49,* 1945
24. This may be viewed at *http://www.taima.org/en/pictures.htm*
25. Benhaim, p. 37
26. Dewey
27. *Ib.*
28. Raja Rudradeva of Kumaon. *Syainika Sastra.* English translation made in 1910, Baptist Mission Press, Calcutta. Some authorities place this in the 16th century.
29. Hunter
30. Da Orta, Garcia. *Colloquies on the Simples and Drugs of India.* London, Henry Southeran, 1913
31. Royle, J. Forbes. *The Fibrous Plants of India.* London, Smith Elder & Co., 1855. p. 320
32. Gibson, Kenyon. *Hemp in the British Crown Colonies.* N.d., n.p.
33. *Ib.*
34. Royle, p. 316
35. *Ib.,* p. 327
36. Drury, Major Heber. *The Useful Plants of India.* Madras, Asylum Press, 1895. p. 109
37. Royle, p. 331
38. *Ib.,* pp. 321-322
39. *Ib.,* p. 325
40. *Ib.,* p. 323
41. Campbell, Dr. J.M. *The Indian Hemp Drugs Commission Report of 1893-1894.*
42. Carter, Herbert R. *The Twisting and Spinning of Long Vegetable Fibres.* London, Griffin & Co., 1904 p. 19
43. Woodhouse, J. and P. Kilgour. *Cordage and Cordage Hemp.* London, Sir Isaac Pitmann & Sons, 1919. p. 20
44. Conrad, p. 6
45. Godwin, Harry. "The Ancient Cultivation of Hemp" published in *Antiquity* vol. XLI, 1967
46. El Mangali, Sid Mohamed. *Traité de Vénerie,* Paris, E. Dento, 1880. p. 125
47. Gibson, Kenyon (ed.) *One Thousand Years of Falconry.* London, The Eryr Press, 2004. p. 2
48. UK Government Publication Office. *Commonwealth Economic Committee.* London, Her Majesty's Stationery Olffice, 1957. p. 177

II. Russia

MIKHAIL LUBIN, KENYON GIBSON,
NICK MACKINTOSH AND CINDY MACKINTOSH

*E*xtreme northern latitudes present a barrier to many forms of agriculture; for certain species, cultivation is out of the question. Hemp, however, is known to thrive in this part of the world, braving the cold in all parts. It "defies the utmost rigors of Siberian frosts,"[1] and is known to grow in the Uralian mountains.[2] In the mid-nineteenth century it was noted that: "Hemp is cultivated in almost every province of Russia, but in the largest quantities in the interior, beyond Moscow, as well as nearer Petersburg, and in the Polish provinces which belong to Russia."[3] A later report (1886) describes the distribution as follows: "The species has been found wild, beyond a doubt, south of the Caspian Sea; in Siberia, near the Irtysch; and in the Desert of Kirghiz, beyond Lake Baikal, in Dahuria (Government of Irkutsh). It is found throughout central and southern Russia and south of the Caucasus, but its wild nature here is less certain. I doubt whether it is indigenous in Persia, for the Greeks and Hebrews would have known of it earlier."[4] By the early twentieth century the chief growing areas were Orel, Poltova, Kalovga, Simbirsk, Thernigow, Mohielew, Koursk, Tambow and Smolenk.[5]

Russia not only grew hemp, but also processed it and exported it in great quantities; she was, in fact, the world's leading supplier for over two-hundred years. This may seem strange, in light of the facts that hemp grows well in so many other regions, and that some nations would have to send their ships halfway around the world to buy it.

The answer lies in the quality of Russian hemp, perfected through long-standing tradition, almost as old as that of China's. In the early nineteenth century Robert Wissett made note of Russia's supremacy in this market, and John Quincy Adams, while stationed at St. Petersburg as the American Minister, wrote an essay detailing modes of cultivation (included here as Chapter XVI). Most was grown on small patches of land, a practice which facilitated getting compost to enrich the soil. Fertilisation was not the only advantage; in 1845 Dr. Francis Campbell asserted:

> The result of long habit has enabled the Russians to excel every other people, as to dressing, sorting, and packing, but more especially in sorting this commodity. Each class... into which it is sorted has its different price as well as its particular distinction and use: and these are the reasons why Russian hemp always commands a ready market.[6]

Also important was the step of retting, (or rotting), the fibres from the stems. In Russia, this was undertaken in streams or retting ponds, thus 'water retted', as opposed to the more prevalent practice of dew-retting. When the hemp was left on the field to dew-ret in Russia, it was often covered by snowfalls and known as 'snow-retted'. This form of retting is inferior to water-retting, but superior to dew-retting.

Конопля – hemp
Коноплянка – linnet
Конопляный – hempen
Коноплянник – hemp field
Конопляное Масло – hemp seed oil
Конопляная Килоста – linoleic acid
Коноплевые – cannabinaceae
Пенъка – hemp fibre
Пенъковый – hempen
Пенъкопрядильня – hemp mill

Hemp was used domestically for ropes and canvas, as well as for other purposes; the Dukabours, a Christian vegetarian freedom sect, were known to have "enjoyed the nutritious but gritty hemp seed as part of their Spartan lifestyle in Russia,"[7] and Russians wore a great deal of the hemp they produced. Most Russian hemp was for sails and cordage, and strength was the desired characteristic. A 1907 record states that "...the fibre obtained from the cold northern districts of Russia is said to be the strongest of all."[8]

Russian hemp was what the mariners were used to and thus it was a necessity to cordage manufacturers. The Plymouth Cordage Co. in Massachusetts, for instance, used Russian hemp exclusively.[9] Russia became synonymous with hemp for the rope spinners in that state; James Duncan Phillips, a historian writing of Salem, notes that:

> St. Catherine's Day, the twenty-fifth of November, was the gala of the ropemaker. Little did they know about the saints of the Catholic Calendar, but the idea that St. Catherine was the Empress of Russssia, where most of the hemp came from, got all mixed up and made November twenty-fifth a good day for rope spinners to celebrate.[10]

So on this commodity the great maritime nations came to depend; they sent their traders to the chief ports of export, Rega, Pernou, Reval

> The soil likewise is much enriched by the manuring it receives from the snow, with which it is so long covered during winter; and in some measure produces the same good effects in Russia as the overflowing of the Nile does on the fertile plains of Egypt.
> *Essay on the European Method of Cultivating and Managing Hemp and Flax,* 1797

and St. Petersburg, where they could select from many different grades, primarily:

- St. Petersburg - divided into 1st sort, 2nd sort, 3rd sort and also; clean, outshot, and half-clean.
- Riga - separated into Rein, Drujana, outshot, pass, and codille, then later by the letters MR, BPH, and POH.
- Koenigsburg - including Rein or clean, the 1st sort, which was the best hemp; cut, Russian Chucken, Lithuanian Chucken, pass and tow (these were of a greenish shade).[11]

This trade was the focus of a bitter dispute, as Napoleon set out to stop the British from having the benefit of it for her navy. At that time Britain was Russia's largest customer, and Napoleon's wishes were not carried out by the Russian merchants.[12] He finally decided to invade, a decision which he was much to regret.

Etch'd by Reeve.

War has been a circumstance that causes most commodities to increase in price, and hemp was no exception to this rule. An 1845 report reads:

The price of hemp fluctuated greatly during the long war, and was sometimes exorbitantly high. In 1792, it was £25 per ton; and in 1808, it had risen to £118. Since the peace, however, the price has had a smaller range, and has fluctuated occasionally only between £25 and £50 per ton. But during the last few years, which form the best criterion, it has scarcely ever risen above £30, and never fallen below £25 the ton. There is another thing to be observed, as worth remembering, the price of hemp in the English market is almost uniformly highest in the months of May, June, July, and part of August, the demand being greatest in these months: the price is lowest in September. The average price for a number of years past, therefore, may be safely taken at about £27 per ton of 2,240 pounds.[13]

From Russia also we receive, for naval stores, and the coarser manufactures, no less than 40,000 tons, which, at present, costs, free on board, nearly 55l. per ton…
Essay on the European Method of Cultivating and Managing Hemp and Flax, **1797**

Total in Quantity of Hemp Exported from Riga to all Places in the Following Years From: *The Linen Trade of Europe,* by John Horner, 1920								
		1790	1791	1792	1793	1794	1795	1796
Hemp Resin	Sh.lb.	72,332	54,303	59,221	50,210	68,199	61,423	62,051
Do.Outshot	Do	2,286	2,061	4,222	5,998	9,121	7,831	12,498
Do.Pass	Do	9,107	11,801	14,834	18,847	16,443	13,027	13,587
Do Codille	Do	21,549	12,438	16,141	13,561	23,029	19,462	22,648
		1797	1798	1799	1800	1801	1802	1803
Hemp Resin	Sh.lb.	48,268	68,252	61,708	53,318	96,430	61,414	75,417
Do.Outshot	Do	7,142	14,470	11,142	8,000	12,549	9,397	6,161
Do Pass	Do	12,535	15,520	20,247	14,700	20,211	13,920	13,493
Do Codille	Do	21,755	27,559	26,470	26,218	22,588	27,150	17,497

Russian hemp prices later fluctuated due to war, going from £38 to £90 between 1851-1855,[14] but becoming more stable as other fibre sources were developed. Britain continued to buy Russian hemp into the early twentieth century, though abaca (Manila hemp) and modern technology decreased the need for hemp. In a strange irony it is noted that it was cheaper to buy Russian hemp than English hemp as the latter involved overland transport costs.[15] This was also the case some two hundred years earlier:

In the early 20th century, hemp was cultivated on peasant farms in Northern Russia close to the northern limit of agriculture, that is, the northern border of cultivation stretched from Arkhangelsk to Mezen (about 66°N) and further to Ust-Tsylma (about 65°N). ...hemp was cultivated in the extreme northeast of Russia, that is along the Kolyma river (about 65°N, 153°E).
Sergey Grigoryev,
Journal of Industrial Hemp,
[vol. 10: 2], **2005**

The rated value of imported Hemp (as stated in the account of imports printed by order of the House of Commons), was, at the commencement of 1807, about £600,000 per annum, which amount, Mr. Arthur Young remarks, indicates 60,000 acres, at £10 per acre. This supply has hitherto been derived principally from Russia, whose cultivators have been enabled to furnish British merchants with Hemp at a price so moderate, that, after the expenses of freight and charges of merchandise had been defrayed, it came to the consumer at a cheaper rate than if it had been grown in Britain. The cause of this superior cheapness has, in a respectable periodical work, been well assigned, viz. that lands in Russia are not "so fully occupied, either by inhabitants or by superior crops, as to be raised in value above what this commodity would repay to the cultivator;" while in Britain, "the rent of land, with the price of labour, and the operation of taxes of various descriptions, when added together, raised the price of the native production to more than and equality with that of the imported commodity,"- notwithstanding the legislators have offered a liberal bounty (3d. per stone) with the view of increasing its cultivation.[16]

After Britain, Russia's second largest customer was the US. This nation cultivated great amounts of hemp on its own, and even encouraged its farmers to water-ret the final product, but to no avail; the US Navy insisted on having Russian hemp, paying twice the price for it than for dew-retted Kentucky or Virginia fibre.

With the advent of metal ships, the demand for hemp declined. In 1904 Russia exported but 39,000 tons,[17] with prices ranging from £35 a ton for top quality Riga, to £24 a ton for St. Petersburg. A 1913 report notes:

> Hemp is cultivated throughout the greater part of Russia, and it is one of the principal crops in the provinces of Orel, Kursk, Samara, Smolensk, Tula and Voronezh. Two distinct types, similar to the tall fiber hemp and the short oil-seed hemp of Manchuria, are cultivated, and there are doubtless many local varieties in isolated districts where there is little interchange of seed. The crop is rather crudely cultivated, with no attempt at seed selection or improvement, and the plants are generally shorter and coarser than the hemp grown in Kentucky. The short oil-seed hemp with slender stems, about 30 inches high, bearing compact clusters of seeds and maturing in 60 to 90 days, is of little value for fiber production, but the experimental plants, grown from seed imported from Russia, indicate that it may be valuable as an oil-seed crop to be harvested and thrashed in the same manner as oil-seed flax.[18]

In 1919 Russia produced 427,000 tons,[19] but by 1937 production had decreased to 200,000 tons.[20] Most of this was by that time for domestic use; production never completely ceased, although the export market did. In 1931 the Institute of Bast Crops was founded; situated in the old city of Glokhiv, it became a centre for research in hemp seed production and breeding. It is the largest in this field, specialising in low THC varieties suitable for industrial use. In 1992 this institute was reorganised, and is now known as the Institute of Bast Crops of the Ukrainian Academy of Agrarian Sciences. Hemp production was at a peak in the Ukraine in 1960, when it was grown on 974,000 hectares, gradually diminishing to just under 60,000 hectares in 1993.[21] Currently the government of the Ukraine is studying the potential of hemp cultivation, with a view to enriching the prosperity of the region. The fact that hemp could be grown there, with the help of the local experts, and also processed into fibre, oil, building materials, and other goods, is of great value to the economy.

Russian Distaff
This style of distaff is peculiar to Russia. The right-angled board at the bottom is weighted or steadied by the foot of the operator, who works standing. On one side of the distaff Russian hemp is bound, on the other side flax; either material is spun by twisting the spindle between the fingers. In the Interior of Russia this mode of spinning coarse yarns is greatly in vogue.

One episode in Russian agricultural history that stands out is the story of the great plant geneticist Nikolai Vavilov. For those familiar with cannabis seed studies, his name brings to mind the Vavilov Research Institute in St. Petersburg. He was passionate about hemp, and in many ways a counterpart to Lyster Dewey who worked for the US Department of Agriculture. Like Dewey, he saw political shenanigans threatening his work, and sadly he was arrested and sent to one of Stalin's gulags shortly after the publication of his treatise *The Origin of the Cultivation of our Primary Crops, in Particular of Cultivated Hemp*. He was to die in this prison, but his work on hemp lives on, epitomised by his words: "...we shall go to the pyre, we shall burn, but we shall not renounce our convictions."[22] Vavilov's work will certainly live on, not only in Russia, but throughout the globe wherever hemp is grown. The institute named after him currently has the world's largest seed bank and continues to undertake research in his style... Viva Vavilov!

1. Campbell, Francis. *A Treatise on the Culture of Flax and Hemp.* Sydney, Statham & Forster, 1845. p. 80

2. US Congress. Report No. 381: *American Canvas, Cables, and Cordage.* Washington, 1830

3. Royle, J. Forbes, M.D. *The Fibrous Plants of India.* London, Smith, Elder & Co. 1855. p. 317

4. De Candole, Alphonse. *The Origin of Cultivated Plants.* 1886. p. 148

5. Carter, Herbert. *The Spinning and Twisting of Long Vegetable Fibres.* London, Griffin & Co., 1904. p. 16

6. Campbell, p. 93

7. Benhaim, Paul. *H.E.M.P.: Healthy Eating Made Possible.* London, Fusion Press, 1999. p. 37

8. Elliott, G.F. Scott. *The Romance of Plant Life.* London, Seeley & Co., 1917. p. 305

9. Morison, Samuel Elliott. *The Ropemakers of Plymouth.* Cambridge, Houghton Mifflin, 1950

10. Phillips, James Duncan. "The Salem Shipbuilding Industry before 1812", as quoted in *America, Russia, Hemp and Napoleon,* by Alfred W. Crosby, Jr. Columbus, Ohio State University Press, 1965

11. Carter, p. 16

12. Crosby, Alfred W. Jr. *America, Russia, Hemp and Napoleon.* Columbus, Ohio State University Press, 1965

13. Campbell, p. 13

14. Anon. "Hemp", entry in *Encyclopaedia Brittanica.* Boston. Little, Brown & Co., 1856

15. Thirsk, Joan. *Alternative Agriculture: A History.* Oxford, Oxford University Press, 1998. p. 159

16. Wissett, Robert. *A Treatise on Hemp.* London, J. Harding, 1808. p. iii

17. Carter, p. 19

18. Dewey, Lyster H. "Hemp", p. 299 in *USDA Yearbook* 1913. Washington, GPO, 1914

19. Woodhouse, J. and P. Kilgour. *Cordage and Cordage Hemp.* London, Sir Isaac Pitman & Sons, 1928. p. 20

20. UK Gov Publications (Commonwealth Economic Committee). London, Her Majesty's Stationery Office, 1957. p. 177

21. Bócsa, Dr. Ivan and Michael Karus. *The Cultivation of Hemp.* Sebastapol (Ca.), 1998

22. McPartland, J.M. , R.C. Clarke and D.P. Watson. *Hemp Diseases and Pests.* Wallingford, CABI Press, 2000. p. 8

III. Branching West

KENYON GIBSON, NICK MACKINTOSH
AND CINDY MACKINTOSH

*F*rom Asia and the Middle East hemp made its way into Africa and Europe. It was well known throughout Egypt, especially for rope making; evidence of this can be found in the pyramid texts, designated by the hieroglyph *'smsmt*.[1] Hemp rope was used in the construction of the pyramids, its great strength ideal for working with large blocks of stone. Dry hemp fibre was stuffed in the rock fissures, and then wetted so that they expanded, thus cracking open the large slabs.[2] Cloth made from hemp was found in the tomb of Pharaoh Alchanaten at El Amarona and hemp pollen on the mummy of Ramses II, dating from 1,200 B.C. Records of apothecary from the time of Ramses III suggest its use for an ophthalmic prescription, and as a poultice.[3]

Hemp spread throughout the African continent and surrounding islands, with the exception of the desert regions. The Punic people, who built the city of Carthage, which dominated North Africa and the Mediterranean Sea between the eleventh and eighth centuries BC, used hemp in ships, rope, and as medicine.[4] Almost two thousand years later, hemp was still grown in North Africa, a fact noted by the Magistrate of Bourges, M. Marcandier in 1758;[5] the American businessman Samuel Boyce in 1900;[6] and British authors J. Woodhouse and P. Kilgour in 1913.[7] These last writers recorded it growing on both east and west coasts. By 1917 cannabis was widely cultivated in tropical Africa, present in Upper and Lower Guinea, Uganda, the Belgian Congo (Zaire) and Mozambique.[8]

At the southern end of the continent hemp is also known to flourish, and was in constant cultivation by the Hottentots. This was outlawed in some areas, but is now being looked into again, with the goal of developement on a large scale as consumer awareness grows. Zimbabwe, shortly before the civil unrest, had started a programme with the help of British consultant Paul Benhaim; other African countries are currently instituting programmes to establish hemp farming for food and fibre.[9]

THE GREEKS AND THE ROMANS

From Africa hemp spread north, crossing over to Italy. A Carthaginian galley which sank in 300 BC near Sicily was recently found to have a cargo of hemp, still identifiable after 2,300 years in salt water.[10] Both the Hellenistic and the Roman empires, then the 'centres of the world', were great users of this fibre, which came from virtually all directions. The Greeks helped spread the cultivation and use of hemp into the Roman Empire, as had the Franks from the north and the Punic people in the south. Hemp spread through Asia Minor to the Mediterranean countries and into the provinces of the Roman Empire (Illyria, Gallia and Hispania).

South Africa's Premier Hemp Company

The Greeks used hemp for clothing and for their ships, as documented by early writers. Hesychius reported that Thracian women made sheets of hemp, and Moschion (ca. 200 BC) wrote of hemp ropes used in the flagship Syracusi, and other ships of the fleet of Hiero II.[11] Herodotus *(Lib. iv., cap. 74* [ca. 450 BC]) noted: "... the people of Thrace cultivated a kind of hemp, that very much resembled flax, excepting that the stalk of it rose higher. Some of it, says he, is cultivated, and another kind grows wild. Both these kinds are preferable to everything of the sort that we have in Greece."

Pedacius Dioscorides, *(Lib. iii., cap. 148)*, a first century Greek physician, made notes describing in detail the different sexes of cannabis, and its use as a potent medicine. Marcandier in his 1758 treatise on hemp recorded that even in those early times the fine qualities of hemp were understood and appreciated.[12] Knowledge of hemp has continued into the twentieth century, with farmers growing it on small lots. In Cyprus, school children were encouraged to grow hemp in the 1950s.[13]

Due to the extensive nature of the Roman Empire, the spread of hemp was facilitated throughout Europe, especially in Italy, where it is like a thread woven throughout the history and culture, from ancient times till the present. The earliest Roman writer to mention hemp was Pausanaius in the second century BC, who noted that it was grown in Elide. A surviving fragment from the work of satirist Luciluis (ca. 100 BC) also mentions the hemp plant. Lucius Columella writing in the period of Emperor Augustus put forward plantation methods in his publication *Res Rustica (II vii. 1 and II xii. 21)*. The Romans grew hemp for its oily fruits, which they used for food, as mentioned by Columella. Crescentius, in *de Agricultura (Lib. iii, cap. de Canapo)*, informs us that it requires the same climate and soil as flax, but it is not necessary to plough the ground so often; Pliny *(xix, cap. 9)* advises a thick sowing so as to obtain a fine fibre. He also records the use of hemp for ships, and states that it was "in common use among the Romans in the first century for ropes and sails, as well as for other purposes."

These other purposes included food, and, later on, paper. Romans consumed hemp seed in cakes, considered a delicacy. The craft of papermaking came to Europe through Arab craftsmen, and this required great quantities of hemp. In 1276 the Fabriano paper mill was established in the marquisate of Arcona; the watermark, or *'filigrano'*, was invented there later that century. This trade flourished, with many other mills opening, shortly thereafter. In 1340 a paper factory was established at Padua, and by 1360 in Treviso, Florence, Bologna, Parma, Milan, Venice and elsewhere there were such ateliers in full swing. To this day the mill at Fabriano still provides paper, most notably watercolour paper. The world's major art collections contain Italian hemp fibres providing long lasting, archival quality grounds.

The best hemp in the world is grown in the Romagna of Italy.
J.H. Maiden,
Agricultural Gazette of New South Wales, 1893

Given the demand for this commodity there was place for its own craft union, which was called the *'Tana'*, in Venice. The sails, cordage, and fabric were spun and guarded jealously by the Venetian government: "The security of our galleys and ships and similarly of our sailors and capital depended on this" was their view, and laws were passed that ships under the Venetian flag should only be rigged with the best quality hempen rope and canvas.[14] Due to its position Venice would continue to be a dominant force in Mediterranean shipping until its conquest in 1797 by Napoleon, who was well aware of the importance of this city, both as a maritime power and as a producer of hemp.

During the Renaissance artists' canvasses and oils were made from cannabis, a fact that is reflected both in the word 'canvas', and *'canapa'*, the Italian word for hemp. One artist known to have used hemp products was Leonardo da Vinci, who mentions it in his notebooks. But of all the uses to which the Italians put hemp, cloth was the most refined. For this, one Italian hemp variety was renowned, the 'Piedmonte', a variety especially sought after and grown in northern Italy. Desirable for its fineness, it was a profitable item of trade throughout Italian history.

Italian Hemp Prices		
From: The *Twisting and Spinning of Long Vegetable Fibers,* by Herbert Carter, 1907		
Italian hose	PC	£36
Naples I	Paesano	£32
Naples II	Paesano	£28.5
Naples I	Maraionise	£28
Naples II	Maraionise	£26.5

An 1804 record notes that it was produced in several of the Italian states, and that Italy was the only hemp-exporting nation in Europe.[15] Several localities became centres of hemp production, such as Lake Armono and environs, in the south, which was the site of great quantities being retted every summer.[16] An 1845 record noted the height of hemp growing in Terra de Lavora as exceeding eighteen feet in height.[17]

The citizens of Naples benefited from hemp as both a crop, and as a plant that cured the land of weeds. Rev. Daniel Smith in 1839 cited an example of its use in this capacity at a swamp near the Lago di Patria where it: "...cleared the *canne,* or reeds, that rose considerably above the head of a man on horseback. They found this to be the most efficient means, and grew Indian corn successfully on the land thus cleared."[18]

Hemp was grown throughout the nineteenth century, and into the twentieth; in 1904 exports totalled 53,000 tons.[19] In 1919, Italy produced 80,000 tons of hemp,[20] and by 1930 her hemp exports accounted for 50 percent of world-wide exports.[21] The market for top quality textiles kept hemp in demand, a niche that Italy has carved for herself in this business. An Italian commission list of 1930s factories devoted to hemp

Tavola Pag. 3

Canape maschio.

Canape femmina.

manufacturing included over twenty Italian "manufacturers of hemp fabric for various purposes."[22] In the 1950s Italy became a centre for hemp research; in that decade the Consorzio Nazionale Produttori Canapa sought to improve production by making studies of cannabiculture and introducing new varieties. In 1960 Professor E. Mancini of the Agronomy Institute of Bologna University and Professor R. Barbieri of Sassari University carried out various comparative field trials in Emiglia and Campania respectively, comparing new strains (Fibridia, Élite, Superélite 56) with old stains (Selected Carmagnola and Common Paesana). These tests, conducted in Emiglia, proved the new varieties to be more productive for fibre.[23] In those two decades Italian scientists produced much literature on cannabis, which, along with earlier material, has given to the world some of the most important sources of technical information on cannabis botany and cultivation.

In 1970 Italy cultivated 36,466 hectares and conducted research on hemp as a non-wood paper source.[24] Exports were continued up to 1982, when it was prohibited. French varieties were re-introduced in 1998, with 126 hectares planted near Turin in Piedmonte and Valle d'Aosta.[25] Awareness of hemp's value is growing, with this deeply rooted part of Italian culture coming into a *'renascimiento'* in the twenty-first century.

THE IBERIAN PENINSULA

On the Iberian Peninsula hemp found fertile soil; both Spain and Portugal were maritime nations, and had a need for sails and cordage to carry on trade, exploration and defence. Hemp came from the Romans and the Arabs, the latter using it mostly for paper and medicine, and establishing the first paper mill in Europe, at Xativa, now known as Denia in the province of Alicante. This was in 1150 AD, and soon afterward more were established in Valencia and Toledo.

As Spain reached the zenith of its powers under Phillip II in the sixteenth century, demand for hemp *(cáñamo)* increased dramatically. Columbus' ships each carried over eighty tons of hemp rigging and sails.[26]

Hemp farming was mandated in Central and South America during the time of its conquest so that the trade could continue.

England, under Elizabeth I, was to become Spain's biggest rival. In those days the English Navy consisted mainly of 'pirates' who worked for the crown. The Spanish galleons plying the seas between the 'Motherland' and her rich colonies became easy prey for this pirate fleet, as the lumbering Spanish galleons loaded with riches were no match for the smaller more manoeuvrable English ships. The interest of the English government was served two-fold by these attacks, as these vessels exacted a large percentage of the booty and also weakened the Spanish Navy, which was a threat to English maritime expansion. The defeat of the Armada in 1588 signalled the decline of Spain as a dominant maritime power and a rise of the English Navy. To maintain its place as a world power, Spain produced more hemp at home and raised quotas for her colonies. Hemp experts were dispatched to the New World to promote production of hemp for export to Europe. In 1564 King Phillip II of Spain ordered the cultivation of hemp for food, fibre and medicine throughout the Spanish territories in the New World.[27]

In 1777 Spain increased hemp production dramatically, and by 1799 every mainland province except Alava and Vizcaya was growing hemp, with Valencia, Aragón, Cataluña and Granada being the main centres of cultivation for the empire.[28] Russia also provided some amount of hemp; in 1804 126,324 lbs. reached Spain from Riga, and 544,800 lbs. from St. Petersburg. In the same year, Portugal imported 233,060 lbs. from Riga, and 669,760 lbs. from St. Petersburg.[29] Hemp has continued to be an important product ever since, but its strategic importance diminished as the age of sail disappeared. In the 1950s the crop was still highly regarded and listed in schoolbooks as a common crop.[30] The production of hemp peaked in 1986 but has since declined. Spain still produces hemp for textiles, paper, and ropes for domestic uses and exports. In the 1970s there were studies of cannabis papermaking with a focus on the use of the hurds for pulp and studies of methods for separating the hurds from the long bark fibres. Other studies were made of mechanical and chemical methods to pulp the hurds as well as oxygen-alkate pulping of fibres.[31]

Spain's cultivation of hemp (as in all EU member countries) is governed by strict regulations. All cultivators are licensed to produce only hemp of the low THC varieties, to be used only for producing paper, textiles, and fibre. Many technological and agricultural advances have been made by the Spanish, who are quietly making improvements in the methods and machinery of this ancient craft. Most of the production of hemp in Spain comes from the Celesa Celulosa mill by Tortosa, near the mouth of the river Ebro, in northeastern Spain.

On the peninsula there has been over the centuries a decline in cultivation, due in part to competition from synthetic products and political pressure. With the availability of new technologies and the general public's greater awareness of pollution, a much closer look is being taken at this crop for use in the near future, as ecological and economic forces play a role in development.

FRANCE

Both the Franks and the Romans brought hemp into Gaul. The former arrived in 253 AD, and eventually occupied most of what is now present day France. Queen Arnemunde, a Frank who died in 570 AD, was buried in hemp cloth, showing a high regard for it by the nobility.[32] During their westward expansion the Romans introduced hemp to Gaul, as Marcandier recorded: "besides the use formally made of hemp, for cloth, thread and cordage it was also the material of other great works, for which there was a very great demand, such as fishing lines, nets, hunting nets and gins (machinery)."[33] When Hiero II of Syracuse (ca. 306-215 BC) "had his splendid ship of state built to which all his subject countries had to contribute their best, he ordered hemp from Gaul for the manufacturer of ropes."[34]

It was from the fifteenth to the seventeenth centuries that cultivation was most developed. Like its principal European naval competitors, France needed cordage and canvas for its growing maritime fleet. In addition to being grown for the military, cannabis was grown for medicinal and household uses. In the sixteenth century, R. Dodoen advised:

The root of hemp bayled in water, doth helpe and cure the finenes and parts that be drawne together and shrunken, also it helpeth against the gout, if it be laved there upon the seed stamped and taken in white wine, is highly commended at this day, against the jaundice and stopping of the liver.[35]

The brilliant French writer, scholar, lawyer, and physician, François Rabelais (1483-1553) devoted three chapters of his great satire *Gargantua and Pantagruel* to a description of *'Pantagruelion'* (his word for hemp). Studies of the remains of the semi-barbarous inhabitants of France indicate that the production of hemp, being of simple cultivation was one of the early developments furnishing the materials necessary for garments and household linens. Boyce noted in 1900: "...the hemp industry first came into prominence when the people cultivated the hemp, prepared the fibres, and by hand labour spun and wove it into cloth for canvas, or for garments and into linens for household use,"[36] and that:

Up to the end of the eighteenth century, and before the invention of machine-spinning by Ray, in 1826 (Ray was a French manufacturer at the time), the hemp produced in Picardy and Alsace was chiefly used for coarse product of cordage and fish net, while that of Dauphiné and

---

*CANNABIS SATIVA *L.*,

Spec., 1457. — H. Bn, *Hist. des pl.*, VI, fig. 129-136.

Ulmacées — Cannabinées.

N. vulg. — *Chanvre, Chanvenon, Carbé, Carvé, Cherbe, Chameret.*

Fleurs dioïques, petites et verdâtres. Calice mâle à 5 sépales, imbriqués dans la préfloraison. Étamines 5, superposées aux sépales, à filets grêles, pendants ; à anthères biloculaires, introrses, déhiscentes par deux fentes longitudinales. Fleur femelle à ovaire supère, uniloculaire, accompagné à sa base d'un petit calice gamosépale et surmonté de deux longues branches stylaires filiformes et papilleuses. Ovule descendant, anatrope, à micropyle supérieur et extérieur. Fruit (*Chènevis*) sec, uniloculaire, monosperme. Graine descendante, à téguments minces, à embryon plissé-enroulé ; la radicule incombante et ascendante. — Herbe annuelle, à tige dressée (haute de 1-2 mètr.), rigide, simple ou rameuse, rude, à feuilles opposées, pétiolées, pourvues de deux stipules ; le limbe palmatiséqué, à 5-7 segments ou moins, lancéolés, acuminés, serrés. Inflorescences mâles en grappes axillaires et terminales de cymes composées. Fleurs femelle en glomérules, dans l'aisselle de bractées foliacées ; chacune accompagnée d'une bractéole. — Fl. en juin-septembre.

Propr. — Plante à écorce textile. Feuilles enivrantes. Embryon huileux. Graine comestible, donne l'huile de Chènevis. Tige (*Chènevotte*) servant à faire des allumettes.

Hab. — Originaire d'Orient, introduit, cultivé et subspontané.

Fl. paris. — Assez commun dans les conditions susdites.

O. Doin, éditeur. Paris.   119   Imp. zinc Monrocq. Paris.

Limoges served partly to supply the hand spinners and weavers of the mountains of the Isère and Puy de Dôme, whose fine fabrics so long had a great reputation in the South of France. The plains of Grenoble produced hemp of a remarkable fineness, which supplied the numerous spinners of Dauphiné whose products contributed so much to the great reputation of the fine linens of Voiron.[37]

Boyce stated that Grenoble was "...so well adapted and so well situated in the shelter of the Alps, enjoying a damp and warm climate, possessing all the natural elements for producing a fine hemp plant," that it "still produces good hemp," and mentioned Limoges much the same way: "Limoges, which unites with the natural elements of a climate warm and moist during the time of the growth of the hemp plant, a rich, deep soil easily cultivated, has been particularly favoured in the culture of hemp."[38]

Thus, by the beginning of the seventeenth century the hemp industry was well established among small farmers. France imported Italian seed for growing the taller varieties, which were esteemed in the millinery trade.

Hemp Exported from Archangel to France, 1802			
From: *The Linen Trade of Europe,* by John Horner, 1920			
Hemp	**Flax**	**Sail-cloth**	**Raven-Duck**
Poods*	Poods	Pieces	Pieces
Bordeaux 4			
1,000	100	60	100
Marseilles 2			
278	–	–	–
Ships			
1,278	100	60	100
* 1 pood - 36 lbs. = 16.3 kg.			

Marcandier asserted the importance of hemp and the fact that France imported more than it should considering how well it grew. He exhorted his nation:

In the north of America and Europe, Hemp thrives exceeding well: that commodity is exported from thence into England, Holland, and even France, to the shame and detriment of those that cultivate it with us. Could no means be fallen upon to encourage them, and increase their number? What country is in better condition to apply to it, and profit by it, than France? All her provinces produce very good Hemp; and, instead of taking it from strangers, we ought to put ourselves in condition to sell it to them. Guyenne, Languedoc, Provence, Dauphiny, Auvergne, Burgundy, and Berry produce as good Hemp as can be wished, and nothing is wanting but the best methods of cultivating and preparing it.[39]

Such advice was not overlooked by Napoleon, especially as the competition between the main European powers for naval supremacy eventually was reduced to Britain and France as the main protagonists, both of whom depended on this commodity for their military. This conflict drew in other powers as well, principally the merchant powers of the US and the Baltic that were to be involved in transporting goods. It was this commerce that Napoleon wished to restrict. The result was a series of quite Byzantine political moves by the countries concerned which ended up by France having an undeclared war on and off with the US from 1797,[40] and a number of changes of alliance over the following years.

CHAP. L.
Of Hempe.
The Kindes.

There are two kinds of Hempe, the one is fruitfull and beareth seede: the other beareth but floures onely.

The Description.

1 The first kind of Hempe hath a round hollow stalke, foure or fiue foote long, full of branches, and like to a little tree: at the top of the branches groweth little small round bagges or huskes, wherein is contayned the seed which is round: the leaues be great, rough, and blackish, parted into seuen, nine, tenne, and sometimes into moe parts, long, narrow, and snipt, or dented round about with notches like the teeth of a saw: the whole leafe with all his parts is like to a hand spread abroad.

2 The second is also in leaues like to the first, and it hath a thicke stalke, out of which by the sides groweth forth sundrie branches: but it beareth neither seed nor fruit, sauing small white floures, the which like dust or pouder is carried away with the wind.

The Place.

1. 2. These two sorts of Hempe are sowne in fields, and (which is a thing to bee marueiled at) they doe both spring of one kind of seed. A man shall sometime find the male Hempe growing in the borders of fields, and by the wayes.

The Time.

The seed of the male Hempe is ripe at the end of August, and in September. The female Hempe is ripe in July.

The Names.

Hempe is called in Greeke κανναβις, ασκεων, ἢ χοινοτειφον: in Latine, and in Shops, Cannabis: in Italian, Cannape: in Spanish, Ganamo, Canauo: in English, Hempe, Neckweed, and Gallowgrasse: in French, Chanure, Chennenis, or Cheneue: And here you may perceiue the cause why the Romans and others do call the cloth made of Hempe, Chennenis, or Canuas, for it soundeth so after the Greeke, Latine, and French: the high Dutchmen call Hempe Zamerhauff: in base Almaigne, Kempe.

The Nature.

Hempe-seede is hote and drye in the third degree.

The rivalry between Britain and France came to a head at this time with each state consuming vast quantities of hemp. In order to strangle Britain's economy the French tried to discourage the Russians from selling hemp to the British. However, even after the treaty of Tilset, which forbade the selling of hemp, was signed in 1807 between Napoleon and Alexander I of Russia, *'les Rosbifs'* continued to import the hemp from Russia. The American historian Alfred J. Crosby noted:

> The struggle between France, and England and their allies, went into its final world-quaking stage in 1805. In that year Nelson caught the combined French and Spanish fleets off the cape of Trafalgar, and Napoleon caught the armies of Austria and Russia at Austerlitz.[41]

The British government then issued 'Orders in Council' forbidding trade with Napoleon's Europe and used her naval power to enforce these orders. Napoleon issued his 'Berlin and Milan Decrees', creating his 'Continental System', and by the beginning of 1812 Napoleon had nearly defeated Great Britain, squeezing her economy and restricting exports to her northern European customers, thus causing great hardship. In 1810 her exports were £13,857,946 but by 1811 they were £3,483,091.[42] Despite this success, Napoleon realised that his political intrigues were not going to achieve the desired results, and he looked to his Grand Army for a solution. Caulaincourt, Napoleon's confidante and previous Ambassador to Russia, used all his abilities of persuasion and logic to turn his Emperor from the course he was taking.[43] Napoleon, nonetheless, invaded Russia in June 1812 reaching Moscow by mid-December, which was eventually torched by the Russians themselves, forcing the French to leave by mid-October. The Russian winter took its toll, as well as the Cossacks who harried their retreat. Of the 600,000 men who invaded Russia only 100,000 managed to escape. One could say that hemp was the undoing of Napoleon; eighteen months later he was defeated at the battle of Waterloo.

During his reign, Napoleon had indirectly affected the production of French hemp production by offering a reward for the invention of machinery that could spin hemp and flax. One million francs was the prize, offered in 1810, and Philippe de Girard was able to offer a solution in six weeks' time. He continued to perfect his apparatus by stages, though circumstances forced him to expatriate to Austria and Poland, but returned to his homeland in 1840, where he died five years later without ever having received a single *'sou'* for his accomplishment. The French people, however, did not forget his labours. In 1853 his family was granted a pension, and in 1882 his statue was erected in the town of Avignon.[44]

Throughout the nineteenth century the demand for hemp continued. US government agronomist Lyster Dewey gave the following account of one of these transactions, which took place in 1846:

> M. Herbert sent the seeds 'tsing-ma' variety home to France. They were grown by M.L. Vilmorin, attaining a height of more than 15 feet but not producing seeds. Later in the same year a M. Itier sent to M. Delite of the garden of Montpellier similar seeds which he called Cannabis chinensis.[45]

These were distributed in southern France where the plants grew well, some reaching heights of twenty-one feet and also producing mature seeds.[46] Another source recorded: "M.L. Vilmorin stated that the two forms of hemp differed very much in habit from the common hemp of Europe, which was shorter and less valuable for fibre production."[47] It was noted at the time that: "...chanvre de Chine did not appear to be the same as the chanvre de Piedmont."[48]

In 1901 France cultivated 25,800 hectares of hemp; Sarthe (5901 hectares), Morbihan (2588 hectares), Maine et Loie (2533 hectares), and Haut-Vienne were the leading areas.[49] Production levels for the first years of the twentieth century averaged around 70,000 tons per annum, with over two-hundred-and-fifty mills engaged in the industry.[50]

By 1919, due to the consequences of WWI, production had fallen to 15,000 tons.[51] Ultimately hemp was grown less as wood-pulp replaced rag paper; recently though, a process was developed in France that uses raw hemp fibres for the production of high-quality strong paper, and hemp for paper production is being replanted. This is in contrast to hemp cultivation for textiles; statistics show that in the 1960s there was a drop in the area of cannabis sown for textiles from 1084 hectares in 1961 to one-hundred-and-forty-seven hectares in 1968, while areas dedicated to paper production increased over the same period from sixty-one hectares to 3181 hectares and by 1977 that had risen to 10,595 hecares.[52] Although some farmers grew hemp for its subsidy of 1405 francs per hectare in 1998, most growers have realised its benefits, of which one author notes: "If it is used in crop rotation its deep roots break and aerate the soil and eliminate weeds, thus making the land ready for direct sowing for a winter wheat crop before the first frost."[53] Thus, in the Bar-sur-Aube the advantages of hemp have been realised by its widespread establishment there, although this particular of France traditionally did not grow cannabis. In 1978 a breaking mill, established by ninety-three farmers, was processing 2,500 hectares of hemp.[54]

French Production from 1840 to 1901 From: *Plantes Textiles*, by L. Bonnetat, 1907		
1840	93.000 hectares donnant	368.000 quintaux de filasse
1881	60.000 hectares donnant	381.500 quintaux de filasse
1892	44.000 hectares donnant	294.200 quintaux de filasse
1901	25.800 hectares donnant	200.000 quintaux de filasse

Recently efforts have been made to up-date the mechanical process of 'breaking' the dried hemp stalks and separating the bast fibres - the phloem fibres, from the woody hurds. This has been very important for the production of crude bast fibre for paper by making it cheaper to produce on a large scale, a process that has meant small mill closings and the openings of co-operatives such as Bar-sur-Aube. Other centres include the traditional Job Cigarette Paper Company in Toulouse and the very large De Mauduit factory in Quimperle (a subsidiary of Kimberly Clark). Added to ordinary wood pulp, hemp fibres make 'speciality paper' particularly pliable and resistant for bank notes and cigarette paper. French farmers received 435 francs per ton for the dried hemp stalks and De Mauduit charged 2,500 francs for the prepared bast paper film.[55]

In 1992, 3,950 hectares of hemp was grown in France; 2,650 hectares in the region of Troyes (eastern France), 1,250 hectares in the region of Le Mans (western France), and fifty hectares in southwestern France. In 1992 two-hundred hectares of hemp was grown for the production of premium seed, and another one-hundred-and-seventy hectares of second rank seed.[56] When grown for fibre it is sown very densely, so as to grow into branchless slender stalks that so resemble straw that French farmers call them '*paille de chanvre'* (hemp straw). After harvest, the long fibres that comprise up to 28 percent of the hemp stalks are removed. In some parts of the world, such as China, the fibres are still spun and woven into cloth. In France, the machinery presently used to remove the fibres from the stalk does not allow processing of the fibre into a thread strong enough to be woven into cloth.

After the fibres have been removed, roughly 72 percent of the plant remains in the form of a bulky product called *'chenevotte'* (hurd). It resembles, but is much lighter than, wood chips, and is very absorbent. It will soak up to five times its own weight in moisture, and is used as bedding for livestock, particularly horses; some is broken and moulded into cat litter. This is also being increasingly used in the building industry. For instance, adding natural lime can petrify it. When water is added it takes on the consistency of cement but when it is hard it is many times lighter and has a texture like cork. It is resistant to both mould and insects, and can be poured as a floor or between sheets of plywood, which are later removed, to make walls. This hemp cement replaces the need for several layers of cement and building material as it offers both thermal and sonic insulation.

The French lead the way not only in production, but in research, much of it carried out at the Institute Nationale de la Recherche Agronomique in Rennes. It is there that the *Journal of Industrial Hemp* is edited, a biannual publication which is the standard reference work in the industry world-wide.

GERMANY, AUSTRIA, HOLLAND & SWITZERLAND

In all Germanic languages, the initial 'k' of cannabis, present in Greek, Semitic, Latin and Slavic languages, shifts to 'h'. Thus hemp, hanf, hampr, hemnef, henf, hänaf, haenep and hampf all reflect a sound shift that is believed to have taken place around 500 BC, which accords with material evidence from a 500 BC burial mound of a Celtic prince near Stuttgart.[57] A yet older find predates this by five millennia, that of a prehistoric vase containing hemp seed, which was found in Thüringen.[58] Rope and fabric have been found in German cities from 400 AD; a find near Brandenburg dates back to the sixth century AD.[59] Charles the Great mandated its cultivation in the ninth century AD,[60] and in medieval times there was a springtime festival held for the hemp to grow tall. The Gutenberg Bibles were printed on hemp, as were most German books until the late nineteenth century when wood pulp came into vogue.

The cultivation and processing of hemp was practised extensively from the medieval ages to the twentieth century, and one can still see this evidenced in the tools and machinery involved; not only in German museums, but in the US as well, brought over by immigrants such as the Moravian Brethren.

In 1919 Germany produced only 2,000 tons of hemp,[61] and until WWII there was minimal production. The German Government published a tract called *Die Lustige Hanffibel* in 1943, encouraging people to grow hemp, and by the end of that war, more hemp was spun than cotton, with 21,000 hectares under cultivation.[62]

After the war, hemp production virtually ceased; it was officially outlawed in 1982, although this was against European Community standards, and subject to challenge in the European Court. One farmer, Martin Butler, who was forced to abandon his crops, was able to settle his claims in the national court.[63] At that time there was also ongoing research using hemp as a soil detoxicant, which was also halted; however, exemption was granted for use of hemp as a pollen insulator.[64]

Interest resurged in 1993, the year that Schneidersohne, Germany's largest paper manufacturer, introduced a line of hemp paper products. By 1994, total annual sales of hempen products surpassed DM 20 million.[65] In 1995 a bill legalising hemp was passed on the state level, and ratified in 1996 by the federal government.

Austria's history of hemp production parallels that of her northern neighbour; one exception is that it was never illegal for Austrians to grow. The Romans kept a hemp storehouse in Vienna,[66] and throughout the middle ages farmers grew hemp in their lands.

In 1766 a businessman named Andreas Kilian from Freiburg in Breisgau operated a factory that specialised in refining and spinning hemp. He sent a detailed petition to the court, describing the processes and costs involved. This petition also contained nine oil paintings showing the processing of hemp, all of which are of historic interest, and are housed at the Viennese Hofkammer Archives.[67]

Ultimately Austria's hemp production declined in the twentieth century, with but 18,000 tons produced in 1919.[68] Only very recently has interest resurged, with a small planting in 1995, when 300 hectares were planted with a French variety called Féline 34.[69] Initially expectations were optimistic, with many wrong notions about the 'miracle' powers of hemp being put into practice. The next year saw more realistic aims, and public interest very high. Currently Austrian farmers are continuing to grow hemp, having found it easy to grow with proper planning and advice.

In the Netherlands, hemp, or *'hennep'*, was a staple crop, used especially for shipping and fishing. Dutch seed production and hemp spinning were considered superior by other European nations, and for this reason Dutch seed demanded a high price, and spinners were enticed away by other nations wishing to enhance their own economies. Holland did purchase some quantities from abroad, sending her traders north to Russia for supplies. In 1804 some 261,000 lbs. of hemp arrived in Amsterdam from Riga;[70] the Dutch were noted for buying top quality, which they used for whaling. At present the government is supportive of hemp research, made public by Dr. Hayo van der Werf's recent book *The Crop Physiology of Fibre Hemp.*

Switzerland also has a history of hemp cultivation, as evidenced by the mills at Dagmersellon and Villmergen. A 1962 record shows hemp growing at an altitude of nearly 8,000 feet in the upper Volais, with processing taking place in nearby Grisons.[71]

CENTRAL EUROPE

Among the Slavic people, hemp has been used extensively. Poland, Romania, Bulgaria, the Czech Republic, Slovakia and former Yugoslavia have all cultivated this crop, as has Hungary. There is a Hungarian record of a royal customs bill from Esztergom, dating from 1198, which mentions hemp. It states that by then hemp was much a part of Hungarian agriculture; it has continued to be so to the present. In the late nineteenth century Italian varieties were introduced, and more was grown on an industrial scale.[72] Historical evidence also exists for hemp cultivation in Yugoslavia, where the Turks taxed production in Serbia, and the Empress Marie-Thérèse insisted that high quality strains be grown. The province of Vojvodnic is the main growing area. At one time, Yugoslav hemp accounted for 25 percent of all hemp grown in Europe, with 60,000 hectares under cultivation. In 1930, this figure was 50,000 hectares, but increased to 108,215 hectares in 1949.[73]

In 1919 Hungary produced 50,000 tons of hemp; Poland, 4,000 tons; Bulgaria, 2,000 tons; and Romania, 1,500 tons.[74] Poland's tradition of hemp production was romanticised by the great Polish poet Adam Mickiewicz in his nineteenth century novel *Pan Tadeusz*. After WWII, US soldiers were surprised to find hemp in constant cultivation, and that the Polish farmers did not share the same phobias towards it as existed in the US, but rather, grew it for their clothing. When the occupying soldiers attempted to destroy the hemp, the Poles stopped them.[75] Sixty years on, the Institute of Natural Fibres in Poznan is a centre of hemp research. In Poland, Hungary and Romania (which in 1957 was noted as the "only country in Europe to export seed in any appreciable quantity")[76] cannabis husbandry has been studied and improved with new seed varieties produced. Today many technical articles are written in Polish, Romanian and Hungarian, with much of the latest research undertaken by Dr. Ivan Bócsa of Hungary.

SCANDINAVIA & THE BALTIC

Pollen and macrofossil evidence places cannabis in the Baltics as early as 3,500 BC. Shoreline samples of hemp seed from Lithuania have been dated at 2,580-2,030 BC, with signs of intense cultivation in the Svetoji lagoon and Nidi, and in Eastern Latvia, at the Lubun Lake Basin.[77] Both of these countries used hemp seed in their religious festivals.

Hemp may have reached Scandinavia through Russia; however, a Germanic influence is seen in the fact that hemp is closer in the language of these countries than to either a Slavic or Latin root.

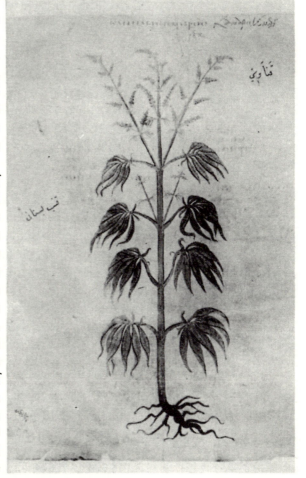

The Earliest known illustration of a hemp plant, 5th century AD manuscript

Cannabis sativa is believed to have reached central and eastern Finland by way of Karelia, around 1,500 AD, but to have reached northern Finland much earlier through Sweden and Norway. The oldest known hemp site dates back to the Viking age (800-1,050 AD), and is situated on a large island called Ahvenanmaa (which is on the Finnish-Swedish border).[78] At that time hemp would have been a major accessory to the seafaring Norsemen, who used it not only for sails and cordage, but for cooking as well. Archaeologists discovered this in 1990, when they found a boat whose hull had been tarred with hemp. The boat, found in Svojuki, Finland, dated back to the thirteenth century.[79]

Other Finnish areas of early hemp cultivation included the southwestern regions and southern Savo, where hemp growing has been dated to the fifth and fifteenth centuries AD.[80] Much agricultural expansion took place in the eighteenth and nineteenth centuries when hemp was grown for many uses, including clothing, cooking oil, and a hemp nut paste which was used like butter. In the early nineteenth century the Finns were briefly brought into the dispute between Napoleon, Britain and the US over the supply routes. In the twentieth century most nations witnessed a decline or complete cessation of production, but Finland continued to grow hemp into the 1960s, as it was used domestically in many ways. Present day Finns can recall rugs or coats made of it in their youth, many of which are still being used. Finland also used hemp for paper, even after the international change from rags and annual crops to tree pulp. The first papermaking factory opened in Tervavoski in 1818, and did not use tree pulp until after WWII. Finnish currency still contains hemp fibres, as does the tender of many other countries.

While Finland did not initially use its trees for paper, it had been selling many of its forests to other nations for just such a purpose; ultimately this has led to concern for the environment and the economy, and as the awareness of hemp's potential became public knowledge, replanting was started.

In the autumn of 1994 the University of Kuopio, in collaboration with the culture secretary of Hankasalmi, Finland started a hemp project with the intention of demonstrating hemp as a non-food agricultural project during the summer of 1995.[81] The two French varieties of hemp seed planted were Futura-77 and Fedora-19. In central Finland a crop was harvested from the Hankasalmi field and retted in a local lake.[82] The public reaction to these trials has been very positive and since then there has been a small resurgence in hemp cultivation with further trial sites.

Another project at the University of Kuopio is a study of hemp oil in food: Tekes, a publicly funded company, is currently sponsoring the study, conducted by Dr. Jace Callaway at the Department of Pharmaceutical Chemistry.

Sweden and Norway share Finland's history of cannabis cultivation, and in the eighteenth and nineteenth centuries not only grew it, but bought it from Russia to process, selling it on to the many vessels that could more easily purchase it from Swedish ports than from Russia. The Swedes were thus unable to avoid the conflict caused by Napoleon, who in 1810 forced them to declare war on Britain. Dissatisfied with Sweden's foreign policy in January 1812, he sent troops to occupy Swedish Pomerania in order to teach them a lesson. This did not produce the desired result as in April, Sweden concluded a secret alliance with Russia, which Britain joined in May, thus reversing Sweden's stance towards Britain.[83]

Swedish cultivation of hemp continued until the 1950s, but has for some time been illegal. In 1999 field trials were made under the direction of Bengt Swenestedt of the Swedish University of Agricultural Sciences; four monoecious varieties were planted, harvested on average 150 days after sowing.[84]

In recent years the Society for Danish Hemp started lobbying for research trials. In 1998 it became legal to grow it commercially so the Danes have been trying to establish a commercial processing facility for hemp in the southern part of Funen, with the intention of cultivating hemp organically.

Before Sweden relegalised hemp, the Swedish authorities had banned The Body Shop's hemp products, which situation their neighbours exploited by encouraging the Swedes to "buy your hemp in Denmark." All of these northern nations are re-evaluating a long-standing practice, not only for its past performance, but also for an even greater role in the future.

1. *www.canablis.blogspot.com/2004_10_01_canablis_archive.html*
2. Guenet, François. *Chanvre.* N.d., n.p.
3. Manniche, Lise. *An ancient Egyptian herbal.* Austin, University of Texas Press, 1989
4. Guenet
5. Marcandier, M. *Traité du Chanvre.* Paris, 1758. p. 7
6. Boyce, Samuel. *Hemp.* NY, Orange Judd Co., 1900
7. Woodhouse, J. and P. Kilgour. *Cordage and Cordage Hemp.* London, Sir Isaac Pittman & Sons, 1928. p. 16
8. Rendle, A.B. *Flora of Tropic Africa,* vol. VI, sect. II, Desk Parain, ed.
9. Benhaim, Paul. Pers. comm.
10. Frost, Honor. pp. 21-22 in *Natural History,* NY, AMNH, 1988
11. Marcandier notes that hempwas the preferred material for ropes in ancient times
12. Marcandier, pp. 1-12
13. Ioannou, Petros and Dimitris Neocleous. Pers. comm.
14. Robinson, p. 115
15. Wissett, Robert. *A Treatise on Hemp.* London. J. Harding, 1808. p. 9
16. Smith, Rev. Daniel. *Natural History for Sunday Schools.* Vol. XII. NY, T. Mason & G. Lane, 1839 pp. 12-13
17. Campbell, Francis. *A Treatise on the Culture of Flax and Hemp.* Sydney, Statham & Forster, 1845. p. 80
18. Smith
19. Woodhouse and Kilgour, p. 20
20. *Ib.*
21. Giacomo, Alberto. *La Canapa nell' Italia.* N.d., n.p.
22. *Ib.*
23. Anon. "Hemp". pp. 2-31 in *CABI Review* 1962/5
24. Bócsa, Dr. Ivan and Michael Karus. *The Cultivation of Hemp.* Sebastopol, Ca, Hemptech, 1994. p. 14
25. A. Nicoletta. *Hemp Cultivation in Italy.* Internet Publication, ca. 1998
26. Lupien, John C. *Unravelling an American Dilemna: The Demonization of Marihuana.* Monterey (Ca.), Pepperdine University thesis, 1995
27. Mosk, S. *Agricultural History* vol. 13, 1939. pp. 171-175
28. Serrera, Contreras, Roman Maria. *Cultivo y Manufactura de Lino y Cáñamo en Nueva Espana.* Sevilla, Escuela de Estudios Hispano-Americanos de Sevilla, 1974
29. Horner, John. *The Linen Trade in Europe.* Belfast, McLaw, Stevenson & Orr, 1920. pp. 507-518
30. Caralambio, Juan, *Cáñamo.* N.d., n.p.
31. Bócsa, Dr. Ivan and Michael Karus. *The Cultivation of Hemp.* Sebastopol, Ca, Hemptech, 1998. p. 15
32. Robinson, p. 116
33. Marcandier, pp. 79-80

34. *Ib.*

35. Dodoen, R. *A New Herball or Historie of Plants.* (Henrie Lyte, trans.) Ninian Newton, 1586. p. 217

36. Boyce. pp. 30-31

37. *Ib.*

38. *Ib.*

39. Marcandier, pp. 46-47

40. Crosby, Alfred W. Jr. *America, Russia, Hemp and Napoleon.* Ohio, Ohio State University Press, 1965. p. 72

41. *Ib.*, p. 99

42. *Ib.*

43. *Ib.*, p. 237

44. Musée Rétrospectif de la Classe 81. *Fils et Tissus de Lin, de Chanvre.* Paris, 1900. p. 10

45. Dewey, Leyster M. "Hemp", pp. 283-346 in the *USDA Yearbook 1913.* Washington, GPO, 1914

46. Vilmorin, L. "Chanvre de Chine", in *Revue Horticulturel,* 1897

47. *Ib.*

48. Guenet, François. *Chanvre.* N.d., n.p.

49. Bonnétat, L. *Plantes textiles.* Paris, Librarie Hachette, 1907. p. 26

50. Boyce p. 23

51. Woodhouse and Kilgour. p. 20

52. Bócsa and Karus, p. 14

53. Guenet

54. Malyon, Tim and Anthony Henman. "No Marijuana, Plenty of Hemp", article in *New Scientist,* Nov. 1980

55. *http://fornits.com/hemp/newscie3.html.*

56. *http://hempmuseum.org/SUBROOMS/HEMP%20CHRONOLOGY.htm*

57. Schreiber, Gisela. *The Hemp Handbook.* London, Vision Paperbacks, 1999 p. 14

58. Heslop, Samuel C.H. *Hemp Fuel and Fibre.* Oxford, Oxford Brookes University thesis, 2000

59. Guenet

60. *Ib.*

61. Woodhouse and Kilgour, p. 20

62. Bócsa and Karus, pp. 7-8

63. Kinzer, Stephen. *New York Times,* 12 November, 1995

64. Anon. *Hemp Research and Market Development in Germany,* Internet Publication, ca.1997

65. Kraus, Michael. *Update: Industrial Hemp in Germany.* Internet publication, ca.1997

66. W.B . "A Series of Pictures on the working of Hemp in the 18th Century", pp. 1791-1792 in *CIBA Review 49.* Basle, 1945

67. *Ib.*

68. Woodhouse and Kilgour, p. 20

69. Bócsa and Karus, p. 14

70. Horner. p. 555

71. Schaefer, Gustav. "Hemp", pp. 1779-1790 in *CABI Review,* April, 1945

72. Bócsa, Dr. Ivan. Internet interview, ca. 1997

73. Berenji, Dr. Jones. *Hemp Cultivation in Yugoslavia.* Internet essay, 2000

74. Woodhouse and Kilgour, p. 20

75. Frazier, Jack. *The Marijuana Farmers.* Peterstown (WV), Solar Age Press, 1974

76. Guenet

77. Latinen, Erkki. *Hompun historia suomessa.* Internet essay, 1995

78. Anon. Internet essay, ca. 1996

79. Callaway, J.G. and T.T. Laakunen, *Cultivation of Cannabis oil seed varieties in Finland.* Internet essay, ca. 1997

80. _____and A.M. Hemmilä. *Cultivation of Cannabis varieties in central Finland.*

81. *http://mojo.calyx.net~olsen/HEMP/IHA/ina03113.html*

82. *Ib.*

83. Crosby, p. 219

84. Guenet

IV. The British Isles

KENYON GIBSON

uropean Celts and Picts were known to have cultivated cannabis, and it is believed that hemp reached western Europe and the British Isles through these tribes. A study published by Professor Harry Godwin of Cambridge University discusses evidence establishing hemp shortly after the time of Christ, the earliest being a well rope from ca. 140 AD found at Bar Hill, Dunbartonshire.[1] This was from a Roman fort on the Antoine Wall, and would be consistent with the habit of hemp use by the Roman army. Godwin analyses cannabis pollen samples from Old Buckingham Mere, in Norfolk, and places them at around 400 AD,[2] a time when Anglo-Saxon settlers were initiating cultivation in England.

He cites two examples of hemp in medieval accounts - the first a mention of hemp fishing line in a tenth century folk legend, the second a written record of *'canab et lin'* from 1341 records of Suffolk. Mention of hemp cultivation in 1304 on monastic estates in Norfolk is made by Joan Thirsk of Oxford University in her book *Alternative Agriculture*.[3] An earlier work by the same author notes that hemp was a speciality of the fenland, and occupied as much as 14.6 percent of the sown area in a sample inventory for the 1500s. She observed: "...the working of hemp and flax...was a subsidiary occupation to agriculture in most households. Hemp, flax, linseed, yarn, and a linen wheel were regularly listed among the farmers' personal property."[4]

Hemp was mandated throughout the British Isles, a fact which allowed the British to take command of the seas. For this a strong cordage industry was needed, which grew up primarily in Bridport, in the southern county of Dorset. Perhaps the earliest known documented evidence of hemp in that industry is a record from 1175, which David MacPherson, a nineteenth century historian, notes in his book *Annals of Commerce* (1805) as having been listed as a commodity subjected to tithe by the council of Westminster. Shortly after that there is a Pipe Roll from 1211, in which the Sheriff of Somerset and Dorset, William Malet, was charged for 1,000 ells of cloth for making ships' sails and for 3,000 weight of hempen thread. King John I is known to have ordered the Sheriff in 1213 to make a great quantity of ropes, cables and twisted yarns for 'cordage and ballistae'.[5] Such orders were followed, making Bridport a centre of England's defence

Cambri Formosa (B.C. 373) the fair oracle, was daughter of Belinus and niece of Brennus. She greatly promoted the building of cities and castles; she taught the women to sow flax and hemp, and weave it into cloth; was a priestess as well as a princess, and made the laws for the Sycambrians. Her grandfather, Dyfnwal Moel-Meod (B.C. 430) is said to have been the first king of Britain who wore a crown of gold.

John Wilson,
Our Israelitish Origin, **1850**

...if the fishery so much desired by us be thoroughly undertakenand our shipping increased, itwill require a much greater production of hemp for cordage, etc., in the fishery, which would set an infinite number of our people on work. Consider how the sowing of hemp and flax may be encouraged.
UK Government Report, **1622**

industry, for which reason King John III granted to the town a Royal Charter in 1253, thus giving it a monopoly on this trade. There not only were hemp items produced for the war effort, but peacetime products were turned out as well, including nets, candle wicks (known as 'lucelli'), and netting for sporting events. Henry VIII, in the sixteenth century, established naval dockyards in Portsmouth, Deptford, Woolwich, Chatham, Sheerness and Plymouth, which led to rope making being established all over the country. Hemp cultivation was then mandated by royal decree, Henry VIII setting a quota of 1/4 acre of hemp per 60 acres of arable land sown; in many cases much more than this was cultivated.[6] By this time botanical and agricultural writings, such as Thomas Fella's *Book of Diveirs Deriges* (first published in 1585), advised the sowing of hemp for its many uses - fibre, food, medicine, and oil.[7] An earlier writer, Thomas Tusser, was quite poetic about it in 1557, writing:

> Hemp huswifely used, looks clearly and bright,
> And selleth itself, by the colour so white,
> Some useth to water it, but some do it not,
> Be skilfull in doing, for fear it do rot.

> Good flax and good hemp, to have of her own
> In May a good huswife will se it be sown;
> And afterwards trim it, to serve at a need,
> The fimble to spin, and the cord for her seed.[8]

While Britons took this advice throughout the realm, Bridport continued to be the centre of this industry, being not only long established in the trade, but also situated in prime hemp growing land. A 1701 report was to note: "What makes the rural management of the environs of Bridport most evidently is the culture of Hemp and Flax - to supply the consumption of Manufacturing of Sailcloth and cordage from the cable of a man of war to the finest packing threads."[9] At that time hemp was imported mainly from the Baltic States, which supplied cordage grades, while the finest grades came from Italy. To encourage British farmers to grow it, the government in 1781 granted a bounty for hemp and also flax. The latter, while also a textile and cordage crop, produces a similar fibre, but is not as useful as hemp, being more useful for clothing than for rope, and further, needing a wet, cold ground in which to grow. From the records of such payments, it can be seen that there were hundreds of families involved in cultivation of these crops from 1782-1793.[10]

On the whole it is evident that a very Extensive Culture of Hemp and Flax is very practical, that the carrying it in execution is highly expedient, and must be attended with general and National Advantages of inestimable value; all this appears from arguments not to be called in question, for the evidence on which it is established is that of stubborn facts.
Joseph Gee of Gainsborough,
Observations on the Growth of Hemp and Flax in Britain, **1765**

Elizabeth I succeeded Henry VIII after a struggle and followed her father's lead in mandating hemp, going yet further to fine those parishes not growing hemp. This insistence on the growing of hemp was part of the prosperity of her reign - its availability enabled both trade and defence. The important naval battles that established British supremacy of the seas were fought with hempen sails and ropes.

From:

Thomas Culpepper's
The English Physician,
18th century

The English Physician Enlarged. 149

Hemp.

THIS is so well known to every good housewife in the country, that I do not need to write any description of it.

Time.] It is sown in the end of March, or beginning of April, and is ripe in August or September.

Government and Virtues.] It is a plant of Saturn, and good for something else, you see, than to make halters only. The seed of Hemp consumeth wind, and by too much use thereof disperseth it so much, that it drieth up the natural seed for procreation; yet, being boiled in milk, and taken, helpeth such as have a hot dry cough. The Dutch make an emulsion out of the seed, and give it with good success to those that have the jaundice, especially in the beginning of the disease, if there be no ague accompanying it, for it openeth obstructions of the gall, and causeth digestion of choler. The emulsion or decoction of the seed stayeth lasks and continual fluxes, easeth the colic, and allayeth the troublesome humours in the bowels, and stayeth bleeding at the mouth, nose, or other places, some of the leaves being fried with the blood of them that bleed, and so given them to eat. It is held very good to kill the worms in men or beasts; and the juice dropped into the ears killeth worms in them; and draweth forth earwigs, or other living creatures gotten in them. The decoction of the root allayeth inflammations of the head, or any other parts; the herb itself, or the distilled water thereof, doth the like. The decoction of the roots easeth pains of the gout, the hard humours of knots in the joints, the pains and shrinking of the sinews, and the pains of the hips. The fresh juice mixed with a little oil and butter, is good for any place that hath been burnt with fire, being thereto applied.

English Hemp Production in 1773 From: *The Linen Trade of Europe,* by John Horner, 1920	
Yorkshire	£10,000
Lincoln	£27,000
Cambridge	£2,000
Norfolk	£19,000
Other English Counties	£150,000

The demand for hemp and its profitability gave it a long-lasting niche throughout the British Isles - Lincolnshire, Norfolk, Suffolk, Dorset, and Kent were the main growing counties.[11] Production was encouraged at home and in the colonies: American hemp was granted a bounty of £6 per ton in 1705, which continued with some modifications for half-a-century.[12] In 1711 Parliament created the Board of Trustees of the Linen and Hempen Manufacturers of Ireland,[13] where both fibre crops were grown and processed as an important part of the agricultural economy.

Many laws existed to encourage and regulate this trade; seed importers were paid bounties and granted citizenship, whilst 'seed cheats' were punished.[14] By 1773 England alone produced £208,000 worth of hemp,[15] of which the table above shows a breakdown.

Mr. Stoddard of Bunratty, in that county, grew last year a quantity of Hemp...This Hemp possessed all the qualities of the Italian, and was particularly well adapted for fine works.

Peter Besnard, *Observations on the Growth of Hemp and Flax in Britain, and extending the linen and hempen manufactures in the south of Ireland,* **1816**

Lincolnshire, at that time, far surpassed any other county in production; a 1767 account reads of it as follows: "In the isle of Axholmes in the county of Lincoln, the culture of hemp and flax is the chief employment

> The hemp plant is of great importance to the Britons, as it forms the sails and tackle of our vessels, from the huge cable of a ship of war, to the more humble but not less profitable net of the herringboat.
>
> *The Library of Agricultural and Horticultural Knowledge,* 1834

of the inhabitant."[16] Domestic cultivation, however, was not enough to meet demand; a first-rate ship required 80,000 lbs. weight of hemp to be completely rigged, [17] and British merchants went to various parts of the globe to secure a supply. The main source was Russia, at whose ports the United Kingdom was the major customer. In this position of preferred trading partner, much of the hemp trade was conducted by British merchants; in Kronstadt, the main mercantile houses were Blandow and Co., Edward James Smith and Co., Cramp and Co., and Gale, Hill, Cazalet, and Co.[18] By 1810 concern over foreign dependence on such a staple was growing, and a communication between Benjamin Tucker, Surveyor-General of the Duchy of Cornwall, written to the Bath and West of England Society, on behalf of the Duke of Wales (later George IV), reflected the mood in the government as follows:

> …this country is interested that the growth of hemp should be encouraged generally and extensively upon all the waste lands in the United Kingdom which will admit of its cultivation.
>
> I beg leave to observe, that the expence of hemp for the use of the royal navy during the last war amounted to the sum of £.5,682,342, and, during the present war, the consumption has necessarily increased with the augmentation of our naval force.
>
> I believe that it will be found upon investigation, that the average exportation of hemp from Russia to this country, during the five years prior to 1809, has been about 30,000 tons per annum; two-fifths of which (about 12,000 tons) have been expended by the royal navy. And taking the whole export at an average of 45l. per ton, for prime cost and expences in Russia, there appears to have been an annual drain from this country of £.1,350,000! of which the publick have paid £.540,000 per annum for the consumption of the navy; besides the freight and insurance, and profits of the contractors.[19]

| **Exports from Archangel to Great Britain 1795 - 1803** ||||||||||
| From: *The Linen Trade of Europe,* by John Horner, 1920 |||||||||| |
Articles		1795	1796	1797	1798	1799	1800	1801	1802	1803
Hemp	Poods	6,285	6,051	11,317	8,143	18,911	31,936	33,413	18,601	25,803
Cordage	Do.	3,376	-	-	440	550	72	-	-	209
Sail-cloth	Pieces	57	-	-	-	-	-	-	120	387

Hemp became more necessary, but also more expensive, in wartime. A 1799 record states: "In peace, the price was £3 or £3. 10d. per acre. It was last year [1798] £5. Price per stone from the breaker was in peace four shillings and sixpence or five shillings per stone: of late it has been from six shillings and sixpence to seven shillings."[20]

Quantities of Hemp Imported Into the United Kingdom From: *The Fibrous Plants of India*, by J. Forbes Royle, 1855					
	1847	**1848**	**1849**	**1850**	**1851**
Russia	544,844Cwt*	540,207	641,548	614,535	672,342
Br.Ter.in East Indies	185,788	258,239	360,362	399,345	590,923
	*cwt = 112lbs/51 kilos				

While Britain did not produce enough hemp for her own needs, other reasons existed for importing this staple. One was quality - most British and Irish hemp was dew-retted, whilst Russian and Indian hemp was water-retted. Transportation costs also, ironically, made it cheaper to ship goods thousands of miles over sea than to use overland routes. This factor was still a reason for buying Russian hemp into the twentieth century.[21] For any country to import a large percentage of an essential product is a weakness. In the early nineteenth century Lord Somerville addressed this:

> Such are the political relations of Great Britain, and such is the unjust, as well as unnatural, alliance of the Continental Powers against our country, that it becomes an imperious duty to make every possible effort that may tend to ensure to her that proud security which her maritime force has hitherto commanded; and on this account I beg leave to call the most serious attention to the cultivators of our soil to the growth of hemp.[22]

At that time, some farmers were forbidden by their landlords to grow hemp, perhaps because of the retting process, which could leave a stream fouled by the effluent, and Somerville addressed that fact in his letter, calling it a 'prejudice which formerly existed against this crop,' and then, as a landlord, put his money where his mouth was by allowing his own tenant farmers in Gloucester and Somerset to grow hemp. He estimated that 140,000 acres of land were needed to grow enough hemp at that time for the UK, which he advised could be grown in the counties of Lincoln, Cambridge, Huntingdon, Northumberland, York (East Riding), Leicester, Warwick, Gloucester, and Somerset. These he saw as well suited to hemp, as well as most of Ireland.[23]

Despite these and other works which advised the cultivation of hemp for reasons of national security, the fact that hemp could be more cheaply bought and transported from Russia kept Britain a hemp importing nation. Ultimately this situation was exploited by Napoleon, who made every effort to persuade the Russians to cease dealing with the UK. He failed at this, but not without severely hurting British trade during the

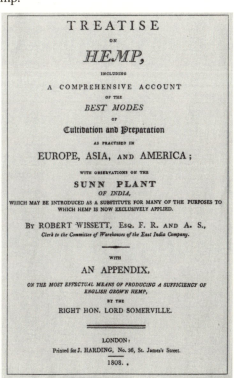

TREATISE
ON
HEMP,
INCLUDING
A COMPREHENSIVE ACCOUNT
OF THE
BEST MODES
OF
Cultivation and Preparation
AS PRACTISED IN
EUROPE, ASIA, AND AMERICA;
WITH OBSERVATIONS ON THE
SUNN PLANT
OF INDIA,
WHICH MAY BE INTRODUCED AS A SUBSTITUTE FOR MANY OF THE PURPOSES TO WHICH HEMP IS NOW EXCLUSIVELY APPLIED.

BY ROBERT WISSETT, ESQ. F. R. AND A. S.,
Clerk to the Committee of Warehouses of the East India Company.

WITH
AN APPENDIX,
ON THE MOST EFFECTUAL MEANS OF PRODUCING A SUFFICIENCY OF ENGLISH GROWN HEMP,
BY THE
RIGHT HON. LORD SOMERVILLE.

LONDON:
Printed for J. HARDING, No. 36, St. James's Street.
1808.

conflict. Napoleon was keen to realise the importance of economic war and the balance of trade; he was to remark after the war that "Britain conquered him with her spindles." [24]

While not enough hemp was grown to outfit the navy, it was continuously grown, and many locations reflect this activity in their names: Hampstead Heath, Hemphill, Hempstead, Southampton, Hampton Court, Hemp Walk, etc. Concern over dependency on Russian hemp was part of the reason for domestic cultivation; another step taken

Imports from Russia and Other Countries			
From: *The Linen Trade of Europe,* by John Horner, 1920			
From Russia		**From Other Countries**	
1851	33,229 tons	1851	31,441 tons
1852	26,857 tons	1852	26,551 tons
1853	40,320 tons	1853	20,619 tons
1854	1,044 tons	1854	35,927 tons
1855	Nil.	1855	28,010 tons

out of such concerns was the sourcing of hemp from other lands. Russia continued to supply much of the demand, but the government was not willing to place itself at the mercy of a sole purveyor, especially after the lesson learned at the hands of Napoleon. The table above shows a decline in imports from Russia against figures from other lands.

Italy was one of these countries, and in fact had been a supplier for centuries. Her hemp, which was used more for clothing than for rope, was of the finest quality, and demanded a higher price than domestic or Russian.

Demand by the twentieth century had slowed down, as ships came to use other types of power. This was to have a secondary effect in the paper trade, where used hempen ropes were recycled into pulp. Jute and abaca, which were used at times to replace hemp, were poor substitutes, and ultimately tree pulp came to replace ropes and rags.

Shortly before WWII, the British government looked to be prepared, contracting to buy from the then re-emerging American hemp

Imports from Italy and Naples		
From: *Cordage and Cordage Hemp,* by J. Woodhouse and P. Kilgour, 1919		
Season	**Italian**	**Naples**
1903-04	62,000 tons	28,000 tons
1904-05	40,000 tons	23,000 tons
1905-06	12,000 tons	27,000 tons
1906-07	58,000 tons	30,000 tons
1907-08	58,000 tons	31,000 tons
1908-09	41,000 tons	20,000 tons
1909-10	55,000 tons	24,000 tons
1910-11	50,000 tons	27,000 tons
1911-12	33,000 tons	30,000 tons

companies. The orders, however, were left undelivered after 1937, when a law went into effect that suppressed production in the US.[25] It was not until the 1980s that any great concern for industrial hemp use was voiced; in that decade world-wide awareness was increasing, as people began to realise the seriousness of deforestation and pollution.

Below:
Poster for 2004 Hemp Fair

Façade of The Hemp Shop,
Gardner St., Brighton
Photograph courtesy of
Bobby Pugh

CURRENT MOVEMENT

In Ireland and the UK there has always been a strong respect for the environment. The Green Party in both countries has actively supported hemp. This support has also come from the church, government, universities and the business sector. In the UK licenses to grow hemp were granted by the Home Office, and in 1993 six-hundred hectares were under cultivation. This increased to eight-hundred hectares in 1994, trebling to 2,400 in 1997.[26]

There is some apprehension about the plant, as cannabis to some people is still an 'evil weed'. Ian Low, director of Hempcore, noted that the "EU is in danger of throwing the baby out with the bath water."[27] This would be a blow to British farmers, especially as demand is increasing. Mercedes and BMW, for instance, are substituting British hemp for polypropylene in door panels,[28] paper manufacturers are using hemp, and GW pharmaceutical, a company devoted to cannabis medicines, is now traded publicly.

Overall support is strong, and since 1999 there has been a yearly Hemp Awareness march in London taking place on or near 1 May. In 2001 it started at Kennington Park and proceeded to Brockwell Park in Brixton. Turnout was significant with over 15,000 people, including a supportive police presence. The Police Foundation has in fact recommended that people not be jailed for possessing cannabis for their own recreational use, and senior officers have made it clear that they would prefer to focus their resources on more serious issues. The debate on this issue has gone back-and-forth many times, with changes to the law being made and then repealed, perhaps obscuring the real issue. One group to take an interest at the 2001 event was a local church, whose members were

Stand at Olympia,
London, **2002**

willing to get involved with hemp by polling attendees as to their views while discussing the environmental and legal aspects. There exists fervent support for cannabis in the Christian community, which looks beyond the propaganda disseminated by certain business interests.

Public events are not limited to the Mayday marches, but take place at all times of the year. In October of 2004 the Wembley Exhibition Centre hosted a Hemp Expo, drawing over one-hundred-and-fifty exhibitors and thousands of attendees, repeating its success the following year, while a second hemp event was held on Brick Lane, in East London. The public is able to shop at many outlets, such as Tony's Hemp Corner in North London which sells clothes, books and other hempen articles. Among the brands found at this shop is Mother Hemp, a Yorkshire based company, which is perhaps the leader in hemp food items, producing oils, seeds, and snack bars that are marketed across the UK. Many companies are in fact producing hemp oils; one purveyor, Paul Dean of Hemp Foods for You, presses his seeds to order, twenty-four hours before delivery, which has made his label one of the most sought after in the health and nutrition world in England. Hemp paper is available as specialty paper from companies such as Wookey Hole, environmentally friendly treefree® paper made by John Hanson of Dorset, and thicker hemp papers, for wallpaper and insulation, by the Hemp Paper Co. in Scotland. A small amount was made by The Hemp Co. in Dublin, including a batch with hemp leaves in a transparent sheet. This company, founded by Jim McDonald, works with designer

Evelyn Campbell and has managed to produce a quality range of hemp products, including a hemp/yak fibre jacket, which has become a top fashion item. The House of Hemp in Cornwall specialises in hemp textile articles, stocking a number of items made from a hemp/silk blend. In the same county Quintessential, based in Truro, sells a number of hemp body care products and papers. The most well known of all UK based enterprises that vend hemp products is Anita Roddick's The Body Shop, which is now found in almost every country of the world, an unbeatable success story that many have tried to emulate.

In 2002 Braintree, originally an Australian firm, established a presence in Camden Market in North London after spending two years in the Portobello Road area. The shop was a flagship address for the complex, situated over the Camden Lock and visible from Camden High Road. With its selection of their own brand of clothes as well as a good range of hemp products, from shampoo to books, it has become a main supplier of hemp products in London. Another immigrant, Jenny McPherson from Canada, has also brought hemp clothes to the British market. Her line, Enamore, is manufactured in Brighton and sells throughout England and Northern Ireland. Hemp threads have been the rage in the UK; Woody

UK edition of
The Reign of Law,
1900

Harrelson, when he arrived in November 2005 to promote his upcoming play *The Night of the Iguana*, proudly displayed his sartorial preference for this fibre by wearing it from head to toe while on the Jonathan Ross show, coincidentally on the same weekend as the Hemp Expo was in session at Wembley. On previous occasions he has been known to share his passion for hemp in the UK, stopping in at Tony's Hemp Corner in London, and The Hemp Shop in Brighton.

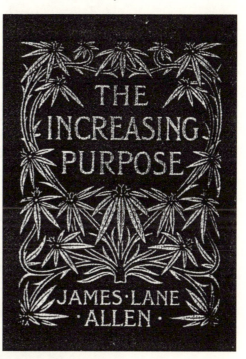

As most of the hemp grown in the UK is currently used for food products, the trend in growth is towards companies such as Yorkshire Hemp which now has the largest range of hemp food of any enterprise, including hemp beer, hemp sauce (akin to soy sauce), hemp pastas, hemp flour and hemp crisps.

Another aspect of hemp that is getting attention is the utilisation of stalks for biomass fuels. As this is a simple process, the turning of a carbohydrate into alcohols, (estimated to cost 17p/lt.) it is of concern to most people, as the price of fuel is several times that amount currently. Added to this are the facts that the local farmers could grow this fuel and that local companies could then process it, with little or no pollution, while providing employment, these realities make hemp a crop that cannot be just ignored. The rise in the price of energy in the 1970s brought about a change in government, when the price of a barrel quadrupled. In the drastic upheaval that resulted, people took to the streets to protest and the Conservatives lost their majority in Parliament. With this recent history in mind, it comes as no surprise to see the government pass a biomass intiative which will increase production of biomass fuel, both diesel and ethanol.

Press coverage of this is at times lacklustre, as many journalists are only beginning to look at the facts regarding cellulose conversion and get sidetracked into such issues as the cultivation of rape, a crop which has become ubiquitious in the English countryside but which offers very little in comparison to hemp.

The hemp issue is one that is constantly in the press, but there a mixed message may be perceived. Some articles tend to concentrate on marijuana laws, while others give only a brief synopsis of the whole picture, which leaves the reader at times confused and not sure why there is such a move to begin with, or, worse, believing that it is all something to do with drugs. *The Ecologist* has perhaps given it the most attention, going so far as to publish sections on treefree® hemp paper. The best press tends to be word-of-mouth, which may be the way in which most people have heard

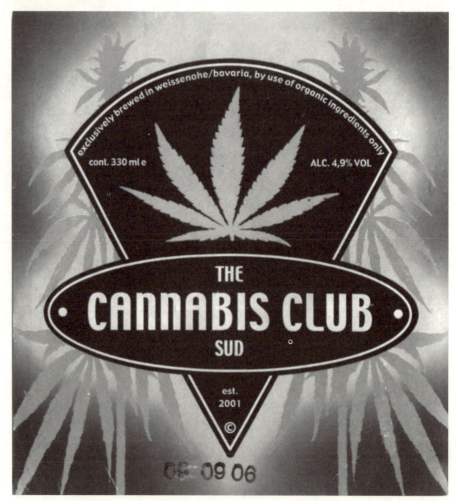

of hemp. As the range of hemp products has been increasingly dramatically over the last five years, people are tuning in. Quality and appeal will be the issues for the hemp movement to deal with today, as they were in the past; in 1724 William Mackintosh, when writing his pamphlet on hemp in Scotland, gave to the modern environmentalist the following advice: "...it is impossible to have hemp, or the manufacturers thereof, brought to any perfection in this kingdom, unless in convenient places throughout this whole kingdom, persons be encouraged to make it their business to acquire a competent knowledge therein."[29]

Three centuries on, hemp products are being brought to perfection, and it is none too soon, as the ecological and economic repurcussions of the way man has been using the planet are impacting on these islands in the north Atlantic, and one can no longer ignore the reality, which, as Joseph Gee of Gainsborough noted in the eighteenth century, are "...of stubborn facts." [30]

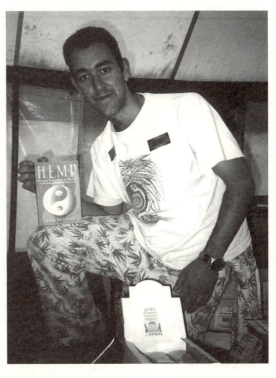

Above:
Daniel Benhaim, London 2002

Left: Plate from
Natural History for Sunday Schools,
Rev. Daniel Smith, 1845

Hemp—*Cannabis sativa*

November 4th, 5th & 6th

THE UK HEMP EXPO 2005

IT'S A GROWING EVENT!

1. Godwin, Prof. Henry. "The Ancient Cultivation of Hemp." Pp. 42-50 in *Antiquity,* XLI, 1967
2. *Ib.*
3. Thirsk, Joan. *Alternative Agriculture,* Oxford, OUP, 1998. p. 16
4. _____. *Fenland Farming in the Sixteenth Century.* Leicester University Press, 1965. p. 48
5. Martin, Celia. *The Bridport Trade: Rope & Net: Hemp & Flax.* Bridport, The Constanduros Press, 2003. pp. 7-8
6. Godwin
7. Fella, Thomas. *Book of Diveirs Deriges.* London, 1585
8. Tusser, Thomas. *Five Hundred Points of Good Husbandry.* London, Lackington, Allen & Co. 1812. [New ed.] p. 153
9. Marshall. *Rural Economy of the West of England.* 1796
10. Trenchard, Diana. *Dorset People Involved in the Growing of Hemp and Flax 1782-1793.* Weymouth, The Somerset & Dorset Family Historical Society, 2000
11. Horner, John. *The Linen Trade of Europe.* Belfast, McCaw, Stevenson & Orr. 1920. p. 26
12. Clark, Victors. *History of Manufactures in the U.S.* NY, McGraw-Hill, 1929. Vol. II, p. 24
13. Horner, p. 47
14. Flint. D.A. *Rules and Directions for Raising Hemp and Flax in Scotland.* Edinburgh, 1750. (UK Gov pub.)
15. Horner, pp. 36-37
16. Wissett, Robert. *A Treatise on Hemp.* London, J. Harding, 1808, p. 128
17. Campbell, Francis. *A Treatise on the Cultivation of Flax and Hemp.* Sydney, Statham & Porter, 1845. p. 80
18. Crosby, Alfred W. Jr. *America, Hemp, Russia and Napoleon.* Columbus, Ohio State University Press, 1965
19. Tucker, Benjamin. Letter of 5 April, 1810, as printed in *Letters and Papers on Agriculture, Planting, &., Selected from the Correspondence of the Bath and West of England Society.* vol XII, 1810
20. Wissett, p. 128
21. Thirsk, p. 159
22. Wissett [2nd ed.], 1808. p. iii
23. *Ib.*
24. Anon. *Report of the Commission of Patents for the Year 1861.* Washington, GPO, 1862. p. 11
25. Lupien, John C. *Unravelling an American Dilemma: The Demonization of Marihuana.* Malibu, Pepperdine University Thesis, 1995
26. Bócsa, Dr. Ivan and Michael Karus. *The Cultivation of Hemp.* Sebastopol (Ca.), Hemptech, 1998
27. Staples. Sally, quoted in *The Times,* 23 Sep. 2000
28. *Ib*
29. Mackintosh, William. *A Treatise concerning the manner of Fallowing of Ground, Raising of Grass-seeds, and Training of Lint and Hemp.* Edinburgh, Robert Fleming & Co., 1724
30. Gee, Joseph of Gainsborough. *Considerations on the Growth of Hemp & Flax in Great Britain.* London, 1765.

V. Brave New World

KENYON GIBSON, NICK MACKINTOSH
AND CINDY MACKINTOSH

*T*he first recorded planting of hemp by a colonial power in the New World took place in 1545, by Spaniards in Chile. Less than a hundred years later the Pilgrims followed suit in New England. Hemp, a most essential item, was quick to take root in North and South America.

However, these were not the first plantings of hemp, as many history textbooks claim. Jack Frazier, in *The Great American Hemp Industry*, cites several early authors who write of hemp growing naturally without any European influence:

John de Verrazano: "...we found these folkes to be more white than those that we found before, being clod with certaine leaves that hang on the boughs of trees, which they sewe together with threds of wilde hemp."[1]

Thomas Hariot: "The truth is, that of hempe and flaxe there is no great store in any one place together, by reason it is not planted but as the soule doth yield of itself."[2]

Lord Delaware: "The country is wonderful fertile and very rich, Hempe better than English growing wilde in abundance."[3]

Du Pratz: "...I ought not to omit to take notice, that hemp grows naturally on the lands adjoining to the lakes on the West of the Mississippi."[4]

Frazier further notes evidence of pre-Columbian voyages to the New World, quoting Cyrus Gordon, whose book *Before Columbus: Links between the Old World and Ancient America*, documents such voyages to 531 BC. Gordon brings to light the discovery of a Hebrew inscription found at Bat Creek, Tennessee in 1890. The inscription, dated to 35 AD, in conjunction with Bar Kohba coins from the next century found in Kentucky, strongly supports the possibility of a Jewish settlement in the New World shortly after the Diaspora.[5] Another writer who Frazier cites is Henriette Mertz, who discusses Asian voyages to the West Coast, in *Pole Ink, Two Ancient Records of Chinese Explorations in America*. It is just possible that the original 'Indians' reached North America in this fashion, and brought with them hemp seeds.[6] Such voyages may not have been possible without hempen ropes and sails, which were of so much a necessity to Europe that hemp was mandated in the New World.

In the Spanish colonies, such orders were taken seriously, with the viceroy of the New World colonies encouraging hemp cultivation by providing seed to settlers. The chief areas of production were Chile, Mexico, and California. In 1795 Spain opened up the Mississippi to international trade to encourage exports, some of which were actually transacted using hemp as barter.[7] With greater access to trade routes, California increased its hemp production, going from 12,500lbs. in 1807 to over 220,000lbs. in 1810.[8] Much of Latin America has a Mediterranean climate, and hemp was of easy cultivation. Remnants of these plantings still thrive, especially in the Valparaiso district of Chile, where it has had the most continuous cultivation anywhere in the New World. The Brazilians in the early nineteenth century entertained hopes of challenging Russia for her hemp sales to Britain, but this hope never materialised, perhaps due to pressure exerted from Portugal which would certainly not have wanted their colonists to be aiding and abetting their rival.[9] At that time European colonial powers looked across the Atlantic for their supply of hemp, including France, whose merchants heard that hemp was growing wild in the New World and sensed opportunity. It was not as easy for them as they thought, but after some initial disappointments, the French believed they could still make a profit on hemp if they could persuade the settlers in 'New France' (French Canada) to cultivate it. To this end, Samuel Champlain, the great explorer and coloniser, brought hemp seeds along on his early expeditions.[10] By 1606, hemp was growing in Port Royal in Nova Scotia under the supervision of botanist and apothecary, Louis Herbert.[11] Both the French and the British had difficulty in finding enough labourers to cultivate the hemp as the early settlers were busy trying to grow food to eat. Jean Talon, the finance minister of Quebec, provided seed free to farmers which they were to plant immediately and return with seed from the following year's crop. He also confiscated all the thread in the colony agreeing only to sell it in return for hemp. This forced the settlers to grow hemp so that they could barter or sell it for thread with which they could sew clothes for their children.[12] By this rather unorthodox method, Talon succeeded in increasing the production of hemp to the satisfaction of the French government. The French traded hemp cloth with the natives in the Louisiana territory,[13] and a French settlement office published a treatise on the cultivation of hemp.

However, there were times as early as 1721 when France, in order to protect its home industries, discouraged production in its colonies. Generally this was not the case; the Governor of Louisiana was told to increase production by offering free hemp seed to the colonists.[14] Towards the end of the eighteenth century New Orleans had a hemp factory which provided ample cordage for ships which docked there. By 1763 French interests in the New World were to subside, as the Treaty of Paris gave up Quebec.

British settlers were encouraged to grow hemp in all the colonies, which was done in Canada by land grant. Perhaps the first orders to

The Indians who originally inhabited Manhattan had learned to twist fibers into fishing lines long before the coming of the white man. According to legend they grew a fiber, which they spun and wove into fabric. Whether this was a grass or some form of cotton is not known.

Frank L. Walton,
Tomahawks to Textiles, **1953**

cultivate hemp were made at Jamestown, Virginia, which Jack Herer, in his 1985 book *The Emperor Wears no Clothes,* notes as the nation's first 'marijuana laws' in 1619. Massachusetts and Connecticut followed suit by mandating cultivation in the 1630s.[15] A 1635 record of Maryland recommends hemp for the soil, and notes that the first American textile mill, built by Ezekial Rogers in Massachusetts in 1638, was used to process hemp.[16] With the government behind the cultivation of hemp, it was not hard to encourage its growth. Another tactic used by the authorities was to allow its use for payments of taxes, as in Virginia, where hemp could be used to pay the poll tax, or even as legal tender, as a statute of 1682 shows.[17] A 1685 account notes both New Jersey and Pennsylvania as good for growing hemp, that much was shipped to England, and that a receipt for hemp from the store house register was as good as money.[18] The hemp industry in Pennsylvania was much worked by German immigrants, who brought with them knowledge from the old country. Many of them settled in Lancaster County, which was the centre of the hemp industry for Pennsylvania in the eighteenth and nineteenth centuries. Over a hundred water mills for processing fibre hemp were working in that county between 1720 and 1870, while neighbouring counties such as York had dozens of such mills. Before the invention of the cotton gin, and possibly for some decades thereafter, hemp was the primary fibre for use in homespun clothing in that state.[19] Oil mills also existed at that time, many worked by the Moravian Brethren who settled in Pennsylvania, and hemp seed was often brought to them to be crushed, the oil being used for food while the remains were fed to cattle.

Subsidies were used at times, as Massachusetts law decks record; in 1701 one subsidy was enacted, giving farmers a farthing per lb. of hemp, which then went for four-and-a-half pence per lb. Virginia was a steady producer of this staple; one 1649 account mentions "an old planter of over 30 years standing who sows yearly of hemp and flax, and causes it to be spun."[20] In 1723 South Carolina encouraged the production of hemp by offering a bounty and in 1733 Richard Hall was paid by the state to write a book in order to promote the production of hemp and flax. He travelled to Holland to study European practices and returned with Dutch seed.[21]

Ultimately the colonies were to become independent, starting with the US. Independence, however, did not curtail hemp production; in many areas production increased, particularly in the US, where the Founding Fathers were hemp growers.

Benjamin Franklin, as the leading paper manufacturer in the colonies, noted the raising of it in his state, of which he was in support. Thomas Paine noted hemp as a strength of the colonies, citing it as evidence of self-reliance that made the revolution plausible.[22] George Washington grew it on his estates, and took an interest in its uses, stopping on one occasion to visit a hemp paper factory in Hempstead, New York.[23]

> The Anglo-Saxon farmers had scarce conquered foothold, stronghold, freehold in the Western wilderness before they became sowers of hemp.
> **James Lane Allen,** *The Reign of Law,* **1900**

Advertisement in the *Pennsyvania Gazzette,* **March, 1766**

Notice is hereby given to the PUBLIC, THAT at Bethlehem, in Northampton County, the Mills for rubbing Hemp, ſtamping Millet, and preſſing Oil, are done and ſet at work already. The Hemp is not rubbed with a Pumiceſtone in the common Way, that being attended with many Dangers ; but it is ſtamped in a particular Manner, and becomes pliabler and fitter than with the Stone. In the Oil Mill every one may alſo have his Flaxſeed cleanſed. The Mills for Groats, peeled Barley, Oatmeal and Spelt, will alſo be finiſhed this Summer, and ſet to work in July or Auguſt next. The further Particulars may be enquired at the ſaid Bethlehem, by

JOHN ARBO.

Thomas Jefferson even took a stand in favour of hemp vs. a native plant, tobacco. He voiced his opinion in his *Farm Journal* on 16 March 1791, stating that tobacco required much more manure, employed less people, and did not contribute to the wealth or defence of the state. He also compared hemp favourably to flax, and invented a method for breaking, which involved a thrashing machine moved by a horse; this was to be the new nation's first patent.[24] John Quincy Adams wrote of Russian hemp cultivation which was printed into government records in the early nineteenth century (Chapter XVI.)

From:
James Lane Allen's
The Reign of Law, **1900**

"THE EARLIEST SOWER OF THE HEMP GOES FORTH INTO THE FIELDS."

After independence, there was new pressure on the young nation to produce hemp, as the need for defence and trade fell solely on its shoulders. Ironically, while great amounts of hemp were grown, they were not water-retted, and thus the US, like other nations, sent to Russia for its supplies. At one stage Yankee ships carried hemp not only to Boston and New York, but also to London and Liverpool, acting as agents for the British whom Napoleon tried to force out of the Baltic.[25]

Many Americans voiced concern over the amount of imported hemp, and two ideas were put forth: tariffs, which were unpopular with the merchants, and subsidies to farmers producing water-retted hemp. While much debate was heard on these proposals, Russian hemp continued to be the choice of the navy, and sold for 100 percent more than American dew-retted hemp,[26] which was used for other purposes; bagging cotton, ordinary ropes, and clothing. In 1824 the Plymouth Cordage Co. was founded in Plymouth, Massachusetts. This firm used Russian hemp, despite a tariff rise of four cents a pound that same year. Bourne Spourner, Plymouth's founder, was an abolitionist, and his dislike of slavery put him off to using the products made by such means. Despite paying higher prices for hemp, the company prospered to become the largest cordage company in the world by 1950.[27]

The following table shows that Kentucky and Missouri had become the centres of production, while the northeastern states had by 1850 just about abandoned hemp growing. Mechanisation and westward expansion were two forces behind this shift, but much was due to the soil and climate in Kentucky being especially favourable to cannabis cultivation. The first recorded crop of hemp grown in that state was by Archibald McNeil of Clark's Creek, who planted it near Danville in 1775.[28] The 'Blue Grass' region especially attracted hemp farmers, and was for over a century to remain the largest growing area of hemp in all of North America. Its fertile soil, formed by the disintegration of lower Silurian limestone was especially rich in mineral deposits.[29]

Comparative Amounts of hemp by state (1850-1870)		
From: *Tabular Statements from 1840-1870 of the Agricultural Products of the States and Territories of the United States of America*, **by Samuel B. Ruggles, 1874**		
1850	**1860**	**1870**
West Virginia —	—	37 tons
Kentucky 17,787 tons	39,409 tons	7,777 tons
Tennessee 595 tons	2,243 tons	1,033 tons
Mississippi 7 tons	—	3 tons
Arkansas 15 tons	447 tons	—
Texas 179 tons	5 tons	—
Maine —	50 tons	—
New Hampshire —	81 tons	—
Massachusetts —	—	2 tons
Connecticut —	3 tons	—
New York —	5 tons	6 tons
New Jersey —	430 tons	5 tons
Pennsylvania —	46 tons	571 tons
Delaware —	1 ton	—
Maryland 63 tons	272 tons	—
Virginia 139 tons	15 tons	31 tons
North Carolina 39 tons	3,016 tons	—
South Carolina —	1 ton	—
Georgia —	31 tons	—
Florida —	1 ton	—
Ohio 150 tons	1,212 tons	25 tons
Indiana —	4,222 tons	22 tons
Michigan —	776 tons	—
Illinois —	1,502 tons	174 tons
Wisconsin —	356 tons	—
Minnesota —	109 tons	—
Iowa —	651 tons	4 tons
Missouri 16,028 tons	19,267 tons	2,816 tons
Kansas —	44 tons	35 tons
Nebraska —	9 tons	—
California —	—	200 tons

Hemp in Kentucky in 1782 -
early landmark in the history
of the soil, of the people.
Cultivated first for the needs
of cabin and clearing solely;
for twine and rope, towel and
table, sheet and shirt.
James Lane Allen,
The Reign of Law, 1900

Early hemp cultivation in Kentucky was hampered by the scarcity of seed and its consequential high price. By 1790 the situation was different; it was noted in the *Kentucky Gazette* in March of that year that hemp was "the most certain crop and the most valuable commodity." The exportation of hemp products from Kentucky was hampered by the difficulties of transport and its consequent costs. As new settlers moved west, crossing the mountains, new markets opened up. The Mississippi was the means by which goods could be transported. At that time the lower reaches of the river and New Orleans were Spanish possessions.

In order to boost trade the Spanish in 1788 opened up the Mississippi Basin, giving special privileges to such men as Gen. James Wilkinson. In 1795, the Pinckney Treaty, concluded with Spain, gave Americans free navigation on the Mississippi and a 'deposit' in New Orleans to land and store goods. The latter was revoked in 1803 for a few months, which caused some inconvenience and a reduction in the export of hemp. However, due to the 'Louisiana Purchase' in 1803, the export market was reinvigorated, and Kentucky was able to send hemp and produce to the southern markets at will. The wars in Europe in the early part of the nineteenth century helped the cultivation and manufacture of Kentucky hemp. In wartime, importation of European hemp products and hemp fibre was curtailed which meant Kentucky took up the slack with exports to the East and the South. After 1815 European imports resumed with the eastern states resuming their trade with European countries. In 1839 Kentucky's hemp crop was badly damaged by drought, but it was able to satisfy its own needs by imports from other states such as Illinois, Missouri, and Minnesota.[30] North Americans tried to raise the best crops they could, and this meant constant revision and a willingness to try new methods. However, Russian, Italian, and Dutch hemp continued to be the most desirable, largely due to the centuries of experience that these

Production, Acreage, and Import of Hemp in the United States From: *Matthews' Textile Fibers*, by Herbert R. Mausberger, 1947			
5-Year Periods	Hemp Grown(acres)	Fiber Produced (tons)	Fiber imported(tons)
1876-1880	15,000	7,369	459
1881-1885	11,000	5,421	5,393
1886-1890	16,000	8,270	10,427
1891-1895	11,000	5,631	4,962
1896-1900	10,000	5,177	5,000
1901-1905	12,000	6,175	5,000
1906-1910	10,000	5,150	6,375
1911-1913	10,000	5,100	6,000
1914-1918	10,500	8,500	5,000
1919-1923	8,600	3,800	4,000
1924-1928	4,300	1,800	2,000
1929-1933	1,200	500	1,000
1934-1938	7,100	600	241

nations possessed. In Europe and Russia there was much literature available along with superior seed stocks, which gave these nations the edge in cultivating hemp.

It was apparent to some producers and distributors of hemp that the Kentucky seed was in need of improvement, and importation of quality seed was encouraged; 'Bologna hemp', grown from imported Italian seed, was cultivated with excellent results.[31] The fibre was white in colour, with a strength and fineness that was much admired. It was at that time put forward that the navy should obtain seed from Russia or Italy and supply Kentucky farmers so that they produce better hemp.[32] In 1851 L. Maltby

Fig. 6. Spreading Hemp on the Ground in Kentucky.
From Report No. 8, U. S. Dept. Agr., Fiber Investigation.

From: *Hemp*,
S.S. Boyce, 1900
[originally from a US gov. publication, 1898]

of Mason County, having learnt of the *So-Na* variety from a connection in France, brought back some of these seeds, some of which were planted successfully in Louisiana.[33] Other varieties included Russian hemp but these were not always successful since some of the seeds were more adapted to northern European latitudes than the southern states such as Kentucky. That is not to say that there were not successful plantings. A French colleague of William L. Vance, a hemp farmer, gave him some Chinese seed similar to *So-Na* with excellent results. This variety was from then on to be known as the 'Vance seed'.[34]

Other factors figured into the equation, such as sorting. Dr. Francis Campbell in 1845 laments the fact that while Canadian hemp was of good quality, it was never sorted properly, and could not be relied upon.[35] But the biggest factor was in processing, as US farmers favoured dew-retting; however, the more desirable fibres were obtained from the water-retting method. Consequently few Kentucky farmers ever achieved top prices for their hemp.

In 1842 the *Frankfort Commonwealth* urged farmers to water-ret most of their crop because of the higher prices they could achieve. The crop that year was expected to be the largest ever recorded. Some farmers did follow this advice, but, despite a growing interest in improving the technique, they were still a minority.[36] Only when the price of dew-retted hemp fell to that of half water-retted hemp did farmers change their age-old practices. Water-retting was a time consuming business, which the farmer was not prepared to undertake unless there was extra financial benefit. Until the Civil War the Kentucky farmer continued to depend for the most part on the manufacture of bail rope and bagging to consign his hemp fibre.[37] The quality of dew-retted cordage was not of an acceptable quality for military or merchant marine use. The US Navy saw the strategic importance to have a home grown supply of cordage and canvas and therefore tried to encourage the growth of superior hemp equal to that of Russia's. Previous attempts were made in 1810, an account of which is as follows:

> In the years 1809 and '10, Russia hemp being scarce and very high, we urged on Messrs. Caruthers, of Lexington, Virginia, (large dealers in the article, and living in the neighborhood of the best hemp country) the advantage and necessity of improving it, and contracted to give them $290 per ton, for 70 to 80 tons, to be clear and well prepared. Mr. W. Caruthers paid particular and personal attention to it and it proved, (with some exception) of excellent quality. This was all grown in Rockbridge, Botetourt, and Montgomery counties, on the James, the Jackson, and Cowpasture rivers, and this has hitherto been the part of the State where it was grown to any extent, the three counties then producing 50 to 100 tons each annually. Knowing that the practice of preparing it was by dew, or air-rotting, which is very tedious, it lying out for months, exposed to all the vicissitudes of weather, and is often thereby injured in strength, always in color, in the year 1810, Mr. Theo. Armistead, who was Navy Agent here, and also had a rope walk, and who was very zealous in the improvement of country hemp, with our establishment, held out strong inducements to have the hemp water-rotted, in place of the usual mode, but so difficult is it to change old habits, that only in one instance did we succeed. Colonel Wilson C. Nicholas, of Albemarle county, and formerly Governor of Virginia, water-rotted his crop; and, to encourage and extend its mode, we gave for the part of it we got, (a few tons) $360 per ton; the quality was excellent, color much improved, and we believe, the fibre also, in strength and fineness, though it was not so well cleaned or prepared as it might have been. The experiment seems satisfactory that it was capable of improvement by proper management.[38]

In 1824 the navy desired American hemp to be used on the USS *North Carolina* so as to compare it side-by-side with Russian hemp. Not enough American water-retted could be procured, so the experiment was delayed and took place some months later on board the USS *Constellation*. The conclusion made was that the Russian hemp was superior for maritime purposes.[39] A further attempt to use domestic cordage took place in 1841 when the navy contracted to buy five-hundred tons of water-retted hemp from David Myerle of Kentucky. Myerle delivered twenty tons to the Charleston, Massachusetts shipyard for inspection, where it was not accepted; tests showed his product to be stronger than the best Riga Rein, but the amount of tow and waste caused the inspectors to reject it under the terms of the contract. This act of rejection of domestic hemp in favour of imported hemp sparked off debates for years, with allegations of corruption voiced in Congress. Commodore John Nicholson sided with Myerle, telling him: "you have been damned badly treated, and your hemp should never have been rejected." Sympathy, however, did not prevent Myerle from bankruptcy. His hemp was seized by creditors, who in turn suffered a loss, as they were not adept in the handling of its sale.[40]

Over the years tariffs have been enacted against Russian hemp, starting in 1792 with the tax of $20 per ton, rising to $60 in 1828, then falling back nearer to original levels until abolished in the twentieth century. [41]

"THEN THE FIELDS ARE AS THE CAMP OF AN ARMY."

From:

James Lane Allen's
The Reign of Law, **1900**

Another attempt at using American hemp failed completely in which un-retted hemp was used. It fermented, putting paid to many attempts to use un-retted cordage.[42] In 1906 hemp was successfully water retted in Northfield, Minnesota in cement tanks with water circulation and temperature carefully controlled. The resultant fibre was similar to Italian hemp in quality.[43]

At that time prices were coming off their highs caused by the wars in Europe, when hemp was fought over. War was the main cause of scarcity and price increase; but other factors had an effect as well, such as drought. Many prominent families in Kentucky, including the Speeds and the Todds, grew hemp and were affected by the changes. The latter were a major force in the hemp industry, and of some historical interest, as Mary Todd was to marry a lawyer from Illinois by the name of Abraham Lincoln.

In 1873 Kentucky produced 10,687 tons, 8,975 of which were from the counties of Bourbon, Foyette, Jossamine, Scott, and Woodford.[44] This figure is well off previous highs from before the Civil War, which caused great disruption; hemp growing came to a standstill and did not ever recover to its previous levels. One interesting use of hemp that the war occasioned was that of movable defences - Secessionist soldiers rolled wetted bundles of hemp towards the Union Army, thus able to fire upon their enemy from behind movable cover. By such means was the battle of Lexington, Missouri, decided.[45]

		St. Petersburg Exports to United States in 1804 From: *The Linen Trade of Europe,* by John Horner, 1920		
No. of Ships	**For**	**Clean Hemp** Poods*	**Out-shot Hemp** Poods	**Half-clean Hemp** Poods	**Hemp Codilla** Poods
14	Boston	47,555	13,991	-	-
14	Salem	34,536	13,772	653	-
11	New York	41,822	27,034	437	652
4	Baltimore	19,804	1,870	-	-
4	Newburyport	-	12,800	507	-
4	Providence	12,889	3,099	712	-
3	Marblehead	4,909	-	-	-
3	Philadelphia	7,584	7,303	-	-
2	Gloucester	5,596	242	-	-
1	Portland	3,441	3,659	-	-
1	Plymouth	3,441	3,659	-	-
1	Newbedford	3,715	3,669	-	-
1	St. Michaels	-	-	-	-
1	Rhode Island	2,652	-	-	-
1	Lisbon	575	255	1,031	-

*1 pood = 36 lbs.(16.3 kg)

By 1879 total hemp production had been reduced to 5,025 tons with Kentucky producing 4,583 tons, the remainder coming from Missouri, Michigan, Kansas, Illinois, Minnesota and North Carolina.[46] The decline in the hemp industry was one of many adversities suffered by both sides in the war, and in 1882, an organisation was founded to address this loss - the American Flax and Hemp Spinners and Growers Association. In 1889, Edwin Willits, then Assistant Secretary of Agriculture, noted the decline in the yearly report and exhorted his countrymen to extend the culture of hemp. Noting that its production is an industry that dates back to the earliest history of the United States, and acknowledging the great changes in the manufacture and economics of hemp, he looks ahead, hoping that the "energy for which the American people are noted" and "data concerning economical production" would encourage cultivation.[47]

That year 11,511 tons were grown in the US, 94 percent of which was grown in Kentucky.[48] Most of this was used for bagging and binding cotton, the price being affected by the economics of the southern states. Ultimately metal bands replaced hemp altogether for cotton baling. As this happened other markets were sought out, and hemp was exported to such places as Cuba to be used for bagging sugar.

Hemp continued to move west, with a hemp mill established at Champaign, Illinois in the 1870s. Its strength and durability gave it great appeal to the settlers, covering the early Connestoga wagons. In 1887 hemp was grown in Freemont, Nebraska, by hemp farmers from Champaign; in 1895 some of the men connected with this venture began growing hemp at Havelock, near Lincoln. The bottomlands of the Platte River produced good crops, although irregular rainfall was a setback.[49]

As the settlers reached California, the 'Golden State', hemp followed; it was first grown in that state on a commercial scale at Gridley, in Butte County, by John Heaney, who had grown it at Champaign and who devised the machine used there for making long tow. Mr. Heaney built a machine with some improvements at Gridley, and after three disastrous inundations from the Feather River moved to Courtland, in the lower Sacramento Valley, where the reclaimed lands were protected by dikes. The work was being continued at Rio Vista, in Solano County, under more favourable conditions and with a machine still further improved. The hemp fibre produced in California was very strong and was generally lighter in colour than that produced in Kentucky. In 1912 hemp was first cultivated on a commercial scale under irrigation at Lerdo, near Bakersfield, California and a larger acreage was grown there in 1918. The seed for both crops was obtained in Kentucky.[50]

In 1895 another government report encouraged the use of hemp; written by Charles Richards Dodge, it noted the forces of market manipulation, conducted by "binding twine manufacturers trying to exclude hemp so as to overcharge the public."[51] He claimed that this was against American economic interests, as it forced imports while denying the farmer a crop to grow on their own soil.

In southern California the valley of the Kern River produced noteworthy crops at the end of the nineteenth century.[52] Much wild hemp was found in these areas, and persists to this day; wild cannabis in the foothills of Santa Barbara is often the progeny of that grown centuries earlier by the Spanish.

WWI occasioned an increase in hemp production which went from less than 5,000 tons to 20,000 tons in 1917 for the whole of the US, Kentucky producing over 7,000 tons. The acreage devoted to hemp cultivation over the same period increased from about 10,000 to 42,000 acres.[53] By 1919 the situation had changed so that the total US

On the 26th of June, 1846, a contract was made with the American Hemp Company to furnish 250 tons annually for three years, at $210 per ton if delivered at Louisville or St. Louis, or $235 per ton if delivered at Charlestown navy-yard. On the 13th of July, same year, a contract was made with Mr. Gideon J. Pillow for 90 tons, in three annual deliveries, at $200 per ton. On the 29th August, same year, a contract was made with George W. Billings for 330 tons, in three annual deliveries: first delivery at $220 per ton; second at $210 per ton; and the third at $200 per ton.

Chris Wm. Skinner,
(letter dated **February 1, 1850**, *to the Secretary of the Navy)*

DEW AND WATER-ROTTED HEMP.—THE PLOW. 401

SOFTENING DEW AND WATER-ROTTED HEMP.

INQUIRY BY A MANUFACTURER.

PATERSON, Jan. 6, 1847.

Dear Sir: I wanted to see your new books and talk farming; but more especially to ask you to make inquiry of some of your *Kentucky* friends as to the process they have in practice there for softening Dew and Water-rotted Hemp, to render it as soft as Flax. They do this here, and in Scotland, but it is by a very imperfect machine and cumbrous withal. In Kentucky, I am told, they do it at little expense and less trouble. If it can be done well, it would bring this hemp into very extensive use. I have done it very successfully without the aid of a machine; but a gentleman from Kentucky, visiting me, assured me it was done better, with less trouble and expense, in that State.

If you should get any information regarding it, I hope it will be of such a character as to avail of the process without farther inquiry. If it be a machine, let us have a drawing; if a chemical agent, let us know what it is that is to be applied to produce the desired effect.

Very many happy New-Years to you from yours, truly,   JOHN TRAVERS.
J. S. SKINNER, Esq.

From:
Monthly Journal of Agriculture,
March 1847

production was a mere 3,000 tons, with Kentucky producing three-hundred tons. Wisconsin had by then replaced Kentucky as the leading producer, harvesting 1,500 tons in 1919; Kentucky moved from producing fibre to producing seed for other hemp growing states.[54]

From:
James Lane Allen's
The Reign of Law, **1900**

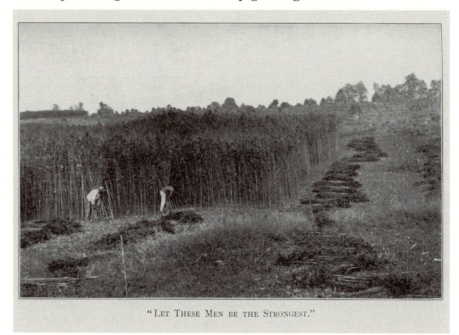

"LET THESE MEN BE THE STRONGEST."

Canada was also growing hemp into the twentieth century. Both the US and Canada were also starting to realise the value of hemp for cellulose, which was, and still is, of major commercial importance. In 1904 and 1906, the *Pulp Paper Magazine* of Canada published two articles on using the waste from cannabis in paper. The US Department of Agriculture in 1908 and 1910 also published articles on this theme, the latter work citing hemp as "one of the most promising."[55] A third article in 1911 was to follow, titled "Paper from Refuse Hemp Stalks." At this time, there was growing awareness of how to separate cellulose from hemp, extracting it even from the hurds, which were then considered waste material. German chemists had made studies of this, and given the multitude of applications for cellulose, it was only a matter of time before the business community responded. John C. Lupien, in his Pepperdine University thesis of 1995, documents this; two figures he mentions are M.J. Conolly, a New York businessman, and H.W. Bellrose, of Minnesota. The former had by 1935 acquired several patents for utilising hemp fibre and hurds in the production of cellulose. He was joined in his efforts by Minnesota businessmen Joseph H. Gunderson and V.A. Batzner, forming the National Cellulose Corp. At that time there were six such patents in the US, and an equal number in Europe.[56]

Bellrose was a very active promoter of hemp as a raw material source for paper, and cellulose based products such as artificial textiles, explosive and plastic. He was also the owner of a patent for the Selvig hemp-decorticating machine, which was uncannily like the Schlicten Decorticator of 1919. Henry Ford was also aware of hemp, and spent over a decade researching plastic automobiles. He hoped to 'grow' automobiles from the soil, and finally succeeded in doing just that, making a stronger body, at only 67 percent of the weight of a steel car. He used cellulose for this, extracted from hemp. Taking an axe to it, literally, he proved that it could withstand great blows, reportedly ten times greater than these which could be withstood by steel.[57] Hemp was in demand, the wave of the future, yet still valued for its traditional uses; 116 million lbs. of hemp seed were used in America just for paint and varnish in 1935.[58]

Thus, during the great depression, a valuable resource was being put to new uses, for which there was a world-wide market. *Popular Mechanics* in 1938 published an article titled "The New Billion Dollar Crop," while hemp companies were starting nationwide, as people realised the potential of this plant which had been so much a part of the development of the country.

1. Frazier, Jack. *The Great American Hemp Industry*. Peterstown (WV), Solar Age Press, 1991. p. 5
2. *Ib.*, pp. 5-6
3. *Ib.*, pp. 5-6
4. *Ib.*, p. 6
5. *Ib.*, p. 10
6. Mertz, Henriette. *Pale Ink: Two Ancient Records of Chinese Explorations in America*. Chicago, Swallow Press, 1972. [2nd ed.]
7. Forster, Erich. *History of Hemp in Chile*. Surfer Seeds, internet essay, 1997
8. Guenet, François. *Chanvre* N.d., n.p.
9. Tucker. Benjamin. Letter of 5 April, 1810, as printed in *Letters and Papers on Agriculture, Planting, &., Selected from the Correspondence of the Bath and West of England Society*. vol XII, 1810
10. Guenet
11. *Ib.*
12. *Ib.*
13. Conrad, Chris. Hemp: *Lifeline to the Future*. LA, Creative Xpressions, 1993. p. 23
14. Guenet
15. Anon. *A Relation of Maryland*. London, 1635. p. 20
16. Walton, Frank. *Tomahawks to Textiles*. NY, Appleton-Century-Crofts, 1953. p. 91
17. Colony of Virginia tax records, 1680-1690
18. Budd, Thomas. *Good Order Established in Pennsylvania and New Jersey in America*. NY, Burt Franklin, 1971 [4th ed.]. pp. 30-41
19. Stark, Les. *Hempstone Heritage I*. Lancaster (PA), Mostof Press, 2005
20. Clark, Victor S. *History of Manufactures in the US*. NY, McGraw-Hill.
21. Conrad, p. 25
22. Paine, Thomas. *Common Sense*. 1776
23. Guenet
24. *Ib.*
25. Crosby, Alfred W. Jr. *America, Hemp, Russia, and Napoleon*. Columbus, Ohio State University Press, 1965
26. Hopkins, James F. *A History of the Hemp Industry in Kentucky*. Lexington, University of Kentucky Press, 1951.
27. Morison, Samuel Eliot. *The Ropemakers of Plymouth*. Boston, The Riverside Press, 1950. p. 3
28. Moore, Brent. *A Study of the Past, the Present, and the Possibilities of the Hemp Industry in Kentucky*. Lexington, 1905. p. 16
29. Peter, Robert. "Chemical Analyses of the Hemp and Buckwheat Plants", in the *Geological Survery of Kentucky*, 1890.
30. Hopkins, pp. 73-74
31. Guenet
32. *Ib.*
33. Hopkins, pp. 106-107
34. *Ib.*
35. Campbell, Dr. Francis. *Treatise on the Culture of Flax and Hemp*. Sydney, Statham & Forster, 1845

36. Hopkins, p. 172
37. Guenet
38 . *US Congress Report No. 381*. Washington, GPO, 1830. pp. 24-25
39. Hopkins
40. *Ib.*
41. Guenet
42. *Ib.*
43. Dewey, Lyster L. "Hemp", pp. 286-343 in the *USDA Yearbook* 1913. Washington, GPO, 1914
44. Peter
45. Frost, Patricia C. *The Encyclopedia of the Civil War*. NY, Harper Perennial, 1986. p. 435
46. Willits, Edwin. "Textile Fiber Production", pp. 46-48 in the *Report of the Secretary of Agriculture*, 1889. Washington, GPO, 1889
47. *Ib.*
48. Guenet
49. *Ib.*
50. Dewey
51. Dodge, Charles Richard. "Hemp", pp. 215-222 in the *USDA Yearbook,* 1895. Washington, GPO, 1896
52. Guenet
53. *Ib.*
54. Kentucky
55. Lupien
56. *Ib.*
57. *http://www.edmunds.com/advice/specialreports/articles/105341.article.html*
58. Herer, Jack. *The Emperor Wears no Clothes*. Van Nuys (Ca.), AH HA Publishing, 1998 [11th ed.]. p. 1

VI. North America

KENYON GIBSON, NICK MACKINTOSH
AND CINDY MACKINTOSH

*T*hese last five chapters have traced hemp's history, showing its long-standing use in clothing, food, oil, textiles, and paper. In the twentieth century it was discovered that even the waste parts of hemp had a value, as they were made of cellulose, for which there was then, and is still now, a large market. Much of this was taking place in the US, where cellulose derivatives were being patented on a constant basis; in fact, the US was in this century to lead the world in such technologies, foremost among them the manufacture of plastics. A major proponent of hemp was the US government.

However, something was to change all this; the plant so favoured by Washington, Jefferson and Adams was to be vilified and prohibited to the point where if one of them were to grow a single acre of this crop, they would be facing the death penalty. To provide an explanation as to why that is the case, history must be explored, and an examination of the characters involved must be made so as to show what forces there are at work. As a start, one might regard the recent statement made in *The Economist*[1] asserting that it was in the interests of Andrew Mellon, the Hearst newspaper syndicate and the Du Pont Corp. to put a stop to the use of hemp. The article maintained that they brought this about through Mellon's nephew-in-law, Harry J. Anslinger. This is not solely the opinion of this one magazine, but rather, is what many have been telling the world for years. Jack Herer asserted this[2] in his 1985 book *The Emperor Wears no Clothes;* authors Chris Conrad and Ed Rosenthal provided a similar opinion in 1994;[3] as did John C. Lupien in his well researched thesis at Pepperdine University in 1995;[4] Dr. Dave West in 1999;[5] and Samuel Heslop in his Oxford-Brookes University thesis of 2000.[6] *The Times,* in September of that year, wrote: "Industrialists such as Hearst and Du Pont backed the 1937 *Marijuana Tax Act* that basically got hemp shot down in America"[7]

Andrew Mellon, who appears to many as an angel of respectability, made his money from Texas oil. He was appointed Secretary of the Treasury from 1921 to 1932, in which capacity he was able to influence tax rebates for his oil interests that would lead ultimately to congressional investigations, the most famous of which was the Teapot Dome Scandal.

Mellon profited from discouring production of safer and better fuels, such as diesel and alcohol, which could compete with fossil fuels. One move that gave him an advantage at this was the loan of money to the Du Pont Corp., which financed their acquisition of General Motors (GM). Thus, while Ford Motors set up a successful biomass fuel facility at Iron Mountain, Michigan, Mellon was supporting the use of cars to be run on oil that he owned. When the Great Depression came, President Herbert Hoover summed up his attitude as follows:

> Liquidate labor, liquidate stocks, liquidate the farmer, liquidate real estate…People will work harder, live a more moral life. Values will be adjusted and enterprising people will pick up the wrecks from less competent people.[8]

Mellon practised 'family values' by appointing his nephew-in-law, Anslinger, to the Federal Bureau of Narcotics, which answered not to any police authority, but to the Treasury. In such a position, Anslinger was able to berate drugs users on one hand, while he supplied morphine to Sen. Joseph McCarthy of Wisconsin with the other.[9] Anslinger, a raging hempophobe, launched tirades against any use of drugs and classed marijuana in with narcotics. At one time he was rebuked for reading the racist phrase "ginger coloured niggers" into government records, and had to be held back from his desire to round up all the jazz musicians in the country in a 'crackdown', a bizarre plan that was overruled by Assistant Secretary of the Treasury Edward H. Foley, Jr. President John F. Kennedy also disapproved, and fired Anslinger.

William Randolph Hearst is perhaps best remembered as 'Citizen Kane'. He owned newspapers, most well-known for 'yellow journalism', which fuelled the Spanish-American War. When the USS *Maine* suffered an explosion in Cuba in February of 1898, it was made clear by the captain of the ship that it was due to an accident; Hearst, however, made it out to be the work of terrorists, and in so doing, urged the public into war, from which he profited. Later on he was to profit from the sale of the editorial opinions of his papers to the Nazis. This he did in person, meeting Adolf Hitler who paid him $400,000 a year.[10] Hearst's relationship with Hitler did not start there; Hitler used to work for Hearst, but was unable to deliver by deadline, and so was let go. While neither of these parties is today regarded as an honest journalist, both knew how to use the press perhaps better than any. When the Reichstag Fire occurred in February of 1933, set by the Gestapo to seize power for the Nazis, Hitler stayed up all night with reporters, fanning the flames of 'patriotism' and succeeding in handing Germany over to the will of the arms dealers.

Some might still remember the pro-Nazi sentiments expressed by Hearst after this date, while others will recall the anti-Latin tone, especially in regards to what he called 'reefer madness', which was a campaign to stir up public hatred of marijuana. While Hitler used lies and deception in Germany, dressing up Polish peasants in soldiers' uniforms and falsely stating that they had attacked the Reich's officers, much the same was used in the US in regards to hemp and minorities that Hearst did not like. The far-right press did much damage to the nation in the 1930s. At one point Hearst's opinions so outraged Americans that one-hundred of them stormed the offices in San Francisco in 1945; the editor called for the police, but no arrests were made; the protestors were US Marines who were tired of opinions from a man who had never served in the military,[11] but who was able to profit so immensely from war.

Last and not least is the Du Pont Corp. Today one of the biggest in the world, it dominates the skyline of Wilmington, Delaware, and its influence is not unfelt in nearby Washington. Its history goes quite a way back, and is of some interest to examine, not only for the context of this present work, but as a glimpse into the history of one of America's, and the world's, most powerful companies.

In the late eighteenth century, France was experiencing political turmoil. The excesses of the monarchy and their supporters had enraged the nation, and the cry for change was to be heard in every town. Among the supporters of the old regime was one prosperous family - the Du Ponts. (In the early nineteenth century they changed the spelling of the family name from Du Pont to du Pont, which serves to differentiate between individuals and the company, which is always spelled Du Pont). Two members of this clan, Pierre and Irénée, were thrown into prison. Pleading senility, and agreeing to leave the country, they were granted release, and on 1 October, 1799, set sail for America under their own banner. Ninety days hence, after an unpleasant journey spent guarding their wealth from the American crew, they arrived. A relief both to them and their crew, this arrival was marked by a singular omen; that of the Du Ponts breaking into a house whilst the owners were at church and eating their meal.[12]

They settled first in New Jersey, finding a mansion to buy at Bergen's Point, acquiring slaves, and setting up offices in New York City at 61 Pearl Street, and later 91 Liberty Street. Pierre tried to come up with a means of launching a private empire, 'Pontiania', which included gold smuggling and land speculation. These and other plans were at best pipe dreams, with the thought of land speculation especially ill advised, as Thomas Jefferson pointed out to them.[13] Finally one thing did work for them: gunpowder. This was a dangerous business, especially for those working directly with chemicals, but lucrative to investors. Early settlers were in constant need of this, and other explosives were added to the product line.

Wars were the most prosperous of times; for this business even the Civil War, with its losses due to a divided market, brought fortune to Du Pont, despite the increase of accidents in the yards. Eleven explosions took place, during that war, killing dozens of workers from 1861 to 1865.[14]

After the war, the du Ponts had to endure the depression, as bitterness ravaged a whole country. They not only endured, but prospered. Led by Lammot, they started a cartel with major manufacturers, cutting prices, and levying severe penalties against anyone who undersold them, undercutting them badly enough to bankrupt them; their Eleutherian

Irénée was openly contemptuous of America and its people: 'The country, the people, the locations are all worthless...'
Gerard Colby Zilg,
Du Pont: Behind the Nylon Curtain,
1974

Mills would "pick up the pieces of the industry for pennies."[15] American Ordinance, New York Powder Co., United States Dynamite Co., and The American Textile Powder Manufacturing Co., were but a few of the smaller companies put out of business or bought out by Du Pont and companies they controlled.[16] "The policy pursued was one of ruthless elimination," wrote H.C. Engelbrecht and F.C. Hanighen in their book *Merchants of Death.*[17]

While the Du Ponts of Delaware were growing richer during the 1890s, most Americans were growing poorer. A public outcry rose against the nation's industries being controlled by a few private corporations. Eventually the country was sick of this situation and the Sherman Anti-trust Act was passed, which was to have some effect in dealing with the du Ponts.

Not only were the du Ponts growing more powerful economically, but they had entered the political arena as well. In 1895 Henry du Pont, having inherited his father's political power, shocked the nation with his dishonesty. du Pont, in a power struggle with John 'Gas' Addicks over the senate seat in the state of Delaware, kept a stalemate going for 10 years in which his state had no senator; his attitude was: 'me or nobody.'[18]

By 1906 the du Ponts had taken on perhaps more then they could handle. They continued to expand monopolistically, and one of their victims, Buckeye Powder, fought back. Robert S. Waddell, the president of Buckeye, published an open letter to the President of the US in which he wrote, "Here is an absolute and exclusive monopoly, superior to the government... it is not safe to entrust... nor is it right to rob the people to fatten millionaires….The welfare of the nation is in balance against the Du Pont Trust."[19]

The government reacted in 1907 with an anti-trust suit against Du Pont. Waddell heaped evidence on the desks of the Justice Department, including Du Pont's collaboration with German interests to keep tight control over the world market. The government was able to use this as well as overwhelming evidence from other sources, and in 1910 Du Pont was found guilty, against a backdrop of national furore.[20] However, the new companies spun off, Hercules Powder and Atlas Powder, were headed by former Du Pont executives.

An anti-trust suit was not the only legal woe of that year; Henry du Pont's political moves were again the focus of national attention. Publicly accused by Willard Salisbury of buying votes, Henry "broke into a cold sweat"[21] as a senate subcommittee investigated. In later years, forced to submit to a vote of the people under the newly enacted Seventeenth Amendment, Henry's forces were noted for "stuffing ballot boxes, shipping repeats, and intimidating voters." Nonetheless, he lost that election (1916) "swamped by a tidal wave of rejection."[22]

Despite public outcry and court rulings, Du Pont's power waxed yet bolder, bold enough for Alfred du Pont to bluff President William H. Taft into submission by threatening to throw people out of work. Taft was to question their bluff with the famous line: "Do you mean to threaten the US government?"[23] Unfortunately, Washington had let a monopoly gain

The rich got richer, the poor got polluted to and lied to.
Paul Benhaim,
Healthy Eating Made Possible,
1999

the upper hand for too long and Taft was at a loss; Du Pont had won. With this kind of clout, there was little to stop them. If a newspaper, for instance, ran an article criticising Du Pont, it was bought out. This was the fate of *Every Evening* in 1911, and it was not long before they "controlled every daily in Delaware."[24]

In 1917 the tide of events once more turned toward US involvement in war, and with it the tide of Du Pont profits, rising from a yearly average of $6,092,000 to $58,076,000.[25] Atlas Powder and Hercules Powder similarly had increased profits - rising 480 percent and 575 percent respectively. Ten days after the US entered WWI, another court case involving du Ponts came to a conclusion, this time with a du Pont as both defendant and plaintiff. Pierre du Pont was the loser, a man whom the court called: "...without principle, money grabbing, greedy, underhanded."[26] It was in this war that they earned the accolade "merchants of death."[27] Perhaps this originated with their workers - who were fired en masse - 37,000 for Christmas, 1918 and 70,000 more by the end of the year.[28] Protest was met with little sympathy: "Du Pont Company lives on, growing bigger and bigger and grander and grander with each day of existence," boasted Du Pont executive Col. Buckner.[29]

Bigger and bigger was certainly true, over the deaths of soldiers and workers, Du Pont rolled on. Charges of holding back on wages and cheating employees out of their belongings began to emerge, as well as charges of cheating the US government. These last were investigated by the Graham Committee, which exposed massive fraud at the taxpayers' expense.[30] Such facts came to light during yet another depression in the US, which Du Pont weathered in part by slashing workers pay by 10 percent and voting against a minimum wage law. They also exercised their power in the realm of foreign language newspapers, insisting that all advertising be placed through an organisation owned by T. Coleman du Pont; in such a way they were able to restrict stories about strikes in immigrant workers' home countries.[31]

At times control of the press was crucial, as in the tetraethyl lead death cover-up of 1923. Workers who handled this substance developed strange symptoms, and then died horrible deaths. The building in which they worked was dubbed the 'House of Butterflies', in reference to men snatching at air and drawing insects on the walls. As profits were expected to be good on this new chemical, silence prevailed. Du Pont owned newspapers in Delaware did not report the workers' deaths.[32] But in October of 1924 the country was given the cry of alarm by other papers. Subsequent investigations showed that the bureau which had certified tetraethyl lead was financed by GM, that no coroner's inquests were held in Delaware, that death certificates were improperly handled or missing, and that poisoned workers were "sent back to the poorly ventilated plant to be poisoned again and again."[33] The public wanted the law to be applied to those responsible, and by standards at that time this was a case for wholesale manslaughter, if not murder. However, those investigating had no desire to bite the hand that had forked over $34,000 to the GOP. No charges were pressed; tetraethyl lead was given the thumbs-up;

Deepwater, the problem plant, was re-opened. Irénée du Pont gave $37,500 to the GOP the next year and mouths were shut.

November 11, 1930 was a day on which a shadow crossed the Du Pont Empire; T. Coleman duPont, the 'general', passed away. His fall, wrote Gerald Zilg, in his 1970 exposé,

> foreshadowed a dark decade ahead, indeed the darkest, most dangerous years of the family's history, years through which the Barons of Brandywine would try every legal and illegal means possible to preserve their new empire and keep millions of hungry, jobless Americans from sharing their fabulous wealth.[34]

In the 1930s an ambitious character was coming into the political stage, stirring up for himself support by means of high pitched speeches and inflammatory writing, which attracted the likes of Madie du Pont and her sons, who had dedicated their lives to 'the Führer'. She took with her on trips snapshots of her offspring, smartly dressed in Nazi uniforms, proud of them and the leader who could "rid the nation of its rotten elements."[35] For material support, this leader, Adolf Hitler, was in a bind, as the Treaty of Versailles forbade him the arms he so wanted. He needed a secret weapons dealer, and this he found in a number of the du Ponts, who were willing to break laws.

On New Year's Day 1926, Du Pont executives signed a deal with Dynamit Aktion Gesellschaft and Köln Rottweiler, both of which were to be part of I.G. Farben.[36] The deal was mainly for explosives, with patents and secret inventions being made open to the Nazis. By 1933 Du Pont had decided to plunge into smuggling arms to Germany.[37] In February A. Felix du Pont, Sr. had a secret meeting with two top agents, naming one of them, Jongo Giera (aka Peter Brenner, a WWI German spy), as Du Pont's sole agent to the Republic of Germany.[38] With the prospect of war, and future sales in mind, Du Pont was diligent in its dealings, inviting Farben officials to the home of Lammot du Pont in Wilmington. In October of 1935, this invitation was accepted by no less than Dr. Fritzler Meer and Georg von Schnitzler, Farben's leading officers. Even then Du Pont knew, and expressed, that all was not quite right; government evidence in a 1945 trial included a letter from a Mr. Haas of Philadelphia, to a Dr. Röhm of Darmstadt, Germany, written in 1936, which included the following statement:

> A matter like this cannot be put into the contract because it would be against the law. We have to rely on our verbal assurance and our experience with du Pont during the last fifteen years has proven that they can be relied upon to live up to an arrangement of this kind.[39]

Du Pont-Nazi agreements had by that time reached a level of great complexity, which would result in numerous indictments against Du Pont and their Axis partners in the 1940s. In 1939, when the UK was buying arms from Du Pont, one clause that Du Pont and its affiliates saw fit to honour was the one limiting what they could send to the Allies; thus Remington supplied the British army with an inferior priming agent for cartridges, putting British ground troops in a critically weakened position on the battlefield.[40]

As Du Pont's relationships with the Nazis grew tight, both sides looked at the future, realising the difficulties that a war could impose. Sen. Homer T. Bone, Chairman of the Senate Patent's Committee, exposed these arrangements, specifically citing a letter of 9 February, 1940, in which Du Pont expressed intention to have Farben participation in Duperial, a Du Pont-Imperial Chemicals joint venture in South America. This, however, was against the wishes of Imperial in the UK,[41] who felt betrayed by the willingness of Du Pont to aid their enemy.

Anastase Vonsiatsky
at his training camp
in Connecticut, **1939**

In 1941 another customer would need to be doing more business with Du Pont; the US military. Lammot expressed the company's sentiments when this happened: "They want what we've got. Good. Make them pay the right price for it."[42]

While the 'right price' was high for Du Pont's clients, it was low for the workforce. Du Pont, financed by the Mellon Bank, had acquired GM, which was then placed under Irénée du Pont. As chairman, he led GM to new strengths, not only in his charismatic speeches about a 'race of supermen',[43] but in reaching new sales, many to the Nazi war machine.

The workers, however, were not included in many of Irénée's ideas. Rather, they came under attack, were spied upon, beaten, tortured, and killed. Obsessed by Hitler's principles[44], he turned them on Americans, and such organisations as the American Liberty League (ALL), the Black Legion (BL) and the Ku Klux Klan (KKK) were to play a hand in suppressing labour; terrorist organisations sponsored by 'patriots'.

For ALL, veteran's bonuses were an extravagance, whilst taxes for pensions and the unemployed were attacked. President Franklin D. Roosevelt was to clash with the du Ponts over this organisation, stating that it: "ganged up against people's liberties."[45] Irénée had founded the league with Lammot and Pierre, and other anti-African-American and anti-Semitic organisations were to follow. Irénée also paid $1,000,000 for gas equipped storm troops to sweep through plants and beat up those who were not in line;[46] moreover, the board kept personal links to Hitler, some signing an agreement of total commitment to the Nazi cause, vowing to stamp out Jewish influence in America. When the Nazis invaded France, James D. Mooney, GM's chief of European operations, went to New York to have champagne and celebrate, renting a suite in the Waldorf-Astoria on Park Avenue specially for the occasion.[47]

GM factories were filled with pro-Nazi sentiment led by the

notorious BL. This group, attired in black hooded robes sporting the Skull & Bones, was divided into special squads - arson, bombing, execution, and membership, which recruited KKK men. If one can imagine an outfit one step below the KKK, this was it; its adherents murdered for thrill as well as political advantage, regarding all 'aliens, Negroes, Jews, cults, and creeds believing in racial equality' as enemies.[48] Several of their murders stirred public rage; even the wealth of the du Ponts could not pacify the country, and the federal government stepped in, as local and state officials were overwhelmed by these atrocities. George H. Earle, then Governor of Pennsylvania, saw it clearly, and spoke out on 8 June, 1936:

> I charge that this organization is the direct result of the subversive propaganda subsidized by the Grand Dukes of the Duchy of Delaware, the duPonts, and the munitions' policies of the American Liberty League.[49]

So out of hand was ALL that it had even hoped to mount an armed rebellion in Washington D.C., trying to use Gen. Smedley Butler of the US Marine Corps, who turned on them and exposed this scheme. By 1936 it had become a total failure, a hated name throughout America. While acts of terrorist organisations were a failure for Du Pont, WWII was a financial boom; the du Ponts emerged as the richest clan in America.

After the war one battle to be fought for Du Pont was the anti-trust suit brought against them for their stake in GM. At first, Du Pont won, which set off another round of buying shares in GM; an error in judgement that caused the government to appeal and ultimately win. Such gloating should have been kept private, as Leonard Mosley notes: "there was no one present with enough common sense to urge them to keep their mouths shut..."[50]

Du Pont today is one of the most powerful companies in the world, and still makes products for war, including nuclear war heads, which they began developing in the 1940s; 'Fat Man' and 'Little Boy' were their babies, developed under the auspices of one of one of their most brilliant scientists and directors, Crawford Greenewalt, a Massachusetts Institute of Technololgy graduate who had married into the family.

Well respected in social and scientific circles, this newcomer was able to give a better feel to this gargantuan corporation. For many, Greenewalt is best remembered for his photography of birds, a passion which he shared with John E. du Pont. Both travelled extensively and wrote lasting works on exotic avifauna, most notably, *Hummingbirds,* by Greenewalt, published in 1960.[51] Greenewalt's direction and that of his antecedents has differed much from that of the earlier organisation ran only by du Ponts, and a greater percentage of their products are geared toward peacetime use. Perhaps these differences have changed everything for the better, and one might well imagine the benevolent scene of a large company now peacefully producing energy while its directors photograph endangered species.

Many, however, do not believe this to be the case. Jack Frazier, an American historian, listed them, along with IBM and EXXON, as "huge monsters that crush and mutilate everything and everyone that crosses their path or stands in their way."[52] Ralph Nader's words are equally descriptive: "a political and corrupt plantation."[53] Colby (1984) listed a number of problems, including crimes committed by then governor of Delaware Pierre S. du Pont IV. That author was himself a first-hand witness to their acts, as they had suppressed his 1974 publication of *Du Pont: Behind the Nylon Curtain.*[54] In the decade between that first printing and the second of 1984, he was to record even more of Du Pont's activities.

Their influence extends today to almost every country, and there are struggles, such as the sale of Valpirone, (aka dipyrone), a drug that the American Medical Association (AMA) evaluated as 'a last resort.' *No problema*, Du Pont sold this through its subsidiary Endo Laboratories in Latin America, where the public was not aware that this was a dangerous product.[55]

In Puerto Rico, pollution in the Monati River destroyed the livelihood of fishermen and farmers, turning the waters black. This led to an ugly scene of threats by Du Pont to close down and throw hundreds of people out of work[56], and the company tried to have the island removed from the protection of the Environmental Protection Agency.[57]

On the mainland Du Pont challenged the authority of the EPA over reductions of lead content in gasoline and that of the Food and Drug Administration over the banning of fluorocarbons. Many Americans have become alarmed at the power and purposes of this company, and the hundred or more in which it exercises power.

While Du Pont's actions can fill volumes, it might be fair to note that there were many other parties whose antics are equally questionable, and that they too acted against the interests of the US in time of war; many of these went so far as to produce war materials on US soil and then clandestinely ship them to Germany through such companies as the Hamburg-Amerika Shipping Line. Some of these companies were quite influential in the 1930s, and also benefited from hemp suppression, including pharmaceutical companies which could easily see hemp as competition. Nazism in the US was accepted in many powerful circles, with such public figures as Charles Lindbergh accepting medals from Hitler and then receiving the support of many in the GOP, members of which put his name forward as a presidential candidate. In Connecticut, a Nazi training camp existed, run by the charismatic Anastase Vonsiatsky, whose fascism was openly embraced by powerful Americans, including the Reams family, into which he had married. Also from that state was Prescott Bush, whose empire, according to US government record, "had been operated on behalf of Nazi Germany and had greatly assisted the war effort."[58] The aforementioned Hamburg-Amerika Shipping Line was one company which Bush took part in. His shares in a number of such enterprises were confiscated under the Trading with the Enemy Act, with government agents arriving at the offices of Brown Brothers, Harriman & Co. on Wall Street to take control of these properties.

Concern over the extent of Nazi activities was glossed over during WWII, when powerful lawyers for these companies exercised undue influence at the White House, much to the consternation of then US Secretary of the Treasury, Henry Morgenthau, Jr. For years the records of their deeds were sealed, but when opened in the 1980s, the truth was made known under the Freedom of Information Act. Once revealed, it was then clear that much of the war had been prolonged by financiers who used US labour to make arms for Hitler so as to keep the war, and with it their profits, rolling as long as they could.

Certainly concern exists over the pattern of large companies taking power in a country, but what can be done? For an answer, let us return to the topic at hand - hemp, which was getting attention and public investment in the 1920s and 1930s as more informed legislators, seeing a use for farm wastes, took an interest in using this plant for its cellulose content. However, this meant competition for a number of businesses, among them a huge paper concern; the International Paper and Power Co. This outfit had interests in wood pulp, and went about negotiations with its largest customer, the Hearst media syndicate, to monopolise the market. Sen. Thomas Schull of Minnesota, seeing the problem, called for the Federal Trade Commission to investigate, which caused International to back off.[59] In 1929 Blair Coan, a Washington reporter, uncovered evidence that the Department of Agriculture had chosen to suppress information on paper production from farm wastes.[60]

One government figure who took an interest in the use of farm wastes for cellulose and paper was none other than Anslinger, who began requesting information on hemp in the 1930s. By 1935, the Bureau actively gathered information on the new hemp industry, even though it possessed no real authority to do so; the file of requests received that year is missing.

The following year one project that caught Anslinger's attention was a series of article about hemp cultivation sponsored by the *Chicago Tribune*.[61] He dispatched an agent to gather information, with specific instructions to report on the machinery involved and the demand for hemp. She sent back her reports, satisfying his need for such sensitive information, but advising against his plans to restrict cultivation.[62]

MARIHUANA TAX ACT

All this poking around by the Bureau was not able to put a stop to hemp cultivation, especially as its potential use as a source of cellulose was being discovered. More effective measures would be necessary, and these were implemented by demonising all cannabis, and then outlawing it.

Hearst accomplished much towards vilifying all cannabis in his papers, with untrue stories evoking fears and prejudice among the ignorant. Anslinger kept a file of this propaganda, calling it the 'gore file'. In it were stories of fifteen-year-olds murdering their parents after one high and cross-racial rapes, the latter especially meant to incite tensions. Lupien summed this up in his 1995 thesis: "From 1935 on, the Bureau actively rewrote the history of hemp by demonizing marijuana... triggered by monopolistic greed and economic insecurity of a few financially threatened industries."[63]

The weed is an annual plant and it grows wild throughout the United States. In a single season recently it was found growing wild in such widespread places as Brooklyn, N.Y. and Los Angeles, Calif.
Det. John Higgins,
True Magazine, **1939**

The Bureau got support in this endeavour not just from Hearst, but from other sensationalists as well. Anslinger especially liked the propaganda of Dr. Jules Bouquet, who claimed to be the world's foremost expert on cannabis drugs. One of Dr. Bouquet's diatribes ran as follows:

> The basis of Moslem character is indolence; these people love idleness and daydreaming, and to the majority of them work is the most unpleasant of all necessities. Inordinately vain glorious, thirsting for every pleasure, they are manifestly unable to realise more than a small fraction of their desires: their unrestrained imagination supplies the rest. Hemp, which enhances the imagination, is the narcotic best adapted to their mentality. When the period of intoxication is over and he is again forced with the realities of his normal shabby life, his one desire is to find a corner where he may sleep…[64]

He also claimed cannabis to be typical of the "poorer classes in urban communities: artisans, small traders, and workmen." Dr. Bouquet failed to produce any credible evidence to support his findings, yet the Bureau still presented this erroneous rhetoric before Congress.

Everyone at the time did not accept their statements. Dr. Woodward of the AMA especially opposed them: "We cannot understand yet, Mr. Chairman," Woodward protested, "…why this bill should have been prepared in secret for two years without any intimation, even to the profession, that it was being prepared."[65] This was in 1937, when Anslinger and Du Pont allies were preparing the final version of their anti-hemp bill. There was at this time some momentum building behind the scare stories about cannabis in Canada where Judge Emily Murphy picked up on the hype and advocated "public whippings and deportations"[66] for people caught using marijuana. Anslinger's campaign caused local police to single out minorities, blaming "Mexicans, Spaniards, Latin-Americans, Greeks, and Negroes" as perpetrators of violent crimes due to the habit of marijuana smoking.[67] All this added fuel to the senseless debate, and the Bureau picked an advantageous moment to take advantage of all the lies and misinformation.

Prior to the 1937 version of the anti-hemp acts, two had been unsuccessfully attempted in 1935; but by a little more secrecy and researching a route that would avoid intelligent debate, Anslinger prevailed. General Counsel Herman Oliphant convinced the anti-hemp fanatics of a more subtle way to tackle the issues; introduction of the bill to the House Ways and Means Committee, where discussion could be kept at a minimum, and which was presided over by a staunch Du Pont ally, Rep. Robert L. Doughton.[68]

Several details bely the craftiness with which this was done, most notably the way the bill was called a 'marijuana' bill (or 'marihuana' bill, as it was then spelt). It was not disclosed that this referred to hemp and, as

> Last week the War Production Board approved plans for planting in the United States 300,000 acres of hemp.and for building 71 processing mills. Plantings will be concentrated in Kentucky, Indiana, Wisconsin, Minnesota, and Iowa..it helps control weeds, needs no tending until harvest, and leaves the soil in good condition.
> *Newseek,*
> **16 October 1942**

> Just outside the nation's capital, for some sixty miles along the Potomac River, on both banks, marijuana was growing in profusion, it had been planted there originally by early settlers who made their own hemp and cloth.
> The workers cleaned out tremendous riverbank crops, destroying plants, seeds and roots. All through the Midwest also, W.P.A. workers were used for this clean-up job. The wild hemp was rooted out of America.
> **Harry J. Anslinger and Will Oursler,**
> *The Murderers,* **1962**

they were using a term then not in the public vocabulary, many parties who had interests at stake simply did not know what 'marijuana' was. Even today, there are people who do not associate 'marijuana' with hemp. Concern over the use of what was then a vague and misleading term was voiced by a representative from Chempco Inc., who stated:

> I do not think the use of the word 'marihuana' belongs in this measure, because that is the word that came up from Mexico and attached to these cigarettes. I see no use in it. This is hemp being grown, not marihuana... we might lose an industry purely by the phraseology of the measure.[69]

TREASURY DEPARTMENT ORIGINAL
UNITED STATES INTERNAL REVENUE

ORDER FORM FOR MARIHUANA, OR COMPOUNDS, MANUFACTURES, SALTS, DERIVATIVES, MIXTURES, OR PREPARATIONS UNDER THE MARIHUANA TAX ACT OF 1937.

TO BE RETAINED BY THE TRANSFEROR FOR A PERIOD OF TWO YEARS

Technically, the bill that was introduced was not completely prohibitive; it was a tax. This was a second underhanded aspect to the whole thing, based on both long-standing precedent and what was then recent action. The long-standing precedent of using a tax to prohibit an activity can be traced back to the reign of Charles I of England, who wanted to close all the coffee houses, as political debate was taking place which was not to his liking. However, an outright ban was contrary to the freedom and the rights of the British people, so he tried to circumvent the Magna Carta by enacting a prohibitive tax that proved burdensome, in the hope of limiting public assembly and free speech.

Of more current precedent was the National Firearms Act, which had been approved as constitutional in the US on 29 March, 1937. It was openly enacted for the purpose of curtailing machine guns, an effort to restrict weapons without violating the Second Amendment which grants the right to bear arms. The Bureau, losing no time, unveiled the Marihuana Tax Act on 15 April of that year. It passed on 2 August and received final ratification on 11 December, 1937. At one point Congress asked if the AMA had been consulted, to which Rep. Carl Vinson, answering for the House Ways and Means Committee, replied incorrectly: "Yes, we have. A Dr. Wharton and the AMA are in complete agreement."[70]

Du Pont, in its 1937 annual report, issued a statement which many hemp advocates see as a reflection of these moves. It read: "radical changes from the revenue raising power of government would be converted into instruments for forcing acceptance of sudden new ideas of industrial and social reorganization." American citizens were facing a tax which was to deprive them of much income and liberty, a concept that many might have argued was treason to support.

This didn't seem to matter; the Tax Act passed, it was a *fait accompli*, with US farmers and businesses forced to accept the loss. Frank Ridgway on 11 October, 1937 wrote in the *Chicago Tribune* that "the prospective complications the new law would create" made it more advisable to "just burn the crops than to try to persevere through the regulatory measures."[71]

Several farmers affected by these new rules, unable to cope with them alone, hired attorney Ojai A. Lende to sort out the difficulties. Lende was himself baffled by the situation and ultimately asked the government to compensate the farmers. In 1938 he wrote:

> ...there was a market for this hemp in processed form but the passage of the Tax Act completely destroyed the market and virtually confiscated this hemp for the growers...the bureau hampered the conduct of legitimate business by strictly enforcing the stipulations of the transfer tax.[72]

Anslinger responded in an apathetic and guarded way, and Lende was to send off another letter, this one more vitriolic:

> If I can find a market for the hemp I have in mind to dispose of that hemp and tell Mr. Anslinger that he can go to the region below and let him present the country with a spectacle of arresting half a thousand farmers in Minnesota for selling an agricultural crop grown off from their farms which were grown long before Congress ever thought of the Marihuana Act.[73]

Ironically, it was war that made America see the folly of hemp suppression.
Yves de Saussure,
Cannabis for Health, Energy, Medicine, Paper and 25,000 Other Uses, **2002**

At last the powerful 'G' man has been given legal authority to stamp out illicit traffic in *marihuana,* America's latest drug peril, the dread sex weed.
Det. John Higgins,
True Magazine, **1939**

Transcript of *Hemp for Victory*, US Government Film, 1942

Long ago when these ancient Grecian temples were new, hemp was already old in the service of mankind. For thousands of yards, even then, this plant had been grown for cordage and cloth in China and elsewhere in the East. For centuries prior to about 1850 all the shops that sailed the western seas were rigged with hempen rope and sails. For the sailor, no less than the hangman, hemp was indispensable. A 44-gun frigate like our cherished Old Ironsides took over 60 tons of hemp for rigging, including an anchor cable 25 inches in circumference. The Conestoga wagons and prairie schooners off pioneer days were covered with hemp canvas. Indeed the very word canvas comes from the Arabic word for hemp. In those days hemp was an important crop in Kentucky and Missouri. Then came cheaper imported fibers for cordage, like jute, sisal and Manila hemp, and the culture of hemp in American declined. But now with Philippine and East Indian sources of hemp in the hands of the Japanese, and shipment of jute from India curtailed, American hemp must meet the needs of our Army and navy as well as of our industry. In 1942, patriotic farmers at the government's request planted 36,000 acres of seed hemp, an increase of several thousand percent. The goal for 1943 is 50,000 acres of seed hemp.

In Kentucky much of the seed hemp acreage is on river bottom land such as this. Some of these fields are inaccessible except by boat. Thus plans are afoot for a great expansion of a hemp industry as a part of the war program. This film is designed to tell farmers how to handle this ancient crop now little known outside Kentucky and Wisconsin.

This is hemp seed. Be careful how you use it. For to grow hemp legally you must have a federal registration and tax stamp. This is provided for in your contract. Ask your county agent about it. Don't forget. Hemp demands a rich, well-drained soil such as is found here in the Blue Grass region of Kentucky or in central Wisconsin. It must be loose and rich in organic matter. Poor soils won't do. Soil that will grow good corn will usually grow hemp. Hemp is not hard on the soil. In Kentucky it has been grown for several years on the same ground, though this practice is not recommended. A dense and shady crop, hemp tends to choke out weeds. Here's a Canada thistle that couldn't stand the competition, dead as a dodo. Thus hemp leaves the ground in good condition for the following crop. For fiber, hemp should be sown closely, the closer the rows, the better. These rows are spaced about four inches. This hemp has been broadcast. Either way it should be sown thick enough to grow a slender stalk. Here's an ideal stand; the right height to be harvested easily, thick enough to grow slender stalks that are easy to cut and process. Stalks like these here on the left yield the most fiber and are the best. Those on the right are too coarse and woody. For see, hemp is planted in hills like corn. Sometimes by hand.

Hemp is a dioecious plant. The female flower is inconspicuous. But the male flower is easily spotted. In seed production after the pollen has been shed, these male plants are cut out. These are the seeds on a female plant. Hemp for fiber is ready to harvest when the pollen is shedding and the leaves are falling. In Kentucky, hemp harvest comes in August. Here the old standby has been the self-rake reaper, which has been used for a generation or more.

Hemp grows so luxuriantly in Kentucky that harvesting is sometimes difficult, which may account for the popularity of the self-rake with its lateral stroke. A modified rice binder has been used to some extent. This machine works well on average hemp. Recently, the improved hemp harvester, used for many years in Wisconsin, has been introduced in Kentucky. This machine spreads the hemp in a continuous swath. It is a far cry from this fast and efficient modern harvester, that doesn't stall in the heaviest hemp. In Kentucky, hand cutting is practised in opening fields for the machine. In Kentucky, hemp is shucked as soon as safe, after cutting, to be spread out for retting later in the fall. In Wisconsin, hemp is harvested in September. Here the hemp harvester with automatic spreader is standard equipment. Note how smoothly the rotation apron lays the swaths preparatory to retting. Here it is a common and essential practice to leave headlands around hemp fields. These strips may be planted with other crops, preferably small

grain. Thus the harvester has room to make its first round without preparatory hand cutting. The other machine is running over corn stubble. When the cutter bar is much shorter than the hemp is tall, overlapping occurs. Not so good for retting. The standard cut is eight to nine feet. The length of time hemp is left on the ground to ret depends on the weather. The swaths must be turned to get a uniform ret. When the woody core breaks away readily like this, the hemp is about ready to pick up and bind into bundles. Well-retted hemp is light to dark grey. The fiber tends to pull away from the stalks. The presence of stalks in the bow-string stage indicates that retting is well underway. When hemp is short or tangled or when the ground is too wet for machines, it's bound by hand. A wooden bucket is used. Twine will do for tying, but the hemp itself makes a good band. When conditions are favorable, the pickup binder is commonly used. The swaths should lie smooth and even with the stalks parallel. The picker won't work well in tangled hemp.

After binding, hemp is shucked as soon as possible to stop further retting. In 1942, 14,000 acres of fiber hemp were harvested in the United States. The goal for the old standby cordage fiber is staging a strong comeback. This is Kentucky hemp going into the dryer over the mill at Versailles. In the old days braking was done by hand. One of the hardest jobs known to man. Now the power braker makes quick work of it. Spinning American hemp into rope yarn or twine in the old Kentucky river mill at Frankfort, Kentucky. Another pioneer plant that has been making cordage for more than a century. All such plants will presently be turning out products spun from American-grown hemp: twine of various kinds for tying and upholsters work; rope for marine gigging and towing; for hay forks, derricks, and heavy duty tackle; light duty firehose; thread for shoes for millions of American soldiers; and parachute webbing for our paratroopers.

As for the United States Navy, every battleship requires 34,000 feet of rope. Here in the Boston Navy Yard, where cables for frigates were made long ago, crews are now working night and day making cordage for the fleet. In the old days rope yarn was spun by hand. The rope yarn feeds through holes in an iron plate. This is Manila hemp from the Navy's rapidly dwindling reserves. When it is gone, American hemp will go on duty again; hemp for mooring ships; hemp for towlines; hemp for tackle and gear; hemp for countless naval uses both on ship and shore. Just as in the days when Old Ironsides sailed the seas victorious with her hempen shrouds and hempen sails. *Hemp for Victory.*

One stipulation that was especially cumbersome was the removal of all foliage. This was burdensome to the farmers, if not nearly impossible, and was in fact no real necessity, as the foliage decomposed naturally during the retting process. There was also the bureaucracy involved, and many farmers simply could not get the necessary paperwork. Illinois and Minnesota growers were especially impeded by the new regulations but Wisconsin farmers were able to continue to grow and harvest their crop, by passing the new laws without any problems; their hemp went to the US Navy, and a laissez-faire policy prevailed in that state.

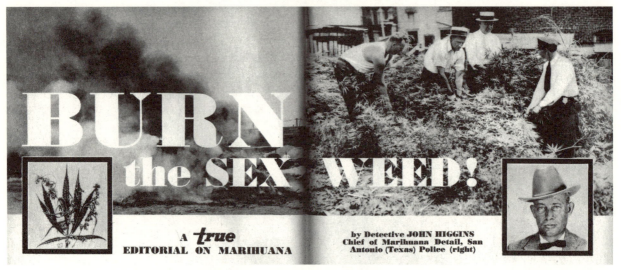

A *true* EDITORIAL ON MARIHUANA

by Detective JOHN HIGGINS
Chief of Marihuana Detail, San
Antonio (Texas) Police (right)

By 1943 however, all American hemp growers had the government behind them. A film titled *Hemp for Victory* was released that year, promoting cannabis growth, and offering all growers the necessary permits. This greatly increased planting to 158,000 acres by 1943, but fell to 5,000 acres just after the war, as the permits were once again an issue. 4-H Clubs encouraged school children to plant hemp patches which would "give 4-H Club members a real opportunity to serve their country in war time."[74]

Not everyone welcomed the patriotism of the hemp growers - the Flax and Fibre Institute of America in a letter dated 30 March 1943, written by managing director Howard D. Salins, ranted:

> New Deal Bureaucrats… offering Hemp Marijuana (dope) narcotic to the American people instead of increased food production…the corrupters of American Life are now engaged in the promoting of 350,000 acres, erecting 100 buildings and building a large volume of equipment and machinery in a number of mid-Western States for production of this narcotic (dope) plant product… Do you want this (dope) narcotic in your community? You are lined up for it.[75]

The government wisely ignored this diatribe and continued support. Sadly however, the position was reversed after the war. One group of farmers tried to start a business using an abandoned hemp mill, but Anslinger shut them down. The anti-hemp policy resumed, and as an added dimension, 'weed eradication' programmes were implemented. These basically spent a lot of taxes on sustances such as 2,4-D (a defoliant used in Vietnam) and paraquat, adding to the wealth of the chemical companies and destroying the environment. Hunting groups were keen to notice the relationship between cannabis and game birds; James Vance's 1971 article "Marijuana is for the Birds", published in *Outdoor Life*, speaks out against the loss of quarry due to such ignorant programmes.

Until the mid-1980s they were just about the only group in the US that took notice of hemp in a positive way. Kennedy had expressed some interest at one point shortly before his assassination. The anti-cannabis band played on afterwards, and the US was to see the 'prison industry', as it is known, become a growth industry. The fact that a large percentage of the incarcerated are in for cannabis related offences has been of concern to the American taxpayer, many of whom would rather see their money spent more wisely. To add to the agony, many in jail for cannabis related offences have been found innocent; in quite a few cases they faced government asset seizure of their property, leading to the ruin of their businesses and personal lives. Life imprisonment and even the death penalty await people for cannabis related crimes. The incarceration of Todd Patrick McCormick, a cancer patient whose mother gave him cannabis as it was the only remedy that alleviated his pain, was a rallying point for many in the US. Actor Woody Harrelson took a personal interest in that case and posted the $500,000 bail, but despite the protests on his behalf, McCormick spent several years in jail. In other cases, AIDS patients and hemophiliacs have died in jail, many of them not charged with anything other than using cannabis. For a certain hardcore segment of people, perhaps themselves not at all representative of America as a nation, this was even welcomed. After the terrible attacks on the East Coast in September of 2001, US TV adverts went so far as to try to associate smoking cannabis with terrorism; ironically, there were no such scare tactics in regards to other drugs which are related to terrorism. Little if any of the marijuana smoked in the US comes from any nation on the 'Axis of Evil' list; most is in fact grown in the US and Canada. In a further irony, similar TV adverts produced by Arianna Huffington linking the use of Arab oil to terrorism were refused by major networks.

As all this irony unfolded, many were questioning the motives of the leaders in regards to why marijuana laws were so draconian while real criminals were in fact getting very little time. The impression that the prison industry was targeting Americans so as to make money was becoming a topic of conversation coast-to-coast. One philanthropist trying to rehabilitate prisoners met with obstacles in his attempts to deal with the bureaucracy; Jimmy Walter, who after initial success, was blocked by politicians in Florida in the 1990s.[76] His efforts and the reaction to his success on the part of the administration in that state sent a message to the nation that this industry was not to be questioned. For many Americans, it was time to talk back and take charge.

One part of the whole debate on the legality of medicinal cannabis was the issue of states' rights. This came to a head in May of 2005, when

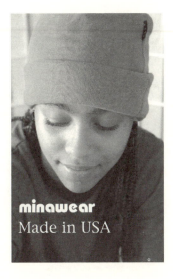

Photograph courtesy of Christie McQueen

Photograph courtesy of Steve Hitter

the Supreme Court voted 6-3 against allowing states to continue to grow cannabis for medicine. For many the whole ideal of liberty was at stake, and the reality that there had been a hard turn to the right taking place,

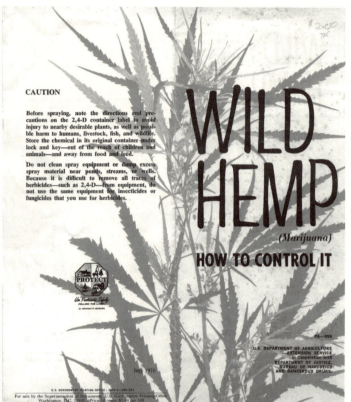

much to the financial detriment of many Americans, was starting to sink in. The ruling came after many other events that were making people uncomfortable about the sudden changes, including an assertion by Bergen County (New Jersey) Police Chief Jack Schmidig that all Americans might have to get a microchip inserted into their skin in order to be able to buy or sell. This, coming on top of revelations about the power of such a chip to integrate with the human system, made many nervous; the chief spoke openly about this at first, but then walked out on Alex Jones, who was doing a radio interview with him.[77]

While the concept that all of this was good for keeping out terrorists was blasted in the public ear on a fairly constant basis, scepticism was growing and people were questioning why it all seemed like a scene out of an Orwell novel. The threat of extraditing Marc Emery from Canada for selling marijuana seeds, legally, from his own country, and, more bizarrely, the threat of extraditing UK citizens Giles Darby, David Bermingham and Gary Mulgrew for undervaluing a Cayman Islands company which they then sold in London, led to massive protests world-wide. Ironically, the very people wanting to extend the long arm of the law were themselves falling prey to indictments and convictions, with charges ranging from abusing young children in government offices to breaching national security laws. Extreme incompetence was also evident, with wealthy government employees playing guitar, fishing, shopping for shoes and making jokes in the wake of a hurricane that devastated New Orleans.

At one point the Senate was left dumbstruck, when badly forged documents were used to calumny a UK Member of Parliament. Andrea Peyser in the *New York Post* noted that the Senators, when confronted, were like "boys with their pants down around their ankles awaiting punishment."

The hard turn to the right, which was doing America no good, affected not only marijuana smokers, but the entire public in general. Big Brother was literally under one's skin, and many reacted by joining forces to prevent a fascist nightmare from destroying the land of liberty. Hemp advocates were finding that their cause was being noticed more and more, as the sensible were ready to roll in defence of the land that had been fought for by hemp advocates George Washington and Thomas Jefferson, but which was presently being hijacked.

Much awareness of the hemp and pot issues came about as a result of a book titled *The Emperor Wears No Clothes* by Jack Herer, published in 1985. It was a rallying point for both environmentalists and civil libertarians; Herer not only chronicled the history and uses of hemp, but called for legalisation of marijuana as well. Whatever his stand, *The Emperor* was not to be ignored. It contained a great deal of documentation, including photocopies of government publications. Since *The Emperor,* there have been a number of other books written in North America, such as Chris Conrad's *Hemp: Lifeline to the Future,* and Ed Rosenthal's *Hemp Today.* The latter rebuts some of Herer's claims, differing not on the major parts of his premise, but on some of the more scientific details. In 2000 the Haworth Press of New York began to publish the *Journal of Industrial Hemp,* (which is now the leading scientific paper on the subject), as well as scholarly books on hemp cultivation such as Paolo Ranalli's *Advances in Hemp Research.*

By the mid-1990s hemp movements were gaining ground. Harrelson planted hemp seeds in his home state of Kentucky, a symbolic act that led to his arrest. A poll conducted in that state by the Kentucky Hemp Museum showed that 77 percent of respondents favoured the growing of hemp: other tobacco states have voiced similar support for hemp, especially as tobacco revenues are falling.

California is the centre of the US hemp industry, with such companies as Green Field Paper Company and Minawear Hemp Clothing. There not only popular support, but political support as well, is evident; pro-hemp bills have not only had an 80 percent endorsement rate by the Democratic party, but have a majority of GOP support as well, according to California activist Sam H. Clauser, who campaigns to farmers and young Republicans.

James Woolsey is another name in California hemp circles; this former director of the CIA believes hemp to be a sensible and patriotic direction. The fact that natural energy sources, produced on America's farms, would not only employ Americans, but would put the whole country in a much safer position financially and strategically, is causing everyone to take a hard look at the future of hemp. Sadly, there are still those parties who benefit from keeping the US dependent on fossil fuels.

Much of the debate in California revolves around the perception of cannabis - is it hemp or is it dope? This controversy was played out recently when Drug Abuse Resistance Education (D.A.R.E.) reacted against the use of the cannabis leaf at bus stops in an advertising campaign for Alterna Shampoo. This ignorance, though not still widespread, does exist and can be used by unscrupulous interests to continue the suppression of hemp.

Photograph Courtesy of
Justin Dennis

Santa Barbara Mayor Harriet Miller summed up the situation: "The industrial hemp strain is different from the marijuana strain, so a public education program is necessary."[78] Her sentiments are those of many legislators, who are fighting cannabis suppression elsewhere. Most noted of such politicians is Jesse 'the Body' Ventura, Governor of Minnesota. A fighter, who beat both major parties and wears Rolling Stones logos at press conferences, he is not afraid to tackle the hemp issue on behalf of Minnesota citizens, who have for years watched as their neighbours in Canada make profits on what used to be a birthright in their own state.

Canada legalised hemp in 1998 after research of this nation's history and studies of cannabis cultivation had shown how valuable this plant could be. Not grown since 1938, this move was welcomed not only for the novelty, but also for the fundamental economics. In Brandon, a town near Winnipeg, Manitoba, it was expected that 1,200 jobs would be created, and local governments expressed their support by providing $500,000 in roads and infrastructure.

Many other locations in Canada have followed their lead, and have been able to sell much of their hemp profitably to the US; however, some difficulties appeared, most notably the confiscation of a truckload of Canadian hemp seeds by US officials, leading to diplomatic tensions. Another discouraging event has been the break-up of Consolidated Growers and Processors, which was in fact a US company that did not move in tandem with the hemp industry; this left many farmers stranded with unfulfilled contracts.

Kenex of Canada was at one time the largest hemp company in North America, and while they have persevered and shown incredible business growth, they have had to deal with a number of obstacles, including the attempt to make any food containing hemp nuts or oil illegal in the US, despite the obvious lack of any evidence showing that it is a danger. Ironically, while one can buy poppy seeds anywhere, grow poppy flowers, and transport poppy products, known to contain trace amounts of a narcotic, hemp is singled out. This attitude has caused much debate among Americans, and on 13 January 2002 *The Washington Post* ran an article on the topic, demonstrating the irony, and describing the range of foods containing hemp, such as hemp pretzels and hemp tofu. As any legalisation barring hemp products would affect Kenex's sales, they have reacted by filing a US$20m suit, alleging that this would be a violation of the North American Free Trade Agreement (NAFTA).

One Canadian company which has been enormously successful despite all the turbulence is Rocky Mountain Grain Products. By late spring of 2005 it was handling 3,000 lbs. of hemp seed a day, most of which was used for 'hemp hearts' (de-hulled seeds). This demand has kept many Canadian farmers busy, growing mostly the USO varieties which produce a large seed. Not only are the 'hemp hearts' in demand for the nutritional boost that they are providing to the consumers, but the by-product, the outer parts of the seeds which are removed, have proven quite useful to the horse breeders who have at times fed them to the older, less successful horses only to see them revive and go on to win races; those privy to such information have been able to place many successful bets at the racetrack.[79]

Another tale is not such a wonderful success story, but is interesting in other ways, the case of Chief Alex Plume of South Dakota; his hemp crops were raided by federal authorities in that state when he was attempting to grow it for paper, a project which he will continue by legally harvesting wild hemp. As the law only prohibits hemp with leaves on it, such plants may be used without the leaves, which are not essential to the papermaking process. Another aboriginal Indian in the same state, Chief Joe American Horse, has been working on using hemp for building material.[80]

Most hemp enterprises do not have any sort of legal entanglements, and entrepreneurs such as Mina Hegaard have been able to trade legally, although they must import the hemp. Hegaard's business, Minawear, purchases the fabric from Hemp Traders in California, which in turn gets it mainly from China. Nutiva is another California hemp business, run by John Roulac, who purchases most of his seed from Canada. While he has always been able to trade legally, there has been pressure coming from the federal government to ban hemp foods, and he has fought lengthy court battles to keep hemp legal. Support for hemp seed comes not only from hemp enthusiasts but from the health food market, as hemp is particularly nutritious and has medicinal value, apart from any THC.

One of Roulac's colleagues and ally in the fight for hemp seed sales in the US is New York City restaurateur Denis Cicero of Galaxy Global Eatery, located at 15th St. and Irving Place just north of Greenwich Village. Not only does he sell food with hemp seeds and oil, but one can also purchase a range of hemp items and books, including his own *Galaxy Global Eatery Hemp Cookbook*. More then just a business, it is also a hangout for many writers and actors who are putting their talents into the hemp movement in an effort to improve the US economy and work for a cleaner environment.

With public support, officials can be effective in reversing the damage done to their country. Ultimately, the wisdom of the Founding Fathers is expected to prevail, as the public is given the facts about their heritage, which country singer Willie Nelson summed up in 1994:

Image from:
Hemporium brochure,
2005

Hemp is intertwined with American history. We grew it to rig the great New England sailing ships, travelled west in Connestoga wagons covered in hemp, dressed in homespun hemp cloth when we got there and wound up wearing hemp jeans. We tied our cargo with hemp rope and fed the poultry with hemp seed. We used hemp to help develop this country.[81]

Photograph opposite courtesy of Juliette Atkinson, **2005**
www.julietteatkinson.com

America and Canada are both taking another look at the reasons why hemp was outlawed; the latter, having relegalised its cultivation, is finding a profit from it, and it is hoped that the US will follow suit. Patriotism is one reason for doing this, as overused as that term may be; not that there need be in fact any such dramatic argument, for, as so many Americans have pointed out, hemp is a sensible crop, and for that reason alone it is expected that the fields of 'living emerald' which so moved Kentuckian James Lane Allen to write of it in 1900 will once again grace the nation's farmlands. When that happens, it will be one of the biggest blessings to be bestowed upon the nation.

**CANADIAN HEMP
TRADE ALLIANCE**

CHTA

ACCC

ALLIANCE COMMERCIALE
CANADIENNE DU CHANVRE

1. *The Economist,* 28 July - 3 August, 2001
2. Herer, Jack. *The Emperor Wears no Clothes,* Van Nuys (Ca.), AH HA Publishing, 1985
3. Conrad, Chris. *Hemp: Lifeline to the Future.* LA Creative Xpresions, 1994 [2nd ed.] pp. 39-41, and Rosenthal, Ed. *Hemp Today.* Oakland, CA. Quick American Archives, 1994. p. 333
4. Lupien, John C. *Unravelling an American Dilemma: The Demonization of Marihuana.* Malibu, Pepperdine University thesis, 1995
5. West, Dr. Dave. "Low, Dishonest Decade" in *Hemp Times,* Fall 1999

6. Heslop, Samuel C.H. *Hemp Fuel & Fibre*. Oxford, Oxford Brooke University thesis, 2000
7. *The Times*. The article quotes Bobby Pugh, proprietor of The Hemp Shop, the UK's oldest and largest retail hemp outlet. 23 September 2000
8. *Oxford History*, vol. 3, 1961. (as quoted in *Hemp: Lifeline to the Future* by Chris Conrad, p.9)
9. Anslinger, Harry J. *The Murderers*. (As quoted in Herer).
10. Hudson, Christopher. *The Daily Mail*. 18 August 2001
11. Newcomb, Richard F. *Iwo Jima*. NY, Holt, Rhinehart & Winston, 1965
12. Zilg, Gerard Colby. *Du Pont: Behind the Nylon Curtain*. Englewood Cliffs (NJ), Prentice-Hall, 1974
13. *Ib.*, p. 12
14. Carr, William H.A. *The du Ponts of Delaware*. London, Fredrick Muller, 1965. p. 181
15. Duke, Marc. *The du Ponts: Portrait of a Dynasty*. NY, Saturday Review Press, 1976. p. 138
16. Guenet, François. *Chanvre*. N.d., n.p.
17. Engelbrecht and Hanighen, *Merchants of Death*. NY, Garden City Publishing, 1937. p. 34
18. Zilg, p. 117
19. *Ib.*, p. 110
20. Colby, Gerard. *Du Pont Dynasty: Behind the Nylon Curtain*. Secaucus, (NJ), Lyle Stuart, 1984. [2nd ed. of the 1974 book, with the authors name shortened]. p. 144
21. Guenet
22. Zilg. p. 130
23. Guenet
24. Zilg. p. 137
25. Engelbrecht and Hanighen, p. 179
26. Duke. p. 290
27. Mosley, Leonard. *Blood Relatives. The Rise and Fall of the du Ponts of Delaware*. NY, Atheneum, 1980. p. 269
28. Zilg. p. 168
29. *Ib.*, p. 169
30. *Ib.*, p. 195
31. *Ib.*
32. *Ib.*, p. 214
33. *Ib.*, p. 216
34. Zilg, p. 258
35. Mosley, p. 354
36. Zilg, p. 303
37. *Ib.*, pp. 305-306
38. *Ib.*
39. Ambruster, Howard Watson. *Treason's Peace*. NY, The Beechhurst Press, 1947 [2nd ed.] p. 327
40. *Ib.*, p. 61
41. *Ib.*
42. Zilg, p. 356
43. Higham, Charles. *Trading with the Enemy*. London, Robert Hale, 1983. p. 162
44. *Ib.*
45. Zilg, p. 318
46. Higham, p. 166
47. *Ib.*, p. 171
48. O'Reilly, Daniel. *Common Sense*. Freedom Club Information Bulletin, 2005.
Here it is noted that the Black Legion in that era was intertwined with the Wolverine Republican League, and members of both were responsible for the murder of Chares Poole, an African-American, who was tortured for thrills in 1936. This and other crimes prompted outcry, as it was found that such far right organisations had links to the Nazis who were in turn infiltrating the US press and the US government; one such organisation was called the "Patriotic League of America."
49. Zilg. p. 329
50. Mosley. p. 388
51. Greenewalt, Crawford. *Hummingbirds*. NY, AMNH, 1960.
52. Frazier, Jack. *The Great American Hemp Industry*. Peterstown, (WV), Solar Age Press, 1991.
53. Colby. p. 700
54. *Ib.*, introduction
55. *Ib.*, p. 712
56. *Ib.*, p. 713
57. *Ib.*
58. Ridgeway, James. *Village Voice*, 16 July 2002
59. Lupien
60. *Ib.*

61. *Ib.*
62. *Ib.*
63. *Ib.*
64. Bouquet, Dr. Charles, as quoted in Lupien
65. Herer, p. 32
66. Conrad, p. 46
67. Lupien
68. *Ib.*
69. *Ib.*
70. Herer, p. 32 Rep. Vinson continued for decades, becoming one of America's longest serving lawmakers, much noted for increasing defence spending.
71. Lupien
72. *Ib.*
73. *Ib.*
74. *Ib.*
75. Salins, Howard Dr. Letter of 30 March, 1943 (as published in Rosenthal)
76. Walter, Jimmy. Personal communication
77. *www.prisonplanet.tv/audio/130505forcedchipping.htm* Plans to microchip the US population, if not the world population, are well underway, some decades after Dr. Jose Delgado experimented with electrodes in human brains and attempted to perfect remote control devices, paid for by the US taxpayer. More recently, victims of Hurricane Katrina were microchipped under the auspices of FEMA and Michael Brown. There is interest in using the mentally disabled, and, much to the consternation of many American parents, there have been discussions with the Pentagon about microchipping US troops; this, however, is not so new, as troops were microchipped in Vietnam, which contributed to their willingness to commit war crimes. There is a belief among veterans that the soldiers who took part in the Abu Ghraib atrocites were also microhipped, as well as those who in Dec. of 2005 broke into a house and bizarrely, tied up the man and then stripped his wife with the family watching. Dr. Delgado wished to see generals in battle controlled electronically, and to achieve this, experiments have been carried out on soldiers. Ironically, the mark proposed would carry a "666" as the bar codes in America are already programmed with this number. Many GOP members endorse this, despite the anti-Christian stigma; GOP heavyweight Tommy Thompson spent much of 2005 promoting the mark, claiming publicly that he would take it; so far at least, he has not done so, but has expressed doubts about getting it before more testing is undertaken. For information on these strange goings-on, see *www.spychips.com/devices/tommythompson.html, www.bilderberg.org* and also *www.rense.com*
78. Hemp Industries Association pamphlet ca. 1998
79. Snow, Roger. Personal communication
80. *Positive News,* Summer 2005. Issue 44

VII. The Antipodes

KENYON GIBSON

Dr. Francis Campbell in 1845 made note of finding hemp growing in New South Wales, on the River Hunter; he has no record of its origin, and leaves open any discussion as to when or how it was first brought to Australia.[1] A recent excavation of the *Metta Caterina,* sunk in 1785 off the coast, showed there to be a large quantity of hemp rope aboard which was intended to be used by the settlers;[2] it was well preserved after its period of submersion.

Campbell's treatise exhorted the settlers to grow this crop for many reasons, including the qualities of the soil: "In respect to soils, no country in the world can boast of any that are better fitted for the cultivation of hemp than New South Wales."[3] He specifically mentions the topography as follows:

> ...alluvial tracts, and the drained swampy lands in the districts of the Hunter, the Wallombi, the William, and the Paterson Rivers; the aquatic meadows of the Parramatta River, where they have been drained, the low flat lands of the Hawkesbury, the Napean, and the fine rich loams of Shoalheaven.[4]

He notes that the soil is rich, and thus not in need of much manure, but recommends a "copious dressing of shell marl given to those soils which are rich, black, deaf, and deep...containing a large proportion of alumina."[5]

His record shows that hemp survived the hot winds and drought, and that it grew during times of famine, twice saving the settlers from starvation.[6]

However, licenses are necessary currently for growing. Recent interest has led to plantings, starting in 1992. Tasmania and New South Wales have been the first areas to get involved, the University of Tasmania undertaking field trials and studies with the Tasmanian Hemp Company to develop a local industry. This has been of significant interest to paper manufacturers, as there are long-range problems as a result of de-forestation, especially of eucalyptus trees. In some areas the water table, due to the loss of these trees, brings up unwanted salt and damages the land for agriculture. Hemp cultivation can be used to reduce this phenomenon, while at the same time playing a role in the economy.

On the mainland one company that is heralding this new industry is EcoFibres. Led by Phil Warner, it has a vision of hemp as a stimulant to local economy, as well as a plan for overseas business. It is expected to be listed on the Australian exchange in the near future, having attracted many international investors in the start-up phase; its shares have already appreciated since the initial offering.

There are several shops trading in a variety of hemp products, the largest of which is the Margaret River Hemp Company in Western Australia, started by Georgina Wilkinson. Her shop stocks a great variety of items, taking its supplies from Asia, the US and the UK. In Victoria, Green Hemp Australia carries an assortment of hemp items from books to clothes to food items. Braintree, specialising in clothing, has several outlets in Australia, where it makes available a range of hemp threads from tank tops to jeans. This has been one of Australia's fastest growing businesses in any category, and since its inception in the Antipodes has branched out to Europe and the Middle East with its fashionable lines.

New Zealand's history also includes cultivation of hemp - Norfolk Island was once intended as a hemp colony in the nineteenth century, and a Mother Aubert grew hemp at Jerusalem starting in 1883.[7] In the early 1940s the Ministry of Agriculture and Fisheries grew ten acres near Foxton, reporting: "...it grew magnificently and fibre yield was excellent."[8]

Interest has recently been expressed in hemp by New Zealanders; several small businesses have begun trading - most notably the Hemp Trading Company of Auckland and Hemporium in Wellington. The New Zealand Hemp Industries Association Inc. (NZHAI) started in 1990 and has been active in bringing an understanding of the hemp industry to the general public.

1. Campbell, Francis. *A Treatise on the Culture of Flax and Hemp.* Sydney, Statham & Forster, 1845. p. 80
2. Maggs Bros. catalogue, London.
3. Campbell
4. *Ib.*
5. *Ib.*
6. *Ib.*
7. Anon. *A Brief History of Industrial Hemp in New Zealand.* Internet essay, n.d.
8. *http://www.norml.org.nz/modules.php?name=News&file=article&sid=298*

PART TWO

USES AND APPLICATIONS

In that building, long and low,
With its windows, all a-row,
Like the port-holes of a hulk,
Human spiders spin and spin,
Backwards down their threads so thin,
Drooping, each a hempen thread...

Henry Wadsworth Longfellow
The Ropewalk

M.L.Upton

VIII. Threads

MINA HEGAARD

*T*he emperor's clothes were hemp, before he traded them in on the advice of some fly-by-night wardrobe consultants. Princesses, vagabonds, soldiers, sailors, cave men and mummies wore or are still wearing hemp. Before spinning, weaving, and knitting were invented, we probably wore fig leaves, animal pelts, matted grasses and peeled bark to protect ourselves from the elements. Ever wonder how Adam and Eve held those leaves on? Consider the hemp plant, producing one of the finest and oldest known spinning fibers. In 1972 archaeologists discovered the oldest preserved hemp product in history, dating from around 10,000 BC on a Chinese mummy.[1] Thus we have the first threads of hemp recorded in history, to be found in every century and every civilized country since. Celtic, Frankish, Egyptian, Japanese and Teutonic nobility wore it; Catherine de Medici wore underclothing of considerable fineness made from it,[2] which was at that time considered to be quite a novelty. Russian peasants are known to have worn it,[3] as well as British shepherds,[4] Chinese laborers,[5] American frontiersmen,[6] and Indian merchants.

Europeans cultivated hemp for all classes of society to wear, going back to times before Christ; Samuel Boyce records:

> A coarse hempen cloth has been found among the remains of the Cave-Dwellers and earliest inhabitants of Europe, by whom it may have been made at a time as remote as when the Pharaohs were laying the foundation stones of the pyramids, six thousand years ago.[7]

The colonisers brought this plant with them to the New World, although, as discussed in Chapter V, American hemp textile fragments and sightings of hemp pre-date Columbus. Settlers wore it, and their records show that "...fiber was produced for the homespun cloth woven by the wives and daughters of the pioneer settlers."[8] Herodotus states that Scythians cultivated hemp in the valley of the Volga four thousand years ago. Research among the remains of the semi-barbarous people first inhabiting France show that the production of hemp was among the earliest of the arts, and furnished the materials for garments and household linens continually.[9]

As early as the beginning of the seventeenth century we find the hemp industry systematically established among the small farmers, who possessed small plots of land adjoining their dwellings, where they sowed their hemp every year.[10] Hemp was of the simplest of cultivation, and its fiber product most easily adapted to the necessities of the people in their everyday tasks. Hemp and flax were the two most important textile fibers of Europe until replaced by cotton. Both of these were cultivated and processed extensively in Italy, whose reputation for hemp was unsurpassed: the finest varieties were grown by 'spade culture', water retted and treated to processing methods that were often trade secrets.

In 1790, Virginia produced 315,000 yards of hemp fabrics, and one Boston company made 3,000 bolts of light hemp canvas in 1792. Hemp and flax production exceeded 21,000,000 yards by 1810,[11] although cotton was gaining ground, and each year replacing other fibers. By the 1820s hemp spinning was at a low: "As far as I can learn, I am the only person in the US that will attempt to spin by machinery; I mean fine threads, capable of making duck," asserted one US manufacturer from New Jersey in 1825.[11] But this was not the case for long; by the mid-nineteenth century Americans had "developed its fiber to the fullest extent", forming "an entirely new staple of that invaluable fiber", noted as "silky- more delicate and beautiful than the finest flax", it was then believed that "this new article will supersede cotton."[12]

At the same time as hemp textiles were being improved, Americans were learning to utilize the wastes of this and other fibers to produce substitutes of higher grade products. The Civil War was to greatly diminish the hemp production, and other world-wide factors contributed to decline in use. In the first part of the twentieth century, hemp was the third most traded fiber, as the following table shows:

World Fiber Production for 1913 From: *La Ramie*, by Félicien Michotte, 1913	
LINEN	882,000 tonnes
COTTON	850,000 tonnes
HEMP	650,000 tonnes
RAMIE	25,000 tonnes

Hemp cloth was still appreciated by many, and was even compared to silk. In the US its cultivation was encouraged, as the *USDA Yearbook* of 1913 noted: "Hemp was formerly the most important long fiber, and it is now used more extensively than any other soft fiber except jute. From 10,000 to 15,000 tons are used in the United States every year."[13] Some of this wound up as trousers, as Chris Conrad noted in a recent book: "Its combination of ruggedness and comfort as duck canvas were utilized in the first jeans by the Levi Strauss company in California."[14]

America in fact had a liking for this cloth, endorsed by no less than Founding Father George Washington. Into the twentieth century many countries continued to grow it for fibers, and even the hempophobe Harry Anslinger was forced to remark:

In 1637 the General Court at Hartford, Connecticut, ordered all families to plant one teaspoonful of hemp. Massachusetts did likewise in 1639. The General Assembly of Connecticut repeated its order in 1640, insisiting that the colonists sow hemp "that we might in time have plenty supply of linen cloth among ourselves."

Rowan Robinson,
The Great Book of Hemp, **1996**

Now this hemp is the finest fiber known to mankind, my God, if you ever have a shirt made out of it, your grandchildren would never wear it out. You take Polish families. We used to see marijuana in the yards of Polish families. We'd go in and start to tear it up and the man came out with his shotgun, yelling: "These are my clothes for next winter."[15]

Sadly, Anslinger referred to it incorrectly as marijuana, even though it was obviously hemp. In the 1930s Anslinger was appointed head of the Federal Bureau of Narcotics by his uncle-in-law Andrew Mellon. Along with the help of media mogul William Randolph Hearst who had agendas of his own, they managed to outlaw hemp by citing racist opinions and made-up stories; by 1937 they had convinced people to trade old-for-new, the new being synthetic fibers made by Du Pont, to whom Mellon had loaned money. Rayon, nylon, dacron and other unnatural fibers were spun, round and round the world, with no one at the time questioning the future effects on the environment and human health; the fig leaf was by then made of plastic, and the slogan 'better living through chemistry' became a mantra for the madding crowd. Transparency, cheapness, flexibility, and water resistance are some of the properties achieved by scientists working in the realm of poly-molecular chemistry and in many cases, these have been worthwhile discoveries with long-lasting applications. However, nature and *Homo sapiens* have had a relationship since our species first appeared, and that will not ever be changed. Each species in nature has its own niche, and its own qualities that give it a purpose; fiber plants especially, hemp quite specifically.

We use textiles every day in our clothing, bedding, flooring, furniture, and automobiles, as well as in industrial applications, such as artificial turf, artificial blood vessels, bulletproof vests and space vehicles. The word 'textile' comes from the Latin *texere* (to weave), originating from woven fabrics; it has evolved with technology into an all encompassing term for fibers and other materials that can be made into fabrics by interlacing or any other construction method, as well as a term for the fabrics as well. Fabrics are classified by the way the yarns, threads, cords, ropes, braids, laces, embroidery, or nets, are constructed; by weaving, knitting, bonding, felting, or tufting them into textiles. The study of textiles has called upon archaeologists, biologists and chemists to decode their historical mysteries, as they play a huge part in the development of humans and our culture including religion, personal appearance, bedding, science, rituals, and the path of commerce.

A fiber is the smallest part of a fabric, an individual, hairlike substance that is either vegetable (cellulose), animal (wool, hair) or mineral (asbestos). Yarns are what fibers and filaments are spun into, before being woven or knit. The structure of a fiber as well as the way a yarn is spun has much to do with the end products, which can range from fluffy to flat, from dull to lustrous and from smooth to slubby. Yarns can be ring spun, open end, wet spun and dry spun. Then the yarns are either woven on looms to make canvas, twill, muslin, and corduroys, or knitted on tubular machines to produce jerseys and fleeces. After that fabrics can be further enhanced with washes, brushing, printing, polishing, dyeing and many other innovations. The making of natural textiles is actually a precise and involved science beginning with the seed, and from farm to factory to finished product, there is a process that sometimes takes more than a year.

Much time has been lost in the development of the hemp fiber for textiles, due to the propaganda that was circulated in the 1930s, but development is on the upswing again as people become more aware of pollutants in the environment and conscious of the impact they have on it; nevertheless, hemp is currently more expensive than cotton, because it must be imported. Many countries have been growing it through the propaganda period, which has kept seed stock development and processing up-to-date knowledge. China is one of the biggest hemp textile producers presently, with Romania, Russia and Poland in tow. Many in the textile industry agree that Chinese hemp has a different 'life' than the European weaves, meaning it is grown, processed and handled in a different manner, thus producing different properties. The 'hand' can range from coarse, like burlap, to smooth and shiny, like a silk blend. China so far has been most innovative with new blends such as silk, cotton, rayon, polyester, wool, jacquards, and knits, as well as Romania and Poland which make their weaves with treatments such as air polishing and brushing. One Irish designer came up with a hemp/yak wool blend. From the finest - velvets which have appeared on the Italian market - (the Italians are rumoured to have the best quality, which is in short supply)- to the simplest - Thailand's primitive burlappy weave - hemp is everywhere.

The number one quality that hemp is most revered for today is its naturalness. It is a well known fact that cotton cultivation is one of the biggest polluting industries in the world due to its use of water, chemical fertilizers and pesticides. But the organicness of hemp is soon overshadowed by the many other brilliant qualities that hemp possesses, including its strength, comfort, absorbency, mildew resistance, UV ray protection and fire retardancy. In a recent study, Dutch researchers note:

> Interest in 'new' fiber crops is increasing...flax, which like hemp is an annual bast fiber crop, continues to be grown in temperate climate zones, demonstrating that a market for bast fibers exists. One of the major problems limiting the market potential of flax fiber is its high price...hemp yields are generally 50-100% higher than flax.[16]

As well as being organic, hemp is an excellent interim crop for farmers because while its long reaching roots choke out the weeds, break up the earth and secure the topsoil; the leaves are sprinkled off after harvesting to enrich the soil for the next crop. Another recent report states: "In some areas of Europe, hemp is an easier crop to grow than flax and, indeed, except by specialists, the two are not readily distinguishable, particularly since it is not unusual to find a mixture of the two in one cloth".[17] Hemp is naturally resistant to many pests and microbes, and it grows rapidly. These qualities make hemp a high profit crop for farmers, with the most

Fiber Bundle.
From:
USDA Yearbook, 1913

expensive part of manufacturing hemp being its transportation. But these facts are just the cotyledons of the mighty plant's versatility. Once it is spun into yarns, knit and woven into goods, sewn into products, then its physical properties can be experienced.

The earliest known description of hemp's qualities is that of Herodotus (iv. 74), who cites it as "equal to linen in fineness." John Baxter in 1840 compared it to cotton, saying, "...hemp would bleach whiter than either flax or cotton, and make the finest fabric, from lace and cambric down to good shirting, and far cheaper than either."[18] In 1865 the US Commissioner of Agriculture also compared it to cotton, calling it a "fiber stronger than cotton, took a better color, could be spun on cotton machinery with less waste than cotton, and was as white or whiter."[19] Boyce calls it a "soft, white silky fiber" while writing on its production:

> worked by hand, hemp furnishes a thread of extreme fineness almost equaling silk, much finer than cotton, and much finer than can be produced by the present imperfect mechanical methods, excepting as manipulated upon 'spun-silk', or on mohair machinery. Lace threads are spun from hemp by hand to the fineness of 600 miles for each two and one-half pounds of hemp fiber.[20]

A recent article in *The Times* notes: "Hemp is half way between linen and cotton: it drapes like linen but is softer than cotton."[21] It is known to also withstand water better than any other fiber,[22] and is relatively fire retardant.

Hemp's high absorption rate, or hydrophilic nature, causes it to retain dye, resist stain and static cling, wick moisture, stay warm in cool weather and cool in hot weather, and 'breathe' better than cotton or flax. Thus it becomes a superior fiber for being active and sweating in. Absorbency is well noted, with a 'regain' rating of 11.75 percent(A.S.T.M.) to 12 percent (Roubaix Conditioning House), compared to cotton, which has an 8.5 percent moisture regain.

Hemp has naturally occurring anti-microbial properties which stave off mold and mildew, which is why sailors found it ideal for use on ships as sails, uniforms and rope, while cobblers and footwear designers use it in uppers on shoes such as Adidas™ or Vans ™.

The strength of hemp is remarkable too; it is said to outlast cotton by five lifetimes. Although hemp's strength would be ideal for use in thread, its present state of technological advancement is in the Dark Ages. The result is that the (polyester) stitching will most likely wear out on a hemp product before the article itself. Its tensile strength is "appreciably greater than linen,"[23] and it has been noted: "Hemp, the strongest of the vegetable fibers, gives the greatest production per acre and requires the least attention...being 2-3 times as strong as any of the hard fibers, much less weight is required to give the same yardage."[24] Thus it is warmer but not bulky.

In order to produce quality and consistency, the preparation of hemp has to be given much attention, beginning with the variety of seed and the care it receives. So important is seed cultivation, that Britain imposed stiff penalties on 'hemp seed cheats', and welcomed immigrants who could supply good seed.[25] Each unique climate requires its own special development of seed qualities according to what end use it is being farmed for. Today specialists such as Dr. Ivan Bócsa of Hungary and Ecofibres of Australia deal with this issue, the latter developing seed and working with manufacturers and designers in perfecting the final product. Ecofibres, which is especially committed to fiber hemp, has a long-term background of farming, and working with the University of Tasmania, has begun careful studies of regional conditions necessary for selected hemp varieties.

There is much literature available on hemp cultivation, which describes the processing of fiber. In 1747 it was noted:

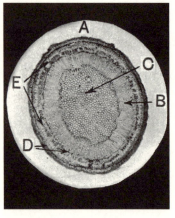

A. cuticle or outer bark
B. woody part
C. pith
D. dark circles enclosing
fibrous layer
E. group of fibres in
fibrous layer

From:
Cordage and Cordage Fibre, by
J. Woodhouse and P. Kilgour,
1919

A fine fibre cannot be obtained without the concurrence of several circumstances. The soil, for as we have already remarked, too strong or too dry soils never produce fibres of superior softness or fineness: on the contrary, they are too woody, and consequently harsh and brittle. But if the hemp-ground be too wet, the bark of the Hemp produced on it will be herbaceous, tender, and easily broken, so that there will be too great a proportion of tow and waste when dressing it. It is soft, rich, and moderately wet soils, which produce a smooth, flexible, and strong fibre the most desirable qualities in Hemp. The seasons; for in hot, dry seasons, the fibres are harsh: on the contrary, they are supple, and sometimes tender, in cold, wet seasons. The degree of ripeness. If the Hemp have been left too long standing on the ground, the longitudinal fibres of the bark adhere too strongly together, so that it comes off the reed like a ribbon, and is very difficult to divide.[26]

Boyce wrote: "Hemp is the king of fiber-bearing plants, - the standard by which all other fibers are measured; No plant is more susceptible to the process of producing a fine, white, soft and silky fiber, and there is not one to take its place in the wide and diversified area of its culture and manufacture."[27] Conrad observes that "for hemp to be its best, it must be treated with due respect. The fiber's characteristics result from the processing it receives."[28] and points out that some countries stretch the fiber beyond its normal length, with shrinkage as a problem down the road.

After harvesting comes the crucial step of retting: Chapter XVIII gives an in-depth account of this process, which is the removal of the fibers from the stalks. On this process Boyce observed:

When perfectly purified and prepared, however, the fibers of the hemp plant are as soft, fine and flexible as those of any other plant... When this is accomplished there are many reasons why the hemp industry will be the greatest one for the production of fine serviceable fabrics.[29]

A second account made a few decades later notes:

> The time taken in the case of water-retting varies from one to three weeks, but it should be noted that the extent to which this treatment is carried has an important influence on the character of the fiber. The longer the retting, the softer the fiber and the finer the subdivision of the fiber layer that is made possible, but at the same time the strength is reduced.[30]

Retting is an art form - a part of 'cannabiculture' as fermentation is to viniculture; anyone can make *'vin aigre'* from a harvest of grapes, just as anyone can make coarse fibers from hemp by tossing it on the ground to dew-ret. Such a practice is not to be taken seriously. Good grapes, in skilled hands will become vintage wine. Good hemp, in skilled hands, can be made into fine, lustrous fabric, as has been produced over the ages: "Hemp fiber, prepared by water-retting as practiced in Italy, is creamy white, lustrous, soft, and pliable. Hemp of best quality is very light in color and possesses a high luster."[31]

Obviously, the different methods of retting freshly sown hemp each produce their own characteristics. Field-retting is the easiest and cheapest method; simply left outside where it is cut while the dew and natural forces have their way with it. However, the quality suffers for lack of control of the elements, and an unpredictable final product is the result. There is also water-retting, enzyme-retting, and steam explosion-retting first explored by the Germans in 1994.

After retting, washing is next; a step sometimes not practiced, though many writers advise it. G.A. Berti, writing in seventeenth century Italy, commented; *"Col laverla replicatamente, e con diligenza,"*[32] best translated as an exhortation to wash many times thoroughly. There are also the steps of crushing and braking, which separate the hurds from the fibers and is also known as decorticating. Scutching and hackling (or heckling) then follow, which remove the last bits of hurds from the fibers by scraping over metal combs. Proper sorting is then necessary. One American grading system had the following classifications: cleaned, open-cut, single, dressed-long, dressed-short, single-dressed, shorts, and tow.[33] Other nations had similar systems, the most precise being the Russian grading, which designated both place of origin and quality. Scutching, hackling, combing and carding organize and groom the hemp. The hackling process was given particular

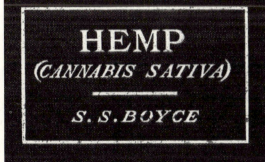

attention, with one writer advising a double hackling, the second time through fine tooth hackles;[34] overdoing it, however, can result in breakage and loss of strength. The hacklers needed to be skilled in their work as too little resulted in impurities adhering to the fiber, while overdoing the job resulted in weak or broken strands.

Although beautiful in its natural colors, hemp takes well to dyes and printing , which have only begun to be explored. Hemp can be yarn dyed, piece dyed or garment dyed with direct, basic, sulfur, vat, azuic, mordant, and reactive dyes as well as with pigments.[35] Hemp and flax are alike in their behavior towards dyes and coloring agents, thus many guide books give the same directions for each. For example, the General Dyestuff Corporation in their 1936 manual recommend boiling either fiber with 5-10 percent soda ash, preferably with the addition of 1-2 percent Igepon T or Laventine H as preliminary treatment. When using basic dyestuffs, tannic acid was used during the boiling process. With direct dyestuffs, General recommends Igepon T or Peregal O, with the addition of salt reduced to effect a slower absorption, and the quantity of soda increased in some cases.[36] However, this particular information may or may not be outdated. More recently, Owen Sercus of the Fashion Institute of Technology in New York City was one of the first to begin investigating finishing treatments on hemp. He has found that hemp is easy to dye and works well with modern dyeing processes. Fiber reactive dye takes well to hemp; after one hour of agitation in the dye bath, it is then spun, and left to sit four hours before the rinse cycle. While direct dye lies on top of the fibers, fiber reactive dye becomes a part of the fibers and therefore lasts longer. Fiber reactive dye is also less polluting than direct dye because it requires less rinsing and the runoff can be done with vinegar before the spin cycle. Hemp can be bleached easily with peroxide, though the best fibers are naturally light to start with.[37]

Even though grey goods (uncolored or bleached textiles) are available to American and Canadian designers, we are still unable to successfully produce our own hemp textiles, mainly because of the cost. Besides needing to import the raw fibers, part of the problem of trying to knit and weave in America has been that our modern machinery is not quite calibrated for hemp. With knitting, which is more problem-fraught than weaving, China has so far been the only nation successful in this because it still has old machinery and the work force to manage it. When coming from a long distance, hemp poses an even greater range of possible defects, and the origin of the fabric is difficult to trace; i.e., where and how it was grown and retted; what mill produced it; how tightly the yarns were spun; if they were wet or dry spun; what settings the machinery was on; how attentive the workers were; and what finishes were applied. Even progressive shrinkage, which is continual shrinking of the garment, has been known to occur on some of the Chinese knits that are meant for wash and wear. Dawn Pickering, of Pickering International, says that knits can have 25 percent shrinkage rates due to varying settings on the machinery, and notes the unpredictability of the source (the farmer), torquing and twisting problems, and runs or holes.[38] Barbara Fillipone, of Earth Goods in Washington, states that when purchasing directly from the mills, one must be familiar with fabric science in order to specify yarn sizes, methods of spinning, number of twists and yarn counts, which are all major variables in the performance of a textile.[39] In less than one year, research and trial and error proved that no knitting mills existed in the US that could handle the condition that hemp was imported in. Defects caused by irregularities (slubs) clogged the needles, breaking them or requiring a worker to monitor them constantly and

The hemp apparel industry has grown dramatically in the last 10 years; Braintree, Enamore. Minawear, Nibus, Sativa, Satori and Swirlspace are becoming well-known brands in Australia, Europe and North America.
Yves de Saussure, 2006

climb inside the tube of the machine and rethread it.

Textile designer Wally Filler, of New York City, notes that the textile industry in the US is dying because it is labor intensive and imported goods pose significantly competitive prices.[40] Therefore it makes it far too expensive to solve the standards issue by importing a container of hemp fiber and having it manufactured and rated in accordance to the Worth Street Textile Market Rules and classifying fabric quality in the textile industry. However, Larry Serbin, of Hemp Traders in California, is currently working in conjunction with the Canadian Hemp Co. to develop a refining process that will groom the hemp fibers to an end yarn of 36Nm, which rivals North American grown flax fibers in quality and price.[41] If Canada can manage to successfully master a new process that brings hemp to an equal level with the price and quality of linen, then many more doors will open and hemp will have a chance to become mainstream.

Until then, hemp designers must devise ways of lowering damage rates. To control shrinkage, particularly in knits, it is wise to piece dye (the entire roll of fabric at once) instead of garment dye (dying after it is cut and sewn). The dye process preshrinks the fabric, but unfortunately when it is re-rolled, it can sometimes restretch it beyond acceptable shrinkage rates. It is best to use dye houses familiar with hemp and its issues. If designers utilize the garment dye procedure, one advantage is that the 'flags' (colored stickers put on the flaws by inspectors as the fabric comes off the machinery) are not washed away. The cutter can be informed to avoid the holes and runs whenever possible, and the sewers are alerted as well. Garment dye is also less wasteful because only the finished product is dyed and not the scraps. However, garment dye is not practical for tailored items due to the shrinkage rates of the different components.

Another issue to contend with in blends is the 'cottonization' of hemp, referring to the arrangement of the bast fibers in length (approx. 1.5 inches), parallelization, and spin-technical characteristics according to those of cotton, necessary to achieve so that it can be processed on modern machinery and blended with cotton. The shortened fibers are sometimes the culprit in the case of pilling, because the fibers can pop out of the surface when dyed or washed, but we are unable to pinpoint exact causes of this phenomenon since there are so many unknown variables in imports. To cope with 'pills' there are finishes and processes such as enzyme washing, biopolishing and singing that help reduce surface fuzz and improve the hand. Both knits and wovens produce a high amount of dust for the workers' environments, and both have a tendency to jam and break needles on the sewing machinery, again proving hemp's durability.

Effects of Ammonia on Oxidized Fibres From: *Phormium Tenax,* by Sir James Hector, 1889		
Coloured Rosa-pink	Coloured brown	Unaltered
Phormium tenax	Wood	Hemp
Yucca	Manila, impure	Sunn hemp
Sisal	Manila, pure	Rhea
Aloe		Raw cotton
		Linum

However, most problems are associated with the knits, not the wovens, and one designer's simple solution is to not use them. But, it is difficult to avoid because there is a demand for the casual comfort and the forgiving nature of these popular fabrics, of which there are several types being consumed as fast as the mills can produce them: jerseys, fleece, mesh knits, and a recently refined, promising yet expensive lycra/hemp/cotton blend. In the end, dedicated eco-determined designers will find ways to maximize the abundant glories of hemp textiles, and work around the hindrances until new developments take shape.

The hemp industry is still in its early stage of rebirth, and only as recently as 1991 has it been allowed into the US. Since its exhumation by historians and enthusiasts, hemp has experienced a global revival and technical advancement in many areas of usage, especially in textiles. Bad press and greed from parties interested in selling oil and plastics rather than natural, domestically grown resources almost erased hemp from American culture. However, hemp is a plant that will not be choked out by removing it from the Smithsonian Museum, spraying Roundup on it, or jailing people for using it. Hemp's importance can not be destroyed or forgotten. It has long roots, a long history, and an even longer resume of uses and talents. The exceptional qualities of hemp make it a superior natural fiber that outperforms all others.

Nibus Clothing - is an environmentally responsible company that was founded on the principle that fashionable clothing can still make a positive impact on the environment and society.
Nibus Clothing
Mission statement

TECHNICAL NOTES

In order to completely understand the physical properties of hemp in textiles, we must examine the technical analysis of the hair-splitting study of the minutiae, fibers and fibrillae which provide insight into the nature of this fiber and how it can be developed. An observation written in 1758 tells us that:

This bark is a kind of natural ribband or scarf, the threads whereof are applied and joined together, lengthways only, by a dirty glutinous humor, which must absolutely be dissolved and separated, because it is equally hurtful to the workmen and the work. The threads themselves also consist merely of a gum, but of one which is of a different quality from the superficial gum; they are supple, strong, and resist the impressions to which the former give way. Every fibre is composed of gummy globules, that are very fine, transparent, and bright, when sufficiently cleared from the superficial gum that surrounds them, and which the microscope shews to be of a different sort. All this will appear plain, if you take a few fibres from a thread that is thoroughly bleached. The fibres of Hemp in this state are nothing different from those of cotton and silk, which makes it reasonable to consider them as materials of the same kind and it is a convincing proof of this, that, when they are mixed and corded together, they appear to be a complete sameness in the whole mixture.[42]

An examination under the lens of the fibers made in the twentieth century reveals: "...each single fiber is in itself a bundle of fibrils, or fibers

of extreme fineness; these are twisted spirally and after maceration may be stretched out to a considerable length."[43] Another researcher gave the following measurements:

models wearing
Minawear in
Venice, California

The fibers are more or less separate, some entirely free, others in small bundles. The fibers vary very much in diameter, some being very broad, others narrow, and they appear like longitudinally striated cylinders. Sometimes a cavity exists, at other times none can be traced. The fibers are, on an average, from .0005 to .0007 in diameter, and in one fiber in which the diameter was .0007 the diameter of the cavity was .0001.[44]

A slightly different set of figures is quoted in 1919: "The ultimate fibers are large and somewhat irregular in shape; they vary in length from 0.2 to 2 inches; with an average length of about 1 inch, while the diameter is only about 1/1000 or 0.001 of an inch."[45] Dewey (1913) gives us a summary and measurements as follows, "Some of the bast fibers extend through the length of the stalk, but some are branched, and some terminate at each node. They are weakest at the nodes."[46] More notes on structure were made in 1933:

> The arrangement of fibers in the stem is similar to that of flax except that the bundle formation is not as well defined. Thus in the case of hemp the surface shows more pronounced markings in both transverse and longitudinal directions and the thickness of the ultimate is not so uniform. The lumen is larger and more irregular in size, while the tips, which are normally rather spatulate, are occasionally bifurcated, a condition which is never found in flax. The fibrillar structure, too, is different.[47]

The above authors make note of an earlier observation by R. Vétillart (1876), who distinguishes two contiguous layers of fiber, the outer one consisting of finer ultimates than the inner. Vétillart also makes note of the interconnectedness of the fibers, which makes for hemp's strength; he makes other observations as to the arrangement of the fiber and stria, and compares hemp to flax and other fibers.[48] More technical analysis in the mid-twentieth century is as follows:

> Under the microscope the hemp fiber is seen to consist of cell elements which are unusually long, averaging about 0.78 in. in length, but ranging from 0.19 to 2.16 in. The diameter averages 22µ and ranges from 16 to 50µ. Hence, the ratio between the length and diameter is about 1,000. The fiber is rather uneven in its diameter, and has occasional attachments of fragmentary parenchyma's tissue. In its linear structure the fiber exhibits frequent joints, longitudinal fractures, and swollen fissures. The lumen is usually broad, but toward the end of the fiber it becomes like a line. It shows scarcely any contents. The ends of the fibers are blunt and very thick walled, and occasionally show lateral branches. The cross section generally shows a group of cells, which have rounded edges and are not so sharp-angled and polygonal as those of jute.
>
> There is also a median layer between the cells, which is evidenced by its turning yellow on treatment with iodine and sulfuric acid and in which the lumen appears irregular and flattened. The cell walls exhibit frequently a remarkable stratification, the different layers yielding a variety of colors on treatment with iodine and sulfuric acid. When examined under polarized light, hemp, like linen and ramie, shows very bright colors. Hemp also gives the following microchemical reactions: (a) with iodine-sulfuric acid reagent, bluish green coloration; (b) with chloriodide of zinc, blue or violet, with traces of yellow; (c) chloriodide of calcium, rose red with traces of yellow; (d) aniline sulfate, yellowish green coloration; (e) ammoniacal fuchsine solution, pale red coloration; (f) With Schweitzer's

reagent the hemp fibers swell irregularly with a characteristic appearance and dissolve almost completely, leaving only the fragments of parenchymous tissue. Hemp is at times difficult to distinguish microscopically from flax; but it may be identified readily by an examination of the fiber ends. Hemp nearly always exhibits specimens of forked or modulated ends whereas flax never has this peculiarity. The fibers of hemp are less transparent than those of linen. Again, the parenchymous tissue which is attached frequently to hemp fibers has star-shaped crystals of calcium oxalate, scarcely ever noticed in flax. It is a mixture of cellulose and lignocellulose (bastose).[49]

The substance of which hemp, and many fibers, are composed of is cellulose, which by all accounts comprises 75-80 percent of the fiber. (An examination of this can be found in Chapter XXII.) Hemp and flax are both composed of this, which is part of the reason why one is oft compared to the other; in fact, hemp resembles flax more closely than any other fiber. The simple test that is used to distinguish the two is that of 'curling'. If soaked in water hemp curls to the left, i.e. a 'Z', while flax curls to the right, an 'S'. A technical explanation of this was made by Dr. Paul W. Allen in 1926:

> The fact that hemp and jute fibers always twist in clockwise direction when drying, while flax and ramie fibers twist in the reverse direction, is the basis of a convenient method for distinguishing flax and hemp. Microscopic examination of these fibers after treatment reveals a fibrillar structure, the fibrils of hemp and jute being arranged in right-handed spirals, while those of flax and ramie are in left-handed spirals. In some cases, internal spirals with a reverse twist may occur. The drying of the fibers is always accompanied by a twisting up of the component fibrils.[50]

Hemp is being returned to the place it once held; this monarch of fibers will once more set the tone in the world of fashion, while naked jokers will find themselves banished from the court. Our world will be better off with this restoration, and, what's more, it will be fun to achieve.

SATIVA™

1. Cheng, Te K'un. *Archaelogy in China,* vol.1 Cambridge. W. Fleffer & Son, 1959
2. Carter, Herbert R. *The Twisting and Spinning of Vegetable Fibres.* London, Griffin & Co., 1904. p. 16
3. Smith, Rev. Daniel. *Natural History for Sunday Schools,* Vol. XII. NY, T. Mason & G. Lane, 1839. p. 45
4. Goodwin, Jill. *BBC* Radio, February, 2001
5. Rosenthal, Ed. *Hemp Today*
6. Guenet, François. *Chanvre.* N.d., n.p.
7. Boyce, S.S. *Hemp.* NY, Orange Judd Co., 1912 [2nd ed.] p. 2
8. Dewey, Lyster H. "Hemp" pp. 283-346 in the *USDA Yearbook* 1913. Washington, GPO, 1914
9. Boyce, p. 36
10. *Ib.*
11. U.S. Congress. *Report No. 381.* Washington, GPO, 1830. p. 25
12. Campbell, Francis. *The Cultivation of Flax and Hemp.* Sydney, Statham & Forster, 1845, p. 93
13. Dewey
14. Conrad, Chris. *Hemp: Lifeline to the Future.* LA, Creative Xpresions, 1994. p. 128
15. Frazier, Jack. *The Marijuana Farmers.* Peterstown, (WV), Solar Age Press, 1974
16. van der Werf, Hayo M.G., W.T.M Mathijssen and Anton J. Haverkort. "Crop Physiology of Cannabis sativa L.", pp. 85-108 in *Advances in Hemp Research,* (Paolo Ranalli, ed.). NY/ London, Food Products Press, 1999
17. Guenet
18. Conrad, p. 27
19. Leavitt, Dr. O.S. *The Culture and Manufacture of Flax and Hemp.* Caber Press, [pre-publication proof, 2001; original 1865 by GPO]
20. Boyce, pp. 48-49
21. Sally Staples. *The Times,* 23 Sep. 2000
22. *www.fabrics.net/default1.asp*
23. Guenet
24. Lower, George. "Flax and Hemp", published in the February 1938 issue of *Mechanical Engineering*
25. de Saussure, Yves. *Cannabis for Health, Energy, Medicine, Paper and 25,000 Other Uses.* London, The Eryr Press, 2002. p. 2
26. Du Hamel, as quoted in Wissett, Robert. *A Treatise on Hemp.* London, J. Harding, 1808. [2nd ed.]. p. 8
27. Boyce, p. 8
28. Conrad, p. 128
29. Boyce, p. 20
30. Morton, W.E. and G.R. Wray. *An Introduction to the Study of Spinning.* London, Longman, Green & Co., 1962. [3rd ed.] p. 84
31. Guenet
32. Berti, G.A. *La Coltivazione della Canape.* N.p, ca. 1657. p. 19
33. Dingus, L.R. "Hemp Words", pp. 60-63 in *Publications of the American Dialect Society,* No.11, 1949
34. Taylor, John. "The Culture of Hemp", pp. 35-43 in *Papers on Agriculture,* Boston, 1804
35. Anon. "Dyeing Bast Fibres", p. 43 in the *CIBA Review,* 1962
36. General Dyestuff Corporation. *Manual for the Dyeing of Jute, Coir, Straw, Bast, Linen, Hemp, Piassava.* Frankfurt am Main, 1936
37. Marcandier, M. *A Treatise on Hemp.* Lyme Regis, John Hanson, 1996, [facsimile text of 1764 Eng. trans.] p. 67
38. Pers. comm. from Dawn Pickering
39. _____from Barbara Fillipine
40. _____from Wally Filler
41. _____from Larry Serbin
42. Marcandier
43. Smith, p. 46
44. Boyce, p. 55 While not noted, Boyce expressed measurements in inches, which were standard at the time.
45. Woodhouse, J. and P. Kilgour. *Cordage and Cordage Hemp.* London, Sir Isaac Pittman & Sons, 1919. p. 27
46. Dewey
47. Morton and Wray pp. 83-84
48. Vétillart, R. *Études sur les Fibres Végétales Textiles.* Paris, Librairie de Firmin-Didot et Cie., 1876. pp. 72-86
49. Mausberger, Herbert R. *Matthews' Textile Fibers.* NY, John Wiley & Sons, 1947, [5th ed.] p. 344
50. Allen, Paul W., M.S., PhD. *The Retting of Flax and Hemp.* Portland, (Or), The Caber Press, 1997. [repr. ed.] pp. 8-9

IX. Paper

KENYON GIBSON

*O*n paper our history is recorded; printed, typed, etched, and lithographed onto these sheets of matted fibre, which by themselves, in their style and substance, tell our history. In the opening chapter mention is made of the Chinese discovery of paper, or rather, of the tale of Ts'ai Lun. However, Chinese paper is known to have pre-dated this event by two- to three-hundred years. The oldest known samples of paper date from the second or first century BC, during the Han dynasty; they are all of hemp, save for the presence of some ramie, and are in an excellent state of preservation.[1]

Long-suffering craftsmen brought about the means of keeping records; their names however, are not recorded. Ts'ai Lun may well have perfected this art to some degree, giving to his country a lasting memorial of its inventive genius. In 1953 it was noted that "knowing antiquarians can readily identify old manuscripts written on so-called 'oriental paper', because it is thick and soft, white, and exceedingly well preserved over the centuries."[2] The famous American papermaker Dard Hunter in 1943 noted the pure hemp content of Oriental paper,[3] such as Japanese dharani of 770 AD.

At Samarkand, the knowledge of this craft passed to the Arabs, who ultimately brought it to Spain, establishing the first European paper mill in 1150. This mill, at Xativa, flourished, and others soon opened in Spain and other countries. Germany acquired its first paper mill in 1411, improving the craft and producing the finest paper of the time. The invention of the movable type press, by Johann Gutenberg in 1453, increased the demand for paper as people grew literate.

In 1680 the Spanish established the first paper mill in the New World at Culhuacon, Mexico; a decade later the first North American paper mill was founded in Pennsylvania by William Rittenhouse, a German immigrant. As people 'ran to and fro, increasing knowledge', paper making materials began to be in short supply. Rags and old cordage, the main sources of pulp materials, could no longer be the only materials used in this trade.

The industry began to review what raw materials could be sourced for pulp. In 1716 an English group called the 'Society of Gentlemen' published an essay advocating raw hemp be used;[4] from 1765-1771 Dr. Schaffer of Germany published a six volume set on papermaking that looked at a wide range of possibilities from asbestos to cabbage. This search for alternatives however, did not turn up a better fibre than hemp; the Société Industrielle de Molhouse, in 1861, offered a reward of 4,000 francs for the discovery of a substance that would make paper at a comparable quality and price to that then produced, but it was never claimed. Palms, ferns, different sorts of leathers, grasses, and all various sorts of materials were put to the test, most notably by Louis Piette; in 1855 he founded the *Journal des Fabriquants de Papier*, in which he published accounts of over three-hundred vegetable substances that he made into paper. Piette's work included research on wood pulp, which had been the suggestion of one of his countrymen from the previous century; René Antoine Ferchouit de Reaumur, who in 1719 was to cause the most drastic change in papermaking for almost two millennia. Observing wasps, he suggested that paper could be made from wood. His idea was not immediately practised, as it was not until 1850 that a method to produce wood pulp paper was devised. This method, invented by Friedrich Gottlob Keller of Germany, was perfected in 1852 by Hugh Burgess of England. Burgess had chemicals 'digest' the wood; in 1867 this step was refined by C.B. Tilghman, a chemist in the US, who added sulphates to the pulp.

> Paper products in which these bast fibers have made their greatest contribution have been heavy-duty, multiwalled papers for the production of sacks for flour, cement, fertilizers, animal feeds, hardware, chemicals, and other industrial items. Special papers used in the manufacture of electrical goods, communications cables, transformer coils, and other electronic or electrical apparatus are prepared in part from these special fibers. Other specialty items include the heavy-duty papers for backing abrasive papers, tag stocks, gasket materials, duplicating papers, and other specialties. The fibers have been selected for their length and strength, which contribute to pliability with maximum resistance to tear and shock.
>
> **Ronald McDonald and John Franklin,**
> *Pulp and Paper Manufacture,* **1969**

This new ingredient was for many the answer, but some were starting to see the folly of destroying the forests. A 1900 French report noted that paper pulp is only short fibre,[4] and, at that time, produced a very imperfect paper. It did not completely foresee the deterioration of books and newspapers that would soon be taking place, but it did voice a concern for the deforestation then taking place, which had become a 'national industry' in Germany. Ultimately the poor quality of chemically treated wood pulp was a painful issue; the Library of Congress found that, "while the paper in volumes three- or four-hundred years old is still strong…ninety-seven percent of the books of non-fiction printed between 1900 and 1939 will be usable for less than fifty years."[5]

UNITED STATES DEPARTMENT OF AGRICULTURE

BULLETIN No. 404

Contribution from the Bureau of Plant Industry
WM. A. TAYLOR, Chief

Washington, D.C.   PROFESSIONAL PAPER   October 14, 1916

HEMP HURDS AS PAPER-MAKING MATERIAL

By LYSTER H. DEWEY, *Botanist in Charge of Fiber-Plant Investigations,* and
JASON L. MERRILL, *Paper-Plant Chemist, Paper-Plant Investigations.*

Other people's money: other people's people: other people's trees; what is going on? These are trends not easy to reverse, and each person on earth is affected in some way. What does the future hold, when even more trees are cut to be mixed into chemical rich slurry? American historian Jack Frazier recently pointed out: "We've now reached the point where 80% of our garbage is paper, but only 20% of it is recycled."[6]

Not many of us remember, for instance, the Pacific Northwest of the US before the Hearst Newspaper Syndicates turned so many trees into paper on which they recorded their propaganda, much of which is an embarrassment to Americans today. Lee Kirk, a resident of these regions, cites a disturbing statistic: only one percent of the original old growth forest is left;[7] much of the 'wilderness' land, supposedly set aside, Kirk adds, is merely barren mountain tops and arid desert, whilst the National Forest Service is in the lumber-selling business.

Analysis of a sample of raw Italian hemp From: *Chemistry of Pulp and Papermaking*, by Edwin Sutermeister, 1929	
Water	8.80%
Cellulose	77.13%
Fat and wax	0.55%
Aqueous extract	3.45%
Ash	0.82%
Pectous substances	9.25%

What is the trade off to such a loss of the ecosystem? Crumbling paper that is not of much use even in recycling, due to the short, weak fibres? Rubbish, to waste away in a landfill? Did we need to mess with the trees? No, according to statistics compiled by the US government: in 1916 it noted that hemp produced 4.4 times as much fibre per acre than wood. The report concluded with a sensible warning: "There appears to be little doubt that under the present system of forest use and consumption the present supply can not withstand the demands placed on it."[8]

The report was not an isolated event; other interest in making paper from hemp hurds, which were at that time considered a waste material, was being expressed. A Canadian study of 1904, entitled *Paper from Refuse Hemp Stalks* gave a viable solution to the use of trees for paper, and re-iterated this premise in a 1906 study, *Hemp Waste for Paper*. The US Department of Agriculture did its own research, and came to similar conclusions. In 1908, it published the article "Papermaking Materials and Their Conservation", in 1910, the "Utilisation of Crop Plants in Paper Making", and in 1911 "Crop Plants for Paper Making".

German scientists followed suit; "The Chemical Composition of Flax and Hemp Chaff", by C.G. Schwabel and Ernest Becker was published in 1919; B. Rassow and A. Zschenderlein, two of their countrymen, further analysed their findings in a study titled "Nature of Hemp Wood", published in 1921. John C. Lupien in his 1995 thesis on the demonisation of hemp noted a total of sixteen articles published in the

The utility of hemp paper is not yet concluded; for after it is completely worn out as cloth, the remnants and rags became of great importance in the manufacture of paper.
Rev. I. Taylor,
Scenes of British Wealth, 1825

1910s and 1920s which advocated bast fibres for paper.[9] However, the role of hemp was that of Joseph, whose coat-of-many-colours brought him harm. Paper manufacturers, such as International Paper and Pulp,[10] reacted in self-interest, as did William Randolph Hearst. Other concerns might have been affected, such as those of the Du Pont Corp., which owned patents on wood pulp processing, and had vast holdings of southern pine.

An irony, that of hemp's suitability, that of its high cellulose content being the cause for its criminalisation; as this is explained in Chapter VI, here let us examine what is more to the point in the making of paper: cellulose. This compound, inherent in nature, is a commercially valuable building block of so many products, paper being chief among them. Hemp fibres are roughly 75 percent cellulose and require less chemical processing than wood to separate this substance. Further, hemp's cellulose is in the form of a long fibre, more appropriate for the making of durable, recyclable paper than the short fibres of wood or cotton. This last is actually higher in cellulose content than hemp, containing 90 percent; a disadvantage to cotton, however, is the amount of harmful chemicals used to grow this crop. 50 percent of all the world's pesticides go to this, a fact that gives incentive to such companies to oppose hemp, which uses virtually none.

Wood is generally 50 percent cellulose, and requires chlorine based chemicals to bleach it in the vat; it was the discovery of chlorine by the Swedish chemist, Karl Wilhelm Scheele in 1774, that ultimately made wood paper more acceptable. For a quarter century afterwards, the process of bleaching underwent many changes. At one stage chlorine gas was used, produced by pouring sulphuric acid onto black oxide of manganese and salt. Charles Tennant developed bleaching powder in 1799, making production safer and more efficient. Much of this resulted in brittle paper, as chlorine combines with moisture to form hypochlorous acid, which damages cellulose. Moreover, bleaching was not effective on some fibres, such as jute; a fact lamented in the trade when jute bags were used instead of hempen bags in the mid-nineteenth century.[11]

Currently chlorine-based bleaching processes are responsible for unwanted byproducts, most notably dioxin. This chemical, which was part of the Agent Orange syndrome, is a monster, causing severe acne, toxic shock syndrome, loss of sexual identity,[12] and a host of other problems. The change from tree-based paper to hemp-based paper, which is naturally whiter, and which can be treated by more natural processes, is a necessity; the call for hemp paper is not an idle gesture; it is based on facts, and affects just about everyone.

Man's fall from Eden involved a tree; man left Eden years ago, and ever since has tried to return on his own terms, always ending in defeat as he spends so much time working on his own destruction, as if in worship of some dark force. Modern man is felling billions of trees, mixing them with dangerous chemicals and turning them into sheets of paper on which

...all paper containing bleach will crumble to dust in a few hundred years...The longer the fiber the stronger and more durable the paper will be.
Dard Hunter,
Ancient Paper Making, **1915**

to write of this diabolical concept. Against this trend, there are those who are taking on the challenge of using hemp, which, one might note, is often used for the printing of Bibles and other religious works. The revival of common sense might be said to have been sparked by Frazier's 1974 article "Hemp Paper Reconsidered", which graced the first issue of *High Times*. His sentiments were repeated in the 1991 article "It's Time to Reconsider Hemp", published in the June issue of *Pulp and Paper*. All cries for a sensible re-introduction of hemp have been backed up by the fact that hemp fibres, longer and stronger than cotton and other sources, are a necessity in certain kinds of paper such as bank notes, facial tissues and cigarette paper; some nations mandate that hemp be used for such sensitive papers. Frazier (1991) quotes Hugh Williamson's (1956) compelling argument: "There are three main sources of cellulose fibre; the first includes cotton, linen, and hemp. The fibres in these materials are known as normal or simple cellulose, and they are weakened less than any other kind of cellulose by the drastic process of purification which leads to paper-making." Williamson states further: "...hemp is scarce and costly, and is rarely used alone; the highest qualities of India paper, however, consist mainly of hemp. The resistance to tearing and folding of papers made from simple cellulose is due in part to the length of the fibres, and of all the fibres mentioned hemp is the longest."[13]

> Hemp's low lignin content reduces the need for acids used in making paper, and its naturally creamy colour means that there is no need for harsh chlorine bleaches.
> **Sally Staples,**
> *The Times,* **2000**

hemptec

The first chlorine-free bleached hemp paper world-wide.

From hemp to Hemptec, a cultured plant develops into paper culture.

Hemp is an extremely versatile plant that has been cultivated for centuries. In the old days hemp was used to make sails and ropes, textiles and even medicine and foodstuff. Hemp paper too, was well known in those days, paper made from the outer raffia fibres coming from the stem of the hemp plant.

Once the raffia fibres had been utilised the wood containing inner part, the so-called shives used to be recycled back into the soil and were thus lost for any further use. What a mistake, as

especially the shives are an extremely valuable substance and are today used by Neusiedler in the manufacture of their **Hemptec** paper.

When it turned out that hemp could also be used in the manufacture of drugs, hemp became a forbidden plant and neither the cultivation nor its use was allowed in the 1930's. Nowadays hemp is undergoing somewhat of a renaissance as a valuable plant and has become a celebrated commercial success. This change of opinion has come about due to the development of a narcotic-free industrial hemp coupled with a conscious promotion by the EU and the availability of ecological cultivation of the hemp plant.

Innovative and aesthetic: Hemptec, a world novelty from Neusiedler.

Hemptec is an innovative product for modern office communication which excels with its high quality and elegance. If you want to help creating a healthier environment, **Hemptec** is the right choice. It is the first totally chlorine-free bleached hemp paper world-wide.

This elegant paper impresses with its aesthetic look. The chamois shade of the paper gives it an elegant presence

which is also easy on the eye. The rattle of the paper attests the high quality character of the sheet formation.

It's your choice with Hemptec.

This high quality paper was developed for multi-functional use. It is highly suitable for copying, laser and ink jet printing, as well as for pre-printing, i.e. multi-colour offset and digital printing. For monochrome as well as for coloured printouts and copies.

For your business correspondence, for high quality handouts of reports, information on evironmental issues, production of antique books and pictorial material, for brochures in offset or digital printing. The usage of **Hemptec** for your office has no limits.

The quality of Hemptec is internationally renowned.

During the world congress for digital printing in New York a book printed on **Hemptec** "R" received first prize in the category "Case for Digital Printing/ Color". The antique book had been re-published by the German group Zander & Meyer.

Promotional letter from
Continuum. ca. 1999

All these voices were starting to be heard, and in 1994 the US imported 2,000 tons of hemp paper from China. Throughout the world many mills have started producing small amounts of hemp paper, such as Greenfield in Southern California and Neusiedler in Austria. One Northern California papermaker, John R. Stahl, makes his from 'donations' provided by local marijuana growers; an irony, as they are breaking the law, technically, to grow high THC producing strains of the same plants George Washington grew, and of which the fibres are to be found in the paper used for the constitution of their country.

British papermaker John Hanson was inspired by an article in the 'Hempathy' issues of *The Ecologist* in 1980. He got started in 1987, coming out with the registered trade watermark treefree® in 1991, and produced three tons of paper in 1993. The previous year *The Ecologist* printed their index on this paper, which is made without chlorine bleaching. Over the years he has seen this put to use in books, including the output by the Eryr Press which specialises in falconry books.

Several other UK hemp paper manufacturers have produced small amounts as well, including the BioRegional Development Centre in Surrey, the Hemp Paper Co. of Scotland, and Quintessential of Cornwall. An Irish hemp entrepeneur, Jim McDonald of Dublin, produced a white writing paper with leaf watermark and also a translucent paper with whole hemp leaves. All of these efforts however did not satisfy the demand, and hemp paper has remained difficult to acquire. Some publishing companies saw fit to stock up so as to have a supply. Often the price is prohibitive, as

Hemp (Cannabis sativa). The fiber is prepared by retting, from filaments, which run the entire length of the stem. The ultimate fibers composing these filaments vary from 5 to 55 mm. and average about 22 mm. long by 0.022 mm. in diameter, the ratio of length to diameter being therefore about 1000. The fibers have very thick walls, which are not very highly lignified. The ends are large and sometimes flattened and the central canal is almost obliterated. In microscopic appearance the fibers are very similar to those of flax; they show the same knots or thickenings and the same striæ, but they differ from linen in having more ability to break down into fibraillæ during the mechanical processes of paper making.

getting hemp pulp can be difficult. In the hemp community one answer has been to recycle old hemp clothes; in California, businesses such as Minawear give hemp scraps to those interested in making their own batch of paper. Such endeavours, however, are small at the moment, largely because the paper making industry has moved to Asia where most mills produce over 500,000 tons a year. Making large amounts of paper in Asia would decrease the basic cost of a sheet, but without immediate demand, the shipping and storage become a burden.

From:
Chemistry of Pulp and Papermaking,
Edwin Sutermeister, 1929

Gmund brochure
ca. **2005**

In addition to the economic obstacles involved, there is the fact that most paper making is now geared for short grain wood pulp, and thus there needs to be more attention paid to the process. In the 1910s a number of studies were carried out by the US government, when paper makers were instructed to attempt to use hurds. The records of their attempts were preserved for future generations, and thanks to Lupien, have been made available to a number of entrepreneurs in the UK who are at present pursuing the idea of making large runs of hemp paper for widespread consumption, among them Sam Heslop in Oxford and Nick Chow, the proprietor of the The Favil Press of London.

It is hoped that their efforts will be successful. While they work towards their goals, the world is losing its trees, not unlike the Easter Islands, which came to be uninhabited as the islanders used up the last of the trees, fighting among themselves for the remaining resources. While the trees were felled from those islands, the statues of their chiefs were left to stand. The thought that this is a harbinger of the way in which it will all end for us today is haunting, and at the rate in which man is felling the trees, who could expect any other fate?

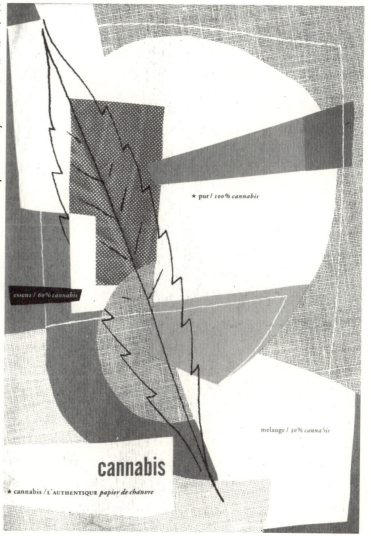

* pur / *100% cannabis*

essenz / *60% cannabis*

melange / *30% cannabis*

cannabis

* cannabis / L'AUTHENTIQUE *papier de chanvre*

1. UNESCO Document - IFLA-CIA, 1987
2. Hayes, William. Cellulose: *The Chemical That Grows.* NY, Doubleday, 1953. p. 35
3. Hunter, Dard. Papermaking: *The History and Technique of an Ancient Craft.* NY, Knopf, 1943. p. 70
4. Rostaing, Leon, Marcel Rostaing & Fleury du Sert. *Précis Historique, Descriptif, et Photomicrographique de Vegetaux propres a la Fabrication de la Cellulose et du Papier.* Paris, 1900. p. 8
5. Guenet, François. *Chanvre.* N.d., n.p
6. Frazier, Jack. *The Great American Hemp Industry.* Peterstown (WV), Solar Age Press, 1991
7. Kirk, Lee. Personal communication
8. Dewey, Lyster H. and Jason L. Merill. *Hemp Hurds as Paper-making Material.* Washington, GPO, 1916
9. Lupien, John. *Unravelling an American Dilemma: The Demonization of Marihuana.* Malibu, Pepperdine University (Thesis) 1995
10. Merrill, Jason J. *The Manufacture of Paper from Hemp Hurds.* Washington, GPO, 1916
11. Tillmans, Martin. *Bridge Hall Mills.* Wiltshire, The Compton Press, 1978. p. 15
12. *Village Voice,* 12 Nov. 1999
13. Frazier

X. Medicine

KENYON GIBSON

*C*annabis has provided humanity with many products, of which medicine may be the most controversial. Early Chinese pharmacopoeia, such as the *Pen T'sao Kang Mu* advocate cannabis, as do Indian, Arabic and European writings. Over long periods of time doctors have used extracts of *Cannabis sativa* for many ailments.

Today's doctors have been able to isolate the chemical compounds that are found in cannabis and study their uses. However, because of the laws in many areas, they are not free to continue this research; the sixty or more cannabinoids that exist in the plant all have a value in modern medicine, but many of them are not used as they have not been completely tested.[1] Thus many people suffering from painful diseases have been ignored in their plight, at the behest of governments that are often linked to pharmaceutical companies which would prefer to sell expensive manmade compounds. Citizens of these countries are betrayed, and at times have little choice but to break evil laws that have been implemented to enrich politicians and their friends. With such a harsh reality, the choice comes down to that of suffering a slow painful death or breaking the law in order to survive.

Given this grim prospect, the latter is what many law-abiding citizens have had to choose. One can hardly ignore this enigma, as the papers have published more and more stories which are educating the public about the reality of the 'reefer madness' syndrome and the ties that the legislatures have to drug companies.

The Independent in March of 2000 ran an article about one person suffering from multiple sclerosis who was arrested with forty cannabis plants at his home in Suffolk.[2] The jury, hearing the facts, acquitted him. While this trial was taking place, public awareness was calling for a review of the laws, with sentiment for decriminalisation expressed by many ministers, including Mo Mowlam; the Prime Minister, Tony Blair, continued to oppose any relaxation of the law,[3] despite public opinion and qualified advice of the medical community.

A less well-known condition known as retinitis pigmentosa is also affected by cannabis use. Sue Arnold, who suffers from this, admits to smoking 'pot', but would prefer to have it available in pill form. This is not presently an option, but could be if money were allocated to research. Money, perhaps, that is now spent on eradicating the 'evil weed' and jailing the sick? In the US hundreds of millions of dollars have been spent on putting medical cannabis users in jail, with lives destroyed and tax money wasted.[4] At times there are prisoners in the US who have only been at the scene of a marijuana related arrest, but have suffered lengthy incarceration, and there are many stories of a tyrannical use of the law in which the property of the accused is confiscated, including their house and vehicles, on the grounds that they 'may have been' used in the sale of drugs; the lengthy process of proving one's innocence does not always guarantee a return of this property, and this has become a bitter issue. To add to this picture, there is the juxtaposition of the sentences handed down to real criminals, such as murderers and those who endanger the public welfare,[5] compared to those of people who have been caught with, or simply suspected of having, small amounts of marijuana. Here again, money skews justice; many politicians have interests in what has come to be termed as the 'prison industry', and the more bodies there are in prison, the more tax money can be given to their friends who have invested in this new growth industry. Despite these facts, the beat goes on in some people's minds; all they need to hear is a speech about the 'evil weed', and they vote for more money to be spent on prisons. After 9/11 in the US, there were even television commercials depicting young Americans who lit up a joint as 'terrorists', yet there were no such attempts to point the finger at crack cocaine users.[6] The Hearst hysteria of the 1930s had taken a hard turn to the right, hijacking once more the public mind and flying it at full speed into a destructive mode.

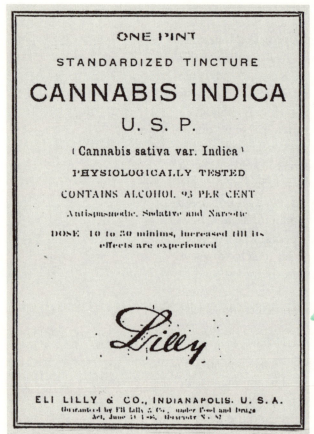

While the intention of much of this legislation is meant to be daunting and to cheat Americans out of their rights, some have turned the tables on the oppressive regime, preferring liberty to stupidity, and have stood up for their rights. One case in point was that of Elvy Musikka, a long-term glaucoma patient who after exhausting all means of treatment, found out about cannabis from other sufferers. Already blind in one eye, she decided to give this natural remedy a go. She grew her own, and was turned in to the police. Her case was harshly treated, with many in authority behaving as if they were blind themselves. Demanding a trial, Musikka placed her case in the hands of her peers in the state of Forida, and they saw common sense; she too was acquitted. Her legal battles were still not over, as she had to threaten the government with a lawsuit in 1998 before they made cannabis available to her.

A later trial involving Kenneth and Barbara Jenkes from Pensacola, Florida did not turn out so well. Kenneth was a haemophiliac who contracted AIDS from a blood transfusion, which was passed on to his wife. In such a painful predicament they turned to cannabis to alleviate their misery, only to find themselves under state prosecution. They were each convicted of felonies; the jury spurning the precedent of medical necessity, sentencing them to harsh jail sentences.[8] They died shortly thereafter; Americans, deprived of liberty, victims of a system that was infiltrated by those who destroy life, best described as 'white collar terrorists'.[9] Many US cannabis growers have been given lifetime sentences, while truly heinous crimes go unpunished.

The backdrop to this is the wrangling debate that goes on in government agencies about the effectiveness of cannabis. Not only are thousands of years of writings and medical precedents ignored, but even rulings by judges of the Drug Enforcement Agency (DEA) are set aside arbitrarily with no scientific reason. In one such ruling, made by Judge Francis L. Young in 1988, it is stated:

> The evidence in this record clearly shows that marijuana has been accepted as capable of relieving the distress of great numbers of very ill people and in doing so with safety under medicinal supervision. It would be unreasonable, arbitrary and capricious for the DEA to stand between those sufferers and the benefits of this substance in this record. The administrative law judge recommends that the DEA Administrator conclude that the marijuana plant considered as a whole has a currently accepted medicinal use in treatment in the United States. [10]

DEA Administrator John Lawn ignored all this in 1989. Five years later the US District Court of Appeals in Washington, D.C. issued a finding indicating that "...in its opinion, cannabis has no medicinal value - none." [11]

Not only does one hand in Washington contradict the other over this issue, but the vote counters throw out or hold back the votes cast by the public. In 1999, an initiative was placed on the ballot to legalise medical marijuana. The outcome was suppressed, as Christopher Hitchens of *Vanity Fair* reported in the *Evening Standard*:

> The vote was an official secret. The following day, while reporting the result of the local and ward elections, a tiny inside-page newspaper item announced that the ballots for the marijuana initiative had been counted but then impounded. How had the capital city of the world's largest democracy voted? We are not telling you! [12]

Eventually a law professor sued to have the count; when the true results of the voting were released, after a lengthy delay, it was found that the people had voted to legalise, by a majority of 60 percent. An un-American minority, however, had its way and many Americans have been treated with contempt.

From:
Colloquies on the Samples and Drugs of India,
Garcia da Orta, [1913 ed.].

MEDICAL AUTHORITIES

There is a plethora of authorities which support the argument for the use of cannabis in medicine, including the British Medical Association. In 1997 the BMA's Annual Representative meeting resolved "That this Representative Body believes that certain additional cannabinoids should be legalised for their medicinal use." [13] The Royal Pharmaceutical Society of Great Britain also believes further clinical research is needed to advance therapeutic uses of cannabinoids. At present four cannabinoids - cannabidiol, cannabichromene, dronabinol and nabilone can be prescribed by doctors in the UK. One conclusion reached by the BMA at that time was that:

> Cannabinoids may have a potential use for patients with spastic neurological disorders such as MS and spinal cord injury. Such patients often have distressing symptoms that are not well controlled with available drugs. Trials, which merit a high priority on this disorder, are for patients who have not responded well to traditional drugs. Depending on their results, there may be a case for considering extension of the indications for nabilone (and allowing THC) for use on named patient basis, in chronic spastic disorders unresponsive to standard drugs. [14]

Dr. Daniel A. Dansala, of the University of Southern Alabama, reports that the use of δ-9-THC reduced both nausea and vomiting by 50 percent, a "statistically significant" result.[15]

Walter Kramp is a doctor in San Francisco, who has treated hundreds of patients with HIV for over a decade. He concludes, "there is an obvious beneficial role for the use of cannabis…Any further delay in making it widely available now, particularly to the ill, is both irrational and cruel." [16]

Robert C. Randall cites conclusive firsthand evidence for cannabis in treating glaucoma. He is not, however, a doctor, but rather a patient who suffers from this disease, and president of the Alliance for Cannabis Therapeutics. Citing a well known study carried out by Dr. Robert S. Hepler of the Jules Stein Eye Institute at UCLA, he states that: "marijuana significantly reduced IDOP…The reduction in ocular pressure was quite significant." Mr. Randall had tried several glaucoma medications, without any improvement. His use of cannabis has been effective and sustained over a twenty-year period.[17]

The University of the West Indies in Jamaica has developed Canasol, an ophthalmic preparation developed from cannabis. The population of this country has a high rate of glaucoma among its citizens, three percent (as opposed to one percent for the US), and the availability of this for many Jamaicans has been crucial, developing treatment from local sources would be of great value in this area, and is supported by the government and the medical establishment.[18]

Spasticity and chronic pain were studied by Dr. Denis Petro, who ruled that: "oral THC was equal in effect to codeine (60mg.)," and cited the relative safety of cannabis - an important consideration in pain medications. Many other alternatives have serious, if not fatal effects. Dr. Petro also noted its use in seizure disorders, asserting that: "evidence should not be disregarded."[19]

In Zurich, a study comparing δ-9-THC to established drugs used in the treatment of muscle spasms, concluded in favour of the former, noting that psychopathic side effects were not observed.[20]

Israeli doctors, studying the therapeutic effects of both δ-8-THC and δ-9-THC in children with haematological cancers, obtained positive, conclusive results with vomiting completely prevented and negligible side effects.[21]

The above-mentioned cases are all recent; the list would be endless if several thousands of years of studies were included. A good number of publications, both ancient and modern, will be described in the bibliography part of the upcoming book *The Hemp Papers*.[22] One of these works, a treatise by Dr. William O'Shaughnessy, of the British East India Company, is Appendix A of this book.

---

1. Arnold, Sue. *The Independent,* 24 March 2000
2. Burrel, Ian. *Ib.*
3. *Ib.*
4. Kent, Norman Elliott. "People Behind the Pain", pp. 13-19 in *Cannabis in Medical Practice,* by Mary Lynn Mathre, (ed.) Jefferson, London, McFarland & Co., 1997
5. The case of Edward Samuels of the New York Law School presents a contrast that has caused outcry worldwide. Caught in 2002 with 150,000 images of children being tortured and such equipment in his apartment, which he shared with young children, he received a six month sentence only, the judge even considering that this was a hardship for him. He is now out, and the whistleblowers, have been fired. Such cases are not in fact rare; top level politicians have been implicated in much of this. Government whistleblowers Cathy O'Brien & Mark Phillips relate one story where top politicians were excused from court appearances for "Reasons of National Security", and similar accounts of little or no prison time spent by wealthy political activists has been well documented by Sen. John De Camp in his 1992 book *The Franklin Coverup.*
6. Drug use in the US by top politicians has at times been restricted to crack, cocaine and heroin; all of which are easier to maintain a monopoly over, as they grow in certain areas; unlike marijuana, the 'weed', which can be grown virtually anywhere. In O'Brien's and Phillips' 1995 book *Trance-Formation of America* they note that these harder drugs flowed quite freely, while George Bush and his entourage would not use pot. In addition to the strategy of economic control, there was the fact that pot did not go well with the mind-control programmes as it activated memories and de-activated programming in control subjects. A more recent book by the same authors, titled *ACCESS DENIED: For Reasons of National Security* gives further insight into government control programming and treason in the US.
7. Zeese, Kevin B. "Legal Issues Related to the Medical Use of Marijuana", pp. 20 - 31 in Mathre.
8. *Ib.*
9. This term has come about due to the many abuses in the system which presently take the lives of Americans. It is believed to have originated among US veterans when details of a plot to seize power in the US by faking hijacking and killing enlisted men in Guantánamo Bay were revealed in 2001. "Operation Northwoods", it was known only to a few top figures in the government. The term 'white collar terrorist' has been applied to those who had any ties to Northwoods, or those who are using secrecy to cloak other harmful programmes, such as the use of depleted uranium. Soldiers using this are now coming back home with lifetime symptoms, their children born usually with birth defects. The GOP cut veterans' benefits during this scandal, while it was found out that they were supporting the use of this radioactive substance. Needless to say, use of this is a war crime in many states, and the populations of the countries where it is used suffer cruelly. Not everyone suffers though; there are many at the Pentagon who are in a position to make a profit off this. The term is currently used not only by US servicemen to describe criminals in the Pentagon, but is used more widely to describe a broader range of characters, including those who to use legislative powers to keep hemp outlawed.

10. Aldrich, Michael. "History of Therapeutic Cannabis", pp. 35-55 in Mathre
11. *Ib.*
12. Hitchens, Christopher. *Evening Standard*, 11 January, 2001
13. British Medical Association. *Therapeutic Uses of Cannabis*. Amstedjik, Harwood Academic Publishers, 1997. pp. 38-39
14. *Ib.*
15. Dansk, Dr Daniel A. "As an Antiemetic and Appetite Stimulant for Cancer Patients", pp 69-83 in Mathre
16. Guenet, François. *Chanvre*. N.d., n.p.
17. Randall, Robert C. "Glaucoma: A Patient's View", pp. 94-102 in Mathre
18. West, Dr Manley. p. 103 in Mathre
19. Petro, Dr Denis. "Seizure Disorders" pp. 125-138 in Mathre
20. Guenet
21. The article, by Drs Aya, Abrahamov & Mechoulam can be found at *http://mojo.calyx.net*
22. Now in preparation at the Eryr Press (UK). This will be both a bibliography of all known hemp books and a large selection of important articles and a book on the making of hemp paper.

XI. Food

PAUL BENHAIM, NICK MACKINTOSH
AND CINDY MACKINTOSH

*H*emp as a food? My first perception was that an edible form of hemp was a most bizarre use for a crop more commonly known for the production of ropes and clothes. That was a decade ago, when information on the nutritional benefits of hemp was scarce. We are now privileged to have facts researched by organisations such as The Hemp Food Industries Association which offers copies of independent laboratories' nutritional analysis on the seed and its by-products, as well as detailed explanations on the benefits of receiving such nutritionally superior foods.

One of the first questions asked about hemp foods is "Can they get you high?" Industrial hemp seed must contain less than 0.3 percent of the active 'euphoric' ingredient commonly known as THC. Hemp foods must contain less than 10-20 ppm of THC (dependant upon country of sale) to be officially considered 'safe', although there are no proven negative effects of doses ten times this quantity. Simply put, you would need to eat 100,000 hemp '9bars' (carob coated snack bar) for any noticeable effects. If we cannot get high from hemp then why is it so special? Is hemp food just another fad or fashion statement?

A little known fact is that hemp seed has actually been used as a food throughout history. The Chinese are the first documented consumers of hemp seed - with references reaching as far back as 8,000 years. Hemp seed has been considered part of the daily meal by Eastern Europeans, and in China toasted hemp seeds are used as our equivalent to popcorn in cinemas. With today's technical instruments and medical understanding we can now explain the reasons why hemp is now being rediscovered in the western world as "one of the most nutritious seeds known to man." Hemp seed and oil are high in omega-3 and omega-6 EFAs, and contain around 24 percent high quality proteins called edestin and albumin. These proteins contain the full spectrum of all eight essential amino acids and the seed also contains soluble and insoluble fibre, vitamins and minerals. Hemp's nutritional profile lacks the negatives associated with soy bean, its closest nutritional equivalent.

Hemp protein was used during and after WWII to treat tuberculosis; a 1960s report documents twenty-six children cured or significantly improved due to their treatment. The protein in hemp is absent of the anti-nutritional enzyme inhibitor tyrosine, which is a major advantage over the type of protein found in soybean. Hemp seed does not contain oligosaccharides, which are soya's cause of flatulence. Also, like all pulses, the soybean lacks the vital sulphur-containing amino acids cystine and methionine. These amino acids are both present in hemp seed.

NUTRITIONAL BENEFITS

Hemp contains 80 percent of its fat as Essential Fatty Acids. These good fats are from the omega-3 and omega-6 family. You may have heard of these fats in reference to evening primrose oil, cod liver oil and safflower oil, more commonly known sources of quality fats. Unlike these oils, hemp provides these fats in what is known as an 'optimal ratio' for long-term use. This balance is crucial to the absorption and balance of the complex nutritional needs of your body.

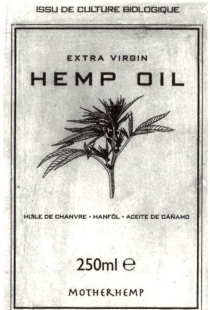

Hemp seed must be eaten in freshly made hemp based food products. Only then can they help benefit a variety of conditions or symptoms such as: heart disease and hypertension, arthritis, asthma, yeast infection, PMS, diabetes, renal, respiratory, dermatological, acne, hair loss, poor blood circulation as well as liver, kidney and gallbladder problems. EFAs are used to facilitate recovery of fatigued muscles, reduce inflammation and swelling in joints and muscles as well as promoting healthy liver functioning.

It is even said that if a pregnant mother has digested a proper amount of EFAs she has the best chance of delivering an intelligent child. Further, consumption of EFAs by growing children may help improve the symptoms of Attention Deficit Disorder (ADD).

Gamma-linoleic acid (GLA), also found in evening primrose oil, is a well-known member of the omega-6 family. A recent study published in the *International Journal of Cancer* states that GLA (found in hemp seed, particularly the Finola variety) can exterminate brain and prostate cancer cells. GLA is also said to inhibit the spread of malignant tumours by restricting blood vessel growth. In a recent study, patients who increased their daily doses of omega-6 equivalent to five teaspoons of hemp oil per day were shown to rapidly decrease elevated blood levels of LDL cholesterol, therefore reducing the risk of thrombosis.

EFAs are damaged when heated at high temperatures. Purchase hemp foods only from reputable, experienced sources, as they will surely know the benefits of using low temperatures when processing foods. A more complete list of documented nutritional benefits for hemp is contained in *H.E.M.P.- Healthy Eating Made Possible.*

SEED

The hemp seed, or nut, is the base for all hemp foods. The seed is where all life comes from, and is naturally protected in nature by a hard shell. This edible shell contains the quality protein, oil and high fibre. Although the seed is often processed further before used as a human food, I still enjoy hemp seed in this, its raw state. Toasting these hemp seeds in a pan with your favourite spices produces a tasty snack.

Analysis of Hemp Seed		
From: *Vegetable Fats and Oils,* by Louis Andés, 1925		
	German Hemp Seed	**Russian Hemp Seed**
	Percent	Percent
Organic matter	54.30	54.95
(containing protein)	(15.95)	(15.00)
Ash	3.45	4.50
Water	8.65	9.13
Oil	33.60	31.42

Inside of the hemp nut there is a small, yellowish seed that is highly concentrated in nutrition. It contains over 30 percent protein and around 40 percent polyunsaturated fats. This soft, de-hulled hemp nut is recommended to be eaten as is, or used as a condiment.

OIL

Hemp oil is best produced from high GLA content seeds such as Finola and USO, which are the best food grade quality seeds available. Hemp oil containing around 80 percent unsaturated fatty acids, provides as much energy as the same quantity of carbohydrate. This energy is much more stable and less intrusive to the body's blood sugar levels than quantities of bread, pasta or rice based foods. Hemp oil also contains beneficial chlorophyll as found in green foods.

Hemp Harvest Hemp Oil

100% Hemp Seed Oil Cold-Pressed with care on our Devon Farm

This high quality cold pressed culinary oil naturally contains a unique balance of omega 3, 6 and 9 essential fatty acids.

Its pleasant sweet nutty flavour makes it ideal for use in salad dressings and as a tasty addition to vegetable, rice and pasta dishes.

1.5 litre €

Keep refrigerated.

FLOUR

Hemp flour is the result of finely ground hempseed or hempseed cake (the by-product of oil production) and is best produced fresh using your own grinder. Hemp is an oily seed and therefore requires grinders designed for oily seeds - ask before you buy. 100 percent hemp flour produces heavy bread and is therefore best used as a substitute for 10-25 percent of regular flour. Hemp flour can also be used as a replacement for any flour in non-bread recipes.

QUALITY CONTROL

The risk of degradation of the fragile oils found in hemp seed and its by-products is severe. Potentially damaging free radicals are unleashed in a

snowball type effect when anything but perfect conditions are present. Farmers and manufacturers must take care at every stage of processing. From the moment of harvest, when drying under the sun's ultraviolet rays to kill potential aflotoxins, to reducing the moisture content to the desired percentage. The bulk seed must be stored in dry non-sweating containers, processed in heat, light and oxygen free environments and then packaged in dark, air-tight containers. European and Australasian manufacturers are guided under the HFIA to use only the best quality food grade seeds that are processed and handled in the delicate manner required to ensure the consumer receives the full nutritional benefits awaiting them in this truly magical seed. A simple yet effective test for quality is to make sure that the hemp food, and particularly any hemp oil product, does not produce a 'scratchy' or rancid taste at the back of the throat.

Alive yeast and bacteria, two potentially under-utilised energy sources on this planet, have been used in fermenting wine, beer, yoghurt, cheese, and bread. The bacteria are decomposers, and in today's energy crises are being called upon in many industries. Current research is being carried out by the HFIA to show how enzymes can be used to produce a stable, high quality protein powder that can be used as a cheap protein source to feed the world. The HFIA believes that the use of enzymes in energy production (foods and fuel) will dominate much of the next century, as mechanical engineering and electronics have dominated the last fifty years.

The HFIA has promoted the use of living foods that aid enzymes in digestion, and are therefore on a par with our own body's energy factory.

This high quality natural vegetable oil has been extracted at low temperature.

Its pleasant flavour and smooth creamy texture make it ideal for use in salad dressings, mayonnaise, dips, and as an accompaniment to vegetable, rice, pasta and noodle dishes. It complements avocado or mashed potato well.

Hemp Foods For You
Lower Pertwood Farm, Wilts SP3 6TA
Telephone 01747 820889

Please telephone for Products Guide with Recipes, Nutrition Info, Tips and Price List.

Also available:
Whole & Shelled Hemp Seed, Hemp Seed Flour, Hemp Burger Mix, Hemp Leaf Tea.

Highest Quality   Cold-Pressed

Hemp Seed Oil

1000/500/250ml

BEST BEFORE:

STORAGE: **Keep refrigerated at all times**

TYPICAL NUTRIENT VALUES	
per 100ml (92g)	
Energy	3400 kJ / 828 kcal
Protein	0.0g
Carbohydrate	0.0g
Fat	91.9g
of which	
-saturates	7.4g
Arachidic acid	0.7g
Eicosenic acid	0.7g
Palmitic acid	4.0g
Stearic acid	2.0g
-monounsaturates	9.0g
Oleic acid (omega-9)	6.0g
Stearidonic acid	2.1g
Vaccenic acid	0.9g
-polyunsaturates	73.5g
Linoleic acid (omega-6)	53.0g
Linolenic acid (omega-3)	18.5g
gamma Linolenic acid (GLA)	2.0g
-cholesterol	0.0g
Fibre	0.0g
Sodium	0.0g
Vitamin E (1150% of RDA)	115mg

Most hemp foods can assist in this process by reducing the cravings for saturated fatty fast foods such as potato chips and other deep fried products. Cravings for such foods often represent a need for an increase in the omega-3 and omega-6 EFAs that our bodies lack due to the constraints of a regular Western diet. Such strong cravings are being exploited by fast food producers who are not restricted from using hydrogenated (heated, processed, damaged) vegetable oils in even the so-called 'healthy' options available today. Such damaging oils are cheap to produce and hold a long shelf-life offering higher profits to the operator, but have shown consistently to be potentially threatening to life after long periods of consumption. You can only guarantee your food does not contain such oils if you produce them yourself or buy fresh organic produce. By reading labels carefully we arm ourselves with knowledge. If it states 'vegetable oil' then it is very likely to be made from these damaging, heated and highly processed fats. We have a choice between carefully produced alive hemp products able to promote a healthy heart over dead processed 'foods' that slowly clog up our bodies mechanisms until we reach a state of dis-ease.

Many hemp products such as Motherhemp's dairy-free hemp ice-cream alternative, Wholebake's 9bar™ and Sunnyvale's Organic Wheat Sprouted Hemp Bread are available commercially. The following recipes are examples of the wide and varying uses of hemp seed in food.

GALAXY GLOBAL EATERY

WINTER MENU

Mixed Leaf Salad with Roquefort, Hemp & Walnuts
Nicky's Very Raj Curry
Three-Bean Real McCoy Vegetable Chilli (veggie option)
Tarte Alsacienne

MIXED LEAF SALAD WITH ROQUEFORT, HEMP & WALNUTS

Serves: 6
Preparation: 15 minutes

400g/ 14 oz mixed leaves (treviso, red mustard, mizuna & rocket)
200g/ 7 oz Roquefort cheese, cubed
114g/ 4 oz walnuts (fresh or caramelised)
55g/ 2 oz hemp seeds (fresh or caramelised)
200ml/ 7 fl oz sunflower oil
100ml/ 3^1/$_2$ fl oz hemp oil
85ml/ 3 fl oz tarragon vinegar
15ml/ 1 fl oz raspberry vinegar
2 cloves garlic
^{1}/$_2$ tablespoon honey
^{1}/$_2$ tablespoon Dijon mustard
juice of ^{1}/$_2$ lemon
fresh ground sea salt & black pepper

Dressing:
1. Place garlic and honey in a bowl and crush with a mortar, to form a paste.
2. Add mustard and vinegars and slowly mix in oil with a whisk.
3. Finish with a little lemon juice, salt and pepper.

Salad:
1. Wash and dry salad thoroughly.
2. Put into a bowl, carefully adding cheese and walnuts.
3. Toss gently with the dressing just before serving.
4. The rest of the dressing can be put into a jug if people want extra.

Caramelised Hemp Seeds & Walnuts: (Optional)

125ml/ 4 fl oz water
2 tablespoons castor sugar
½ tablespoon butter

In a small heavy based saucepan boil water, slowly adding sugar and butter. Cook until water is reduced and mixture becomes a caramelised (golden) colour. Mix in nuts with a wooden spoon and turn out onto greaseproof paper. As it cools separate nuts to avoid clumps forming. Put aside in a cool place until needed.

Note: The mixing of different oils is important in obtaining the right balance.

NICKY'S VERY RAJ CURRY

Serves: 4
Preparation: 30 minutes
Cooking: 45 minutes

2 carrots diced
2 celery sticks diced
2 small onions sliced
1 large potato diced
4 cloves garlic chopped
2.5cm/ 1 inch piece ginger coarsely chopped
7 tablespoons ghee or sunflower oil
2 tablespoons hemp seed oil
3 tablespoons white flour seasoned with salt and paper
2-3 tablespoons hot curry paste (hotness to taste)
1 teaspoon tomato puree
1 tin plum tomatoes sieved to remove seeds.
1 tablespoon mango chutney
450g/ 1 lb lamb cubed (leg cut)
1 apple (eating) peeled, cored and diced
1 tablespoon cream of coconut
1 tablespoon grated coconut
55g/ 2 oz sultanas/raisins
2 teaspoons white wine vinegar
¾ litre/ 14 fl oz stock/water
3 hard boiled eggs
½ lemon, juiced
1 tablespoon hemp seed, lightly toasted (heat in dry pan until they pop) & crushed

1.   Add 2 tablespoons hemp oil and 2 tablespoons ghee to a heavy base saucepan and sweat the onions for 2 minutes.

2. Add celery, carrots, garlic and ginger for another 2 minutes. Stir constantly.
3. Add potato and apple and cook for another 2 minutes, then put pan to one side off the heat.
4. Roll the lamb in 2/3 of the seasoned flour.
5. Quickly brown lamb in remaining ghee or oil then place on kitchen towel to drain.
6. Put the pan containing the veg back on medium heat, stir in tomato puree and then add drained meat, hot curry paste, remaining flour, hemp seeds and cook for 2 minutes.
7. Add sieved plum tomatoes, creamed coconut, sultanas, dried coconut. Stir well, add stock and bring to a simmer.
8. Add wine vinegar, mango chutney and lemon juice.
9. Place on a low heat for about 40 minutes or until meat is tender, stirring from time to time.

Condiments:
poppadoms
pickles
eggs
bananas
tomatoes
chutney
crushed toasted hemp seeds

Note: In this recipe the hemp seed and oil gives a mellow nutty flavour, rounding out the heat of the curry.

THREE-BEAN REAL McCOY VEGGIE CHILLI
(veggie option)

Serves: 8
Preparation: 30 minutes
Cooking: 45-60 minutes

170g/ 6 oz medium or coarse bulgur wheat
85ml / 3 fl oz hemp oil
2 large yellow onions, peeled & coarsely chopped (about 4 cups)
8 medium garlic cloves, peeled and minced
2-4 tablespoons chilli powder (to taste)
3 tablespoons ground cumin
3 tablespoons lightly crushed hemp seeds
3 tablespoons dried oregano
1½ tablespoons dried thyme
2 teaspoons cayenne pepper

½ teaspoon ground cinnamon
1 kilo (35 oz) plum tomatoes, remove seeds
875ml/ 1¾ pints vegetable, chicken stock or water
250ml/ 1 cup of water
225g/ ½ lb fresh green beans, trimmed and cut in half & blanched
2 large red peppers, diced
225g/ 8 oz corn kernels
450gm/ 16 oz dark red kidney beans, rinsed and drained
450gm/ 16 oz chick-peas, rinsed and drained
450gm/ 16 oz borlotti beans
450gm/ 16 oz white kidney beans
sea salt (to taste)
freshly ground black pepper (to taste)

1. In a small bowl, cover the bulgur in water (about 1 cup) and soak.
2. In a large saucepan, warm the oil and add the onions and garlic, cook for 10 minutes on a low heat. Stir in chilli powder, hemp seeds, cumin, oregano, thyme, cayenne pepper, sea salt and cinnamon and cook for 5 minutes.
3. Add the tomatoes, canned beans, and warmed stock. Bring to a boil then cover and simmer for 25 minutes, stir occasionally.
4. Uncover chilli and stir in peppers and green beans, cook for a further 10 minutes, check seasoning and serve.
5. Serve with freshly grated cheese, chopped spring onions and sour cream.

Note: This chilli is best made the day before giving all the flavours a chance to rest and mingle. The bulgur wheat gives this chilli a rich, meaty texture.

TARTE ALSACIENNE

Serves: 12
Pre-heat oven 350 F
Preparation: 1 Hour
Cooking: 1 Hour

For the Pie Base:
250g/ 8 oz plain flour
25g/ 1 oz ground hemp seeds or flour
1 whole egg
100g/ 3.5 oz unsalted butter (cold)
25ml/ 1 fl oz hemp oil
25ml/ 1 fl oz water
75g/ 3 oz castor sugar
a pinch of salt

1. Sift flour and salt into a bowl. Dice butter and hemp oil, and add it to the flour.
2. Gently work the butter into the flour until it resembles crumbs.
3. Add the egg and water and gently work until smooth dough is formed.
4. Wrap in cling film and rest in fridge for about 15 minutes.
2. Take out of fridge and roll out dough.
3. Line a loose bottom 30cm/12inch (flan) tart tin (5cm/2inch deep).
4. Blind bake with weights until firm (light brown).

For the Filling:
4 free range eggs
55g/ 2 oz castor sugar
400ml/ 14 fl oz single cream
4-6 golden delicious apples, sliced quarters
vanilla essence
rum (1 shot)

For the Topping:
250g/ 8 oz castor sugar, 250g/ 8 oz sliced almonds, 30g/ 1 oz. lightly crushed hemp seeds, 125 g/ 5 oz raisins and 2 egg whites (froth); mix with dry ingredients just before placing on top.

1. Filling: Combine cream, eggs, sugar, vanilla and rum together.
2. Fan sliced apples into base, then pour mixture over apples.
3. Bake for 15-20 minutes or until egg mixture is nearly set.
4. Top with almond mixture (adding whites at last moment), then bake until golden brown, usually about 5-10 minutes in a hot oven.
5. Let cool then de-mould and serve warm with vanilla ice cream.

SPRING MENU

**Spring Salad
Chicken Lucia
Linguini with Eggplant & Hemp Tofu (veggie option)
Hempaglione**

SPRING SALAD

Serves: 4
Preparation: 15 minutes

250g/ 8 oz mixed leaves (treviso, red mustard, mizuna & rocket)
1 bunch spring onions
1 ripe avocado, sliced with a squeeze of lemon (to keep from browning)
2 roasted red peppers, sliced
8 small artichoke hearts in oil, cut in half
4 tablespoons hemp seeds

Dressing:
80ml/ 3 fl oz of white vinegar
20ml/ ¾ fl oz balsamic vinegar
2 teaspoons of Dijon mustard
squeeze of ½ lemon
1 garlic clove
220ml/ 8 fl oz extra virgin olive oil
80ml/ 3 fl oz hemp oil
1 tablespoon honey

1.   Put vinegar, mustard, and garlic in a blender on low speed.
2.   Add the vinegars, then after a minute slowly add oil until blended.

For the salad:
1.   Mix leaves with peppers, avocado & artichokes. Toss in vinaigrette.
2.   Top with toasted hemp seeds.

CHICKEN LUCIA

Serves: 4
Preparation: 20 minutes
Oven: 180°C/350°F
Cooking: 25 minutes

4 chicken supremes (free range)

For the stuffing:
110g/ 4 oz spinach, blanched and drained; squeezing out excess water
55g/ 2 oz feta cheese
2 tablespoons white wine
2 tablespoons pernod
1 tablespoon hemp sauce (akin to soy sauce)
2 tablespoons toasted hemp seeds
1/2 teaspoon paprika
pinch of cayenne pepper
Mix the stuffing, cut a slit about 5cm/ 2 inches horizontally in breast and stuff.

For the coating:
225g/ 8 oz of flour seasoned with salt & pepper
3 eggs
1 teaspoon hemp sauce (akin to soy sauce)
1 teaspoon water
1 tablespoon white wine
285g/ 10 oz of fresh bread crumbs
2 tablespoons of crushed hemp seeds
1 teaspoon of sesame seeds
1 teaspoon of hemp oil
1/2 teaspoon paprika

For the Sauce:
225g/ 8 oz of apricot preserves
125ml/ 4 fl oz soy sauce
2 cloves of garlic
1/2 lemon, juiced

1. Get three bowls. In bowl #1 place the seasoned flour, in bowl #2 place beaten eggs, hemp sauce, water, wine & hemp oil and in bowl #3 place bread crumbs, hemp seeds, sesame seeds, cayenne pepper and paprika.
2. Take each stuffed supreme and first coat in flour, then egg mixture then lastly in bread crumb mixture.
3. Place on an oiled baking dish and bake for 25 minutes.
4. Make the sauce by placing all ingredients into a blender and liquefy. Place in a saucepan and warm before serving.

LINGUINI WITH EGGPLANT & HEMP TOFU

Serves: 6
Preparation: 15 minutes
Cooking: 15 minutes

5 tablespoons hemp oil
2 eggplants, slice into inch strips
2 red peppers, roasted, seed and pith removed, sliced
2 tablespoons balsamic vinegar
3 cloves garlic, finely chopped
3 tablespoons toasted crushed hemp seeds
1 small chilli, finely chopped
125g/ 5 oz hemp tofu, cut into strips
1 tablespoon hemp sauce (akin to soy sauce)
450g/ 1 lb linguine
1 tablespoon torn coriander leaves
freshly ground black pepper and sea salt

1.   Heat half the oil and sauté quickly the eggplant strips and then when
     brown add 2 tablespoons of hemp seeds, then the vinegar and garlic,
2.   Cook for about 3-4 minutes, add chilli and coriander and put into a
     bowl with sliced red peppers and hemp sauce.
3.   Using same pan add remaining oil and sauté until the tofu is slightly crispy.
4.   Boil linguine and drain. Put pasta back in pot and toss with tofu and
     eggplant mixture.
5.   Serve and garnish with remaining sesame seeds and coriander leaves.

HEMPAGLIONE

Serves: 4
Preparation: 10 minutes
Cooking: 15 minutes

75g/ 3oz castor sugar
grated rind of ½ lemon
4 egg yolks
½ teaspoon ground cinnamon
1 drop of vanilla extract
150 ml/ 5 fl oz Marsala
1 tablespoon, plus 1 teaspoon finely ground hemp seeds
1 tablespoon crushed toasted hemp seeds
125 g/ 4 oz of fresh peaches

Instructions

1. Place sugar, lemon rind, cinnamon, 1 tablespoon ground hemp seeds, vanilla and egg yolks into a double boiler and beat until thick, pale and creamy.
2. Place the bowl over simmering water and continue whisking. Slowly add the Marsala and whisk until the mixture warms, frothy and thick.
3. Dip the rims of 4 glasses in water, then in sugar to frost them.
4. Toss the fruit with 1 tablespoon of crushed toasted hemp seeds then divide the fruit among the glasses.
5. Spoon in the hempaglione.
6. To serve, dust with a mixture of cinnamon and ground hemp seeds.
7. Top with a fresh green hemp leaf !

Hemp Seed Pesto Sauce

55g/ 2 oz toasted hemp seeds
25g/ 1 oz grated Parmesan
25g/ 1 oz grated Gruyére cheese
2 cloves of garlic-crushed
2 cups fresh basil
150 ml/ 5 fl oz hemp oil
dash of fresh lemon juice
salt & pepper to taste

Place all ingredients into a blender and blend to a paste.

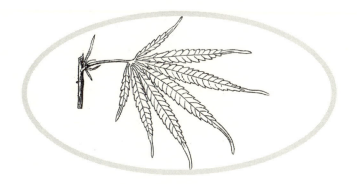

SUMMER MENU

Hemp Pizzas
Moroccan Prawns
Chocolate Hemp Brownies

HEMP PIZZAS
Serves: 6 (8-10 inch)
Preparation: 1 hour 20 minutes
Cooking: 15 minutes

For the dough:
465g/ 1 lb white bread flour
25g/ 1 oz whole meal flour
15g/ ½ oz fresh yeast or 7g /¼ sachet of dried yeast
2 teaspoons salt
25ml / 1 fl oz hemp oil (a little extra for greasing)
25ml / 1 fl oz warm water
1 heaped teaspoon of ground hemp seeds

For the topping:
Hemp pesto sauce
680g/ 24 oz grated mozzarella
225g/ 8 oz roasted peppers
225g/ 8 oz roasted artichokes
225g/ 8 oz grilled red onions, sliced
2 tablespoons toasted hemp seeds
6 teaspoons grated Parmesan

1. In a jug mix the water, yeast and oil.
2. Place the flour onto your marble and make a hole in the middle. Pour water into centre of mixture and mix well. Add a little water if the mixture is dry or a little flour if it's too wet.
3. On your floured surface, kneed the dough for about 8 minutes until smooth and elastic. You should be able to clean the surface, leaving it sparkling clean with the dough.
4. Form it into a large ball and place it in a floured bowl. Lightly oil.

the dough and cover the bowl with a damp cloth. Leave at room temperature for an hour.

5. When it has doubled in size take it out of the bowl and knock back.
6. Make six balls and roll each out into circles about 3mm/1¼ inch thick.
7. Place pizzas on a lightly floured baking tray. Spoon and lightly cover the top of each pizza with the pesto sauce.
8. Sprinkle mozzarella, then toppings of sun-dried tomatoes, hemp seeds, artichokes, onions, grated Parmesan cheese and roasted peppers.
9. Cook in a preheated oven 220°C for 15 minutes or until golden.

MOROCCAN PRAWNS

Serves: 4
Preparation: 20 minutes
Cooking: 10-15 minutes

450g/ 16 oz un-peeled headless raw prawns
2 tablespoons white wine vinegar or coconut vinegar
1 teaspoon turmeric powder
1 teaspoon black peppercorns
1 tablespoon coriander seeds
1 teaspoon cumin seeds
2 tablespoons toasted hemp seeds
4 tablespoons hemp seed oil
3 cloves garlic, sliced
25mm/ 1 inch fresh ginger root
400ml/ 14 fl oz coconut milk
150ml/ 5 fl oz water
5 mild green chillies, halved, cut thinly
2 tablespoons chopped coriander
pinch of cayenne pepper
sea salt

1. Peel the prawns, leaving the tail. Mix the prawns with the vinegar and ½ teaspoon of salt. Set aside for 5 minutes.
2. Grind the turmeric powder, peppercorns, coriander seeds, cumin seeds and hemp seeds in a spice grinder to a fine powder.
3. Heat the hemp oil in a saucepan and add onion, garlic and ginger, fry gently for five minutes. Stir in the ground spices and fry for one minute. Add the prawns, brown quickly for two minutes. Add coconut milk, water, sliced chillies and salt to taste. Bring to a simmer and cook for a further 2 minutes.
4. Stir in the coriander and serve with saffron rice.

CHOCOLATE HEMP BROWNIES

Serves: 12 brownies
Preparation: 30 minutes
Cooking: 45 minutes

340g/ 12 oz unsalted butter
170g/ 6 oz bittersweet chocolate
680g/ 24 oz sugar
6 large eggs
2 drops vanilla essence
285g/ 10 oz sifted flour
4 tablespoons hemp seeds, crushed
115g/ 4 oz pecans, chopped

1. Melt chocolate and butter over a low heat. Stirring to blend.
2. In mixing bowl beat eggs and sugar until a ribbon of egg mixture falls from the whisk. Add vanilla.
3. Now slowly add melted chocolate & butter and mix thoroughly.
4. Fold in sifted flour, hemp seeds and pecans.
5. Pour mixture into a paper lined baking tray.
    Cook at 350°F in a preheated convection oven for 45 minutes. Let cool in tray.

Note: You will know when you are eating the best chocolate brownies when the top breaks away from base. The middle of this brownie will be very moist.

AUTUMN MENU

Parsnip Soup
Chili Crusted Salmon Steaks
Wild Mushroom & Toasted Hemp Risotto (veggie option)
Fig & Gingered Millefeuille

PARSNIP SOUP

Serves: 6
Preparation: 15 minutes
Cooking: 20 minutes

1 tablespoon hemp garam masala powder
1 medium onion, chopped
1 tablespoon crushed hemp seeds
1 large clove garlic, chopped
1 large parsnip, peeled, cut up
2 tablespoons hemp oil
1 tablespoon flour
1 litre/16 fl oz veal or chicken stock
150ml/5 fl oz cream
chopped chives or parsley

1. Cook the onion, garlic and parsnip gently in the hemp oil; lid on the pan, for ten minutes.
2. Stir in the flour, the curry powder and the hemp seeds.
3. Cook for two minutes, stirring from time to time.
4. Pour in the stock, stirring at the same time and cook until the parsnips are tender.
5. Puree mixture in the blender and return to pot and season with salt and pepper.
6. Add cream and serve immediately.
7. Decorate each bowl with chopped parsley or chives.

Hemp Garam Masala (*Makes 4 tablespoons*)

1 tablespoon cardamom seeds
1 tablespoon black cumin seeds
1 tablespoon hemp seeds
1/4 nutmeg

5cm / 2 inch stick cinnamon
1 teaspoon whole cloves
1 teaspoon black peppercorns
Grind in a spice grinder to a powder.

CHILLI & HEMP CRUSTED SALMON STEAKS

Serves: 6
Preparation: 30 minutes
Cooking: 10 minutes

5 tablespoons Cajun spices (our special, never before published recipe, see below).
6 (170g/6-oz.) salmon steaks
125ml/4 fl oz olive oil
1 tablespoon hemp oil
275ml/11 fl oz yellow pepper sauce (see p.134)

1.	Combine spices and dredge the salmon steaks in the mixture on one side only.
2.	In a large sauté pan over high heat, heat the oils until they begin to smoke. Cook the salmon steaks, pepper side down for 2-3 minutes, then turn over and cook for a further 3 minutes.
3.	Make the yellow pepper sauce.
4.	Place salmon pepper side up on a plate and drizzle yellow pepper sauce around the salmon.

Note: You can substitute any fish for this recipe such as tuna, scallops or prawns. It has a lovely balance of hot spice and mellow-yellow pepper.

14 Ingredient Cajun Spice Mix

110g/ 4 oz salt
110g/ 4 oz chilli powder
55g/ 2 oz ground cumin
55g/ 2 oz black pepper
55g/ 2 oz dried thyme
55g/ 2 oz dried marjoram
55g/ 2 oz ground hemp seed

110g/ 4 oz tomato powder
55g/ 2 oz ground fennel seed
55g/ 2 oz paprika sweet
55g/ 2 oz ground bay leaf
55g/ 2 oz powdered garlic
55g/ 2 oz dried dill
55g/ 2 oz oregano

Yellow Pepper Sauce *(Makes about 275ml/11 fl oz)*

2 yellow peppers, lightly roasted, peeled, and seeded
1 red onion, chopped   3 tablespoons fresh lime juice
75ml/ 3 fl oz olive oil   75ml/ 3 fl oz hemp oil
1 teaspoon sugar   salt and pepper to taste

Mix in a blender the peppers, onion & lime juice. While blender is running slowly, add the oil. Add sugar, salt & pepper and serve.
Can be prepared up to two days ahead and refrigerated.

WILD MUSHROOM & TOASTED HEMP RISOTTO
(veggie option)

Serves: 6
Preparation: 15 minutes
Cooking: 40 minutes

1 medium onion, peeled and finely chopped
3 cloves garlic, peeled and sliced
1 litre/ 16 oz chicken stock
300g/ 11 oz risotto rice
75ml/ 3 fl oz white wine
200g/ 7 oz wild mushrooms, sliced
3 tablespoons olive oil
3 tablespoons hemp oil
½ fresh lemon, juiced
1 tablespoon fresh basil chopped
150g/ 5 oz unsalted butter
1 tablespoon toasted hemp seeds
175g/ 6 oz Parmesan cheese freshly grated
sea salt and freshly ground black pepper to taste

1.   Heat butter and oils in heavy-based frying pan until hot. Throw in sliced mushrooms & garlic and cook for about 10 minutes until tender. Drain any mushroom juices and add to the chicken stock.
2.   Add lemon juice to mushrooms & garlic mixture and put aside.
3.   Take a heavy-based saucepan and heat remaining olive oil until hot. Add onion and sweat for 5-10 minutes making sure they do not brown.
4.   Over medium heat add rice and cook for 1-2 minutes until rice is thoroughly coated with oil/onion mixture. Add white wine and stir constantly until liquid is absorbed.
5.   Add hot chicken stock, a little at a time, stirring constantly until liquid is absorbed. Continue to add more stock as the previous addition is

absorbed. Make sure your risotto is simmering at all times. After 15-20 minutes the rice will appear to have a creamy consistency but will remain 'al dente'. When the rice has absorbed all the stock, carefully fold in the mushrooms, hemp seeds, Parmesan cheese, basil and salt & pepper to taste. Just before serving stir in slowly the remaining butter which has been cut into pieces. This will give the risotto an extra creamy texture. Serve immediately.

FIG AND GINGERED MASCARPONE MILLEFEUILLE

Serves: 6
Preparation: 20 minutes
Cooking: 20 minutes

Pre-heat oven to 180°C.
For the Base: 500g frozen puff pastry

1.   Roll out puff pastry to 35cm/14in square, about 3mm/⅛ inch thick.
2.   Place on a non-stick-baking tray, prick with a fork and lightly bush with a little hemp oil.
3.   Put in oven for about 20 minutes then turn over and cook other side until pastry is golden in colour.
4.   Take out of oven and cut into three wide strips; making one strip slightly narrower than the others.

For the Filling:
275ml/ 11 fl oz mascarpone
16 small firm ripe figs
2 tablespoons toasted hemp seeds
1 tablespoon finely chopped crystallised ginger
1½ tablespoons sugar
vanilla icing sugar for dusting
fresh sprigs of hemp leaf

1.   Mix together mascarpone, ginger, sugar, vanilla and 4 chopped figs.
2.   Now assemble the dessert; slice remaining figs into 2cm/ ¾ inch slices.
3.   Take the larger puff pastry strip and spread the mascarpone filling evenly over it.
4.   Layer 4 slices of fig with a little hemp seeds, then take narrower sheet of puff pastry and repeat process.
5.   Place remaining sheet on top. Pressing down evenly using flat tray.
6.   Now cut across using a sharp serrated knife for your 6 portions.
7.   Place on a plate; decorate each with remaining figs and dust with icing sugar.
8.   Decorate with a sprig of fresh hemp leaf.

LAÑAPE

GLOBAL BEEFSTEAK TOMATOES

Serves: 6
Preparation: 20 minutes
Oven: 190ºC/375ºF
Cooking: 25 minutes

3 firm beefsteak tomatoes
1 onion
40g/ 1½ oz butter
55g/ 2 oz breadcrumbs
30ml/ 2 tablespoons sage flowers
10ml/ 2 teaspoons hemp seed oil
30ml/ 2 tablespoons toasted hemp seeds (lightly crushed)
25g/ 1 oz grated Parmesan cheese
6 cloves garlic (slowly roast in the oven with skin)
pinch of cayenne pepper
sea salt

1. Cut the tomatoes in half.
2. Finely chop the onion and gently cook with butter & hemp oil.
3. Add bread crumbs, sage flowers, garlic (peeled and mashed) and hemp seeds to pan and toss for a minute. Season with salt & pepper.
4. Place tomatoes on a baking dish, cut side up and top with mixture.
5. Top with Parmesan cheese and bake until golden.

Note: Roasting the garlic makes it not as pungent, while giving it a softer mellower, flavour.

HEMPINI

Serves: makes 1½ cups
Preparation: 10 minutes

55g/ 2 oz hemp oil
55g/ 2 oz sunflower oil
55g/ 2 oz toasted hemp seeds
55g/ 2 oz sesame seeds
2 tablespoons hemp sauce (akin to soy sauce)
2 cloves garlic
pinch of cayenne pepper
juice of ½ large lemon
125ml/ 4 fl oz water
1 teaspoon honey

Rasta Pasta
Photograph courtesy of
Juliette Atkinson
www.julietteatkinson.com

1. Place hemp seeds, sesame seeds, hemp seed oil, sunflower oil and garlic into blender. Blend thoroughly.
2. Slowly add the tamari sauce, cayenne pepper, honey & lemon juice.
3. Once the mixture is thoroughly blended and creamy slowly add water until Hempini has become a smooth creamy mixture. Adding water will allow it to blend more easily and avoid separating.

Note: This dressing makes a perfect dip for crudités.

XII. Ropes

KENYON GIBSON

A variety of vegetable fibres have been used for rope and twine throughout history, but none so widespread and in demand as hemp. Pliny records Roman use of hemp, and archaeological finds support this. Every nation in Europe grew it for this very purpose, and at times it was a life or death matter. The Italians instituted a guild for the manufacture of sails and cordage, the British fought Napoleon over access to Russian hemp, and the Americans set up their own rope walks to ensure a steady supply of rope and cables for their navy. The following is an article reprinted from the *Book of Trades*, published in 1835.

> The rope maker twists several kinds of materials, and particularly hemp, into yarn, and afterwards several strings of such yarn, assisted by a wheel, into a larger and more compact cord. When the article is of a small description it is called a cord, when larger, a rope; the largest is called a cable.
>
> Ropes are made of many vegetable substances that are sufficiently fibrous, flexible, and tenacious, but chiefly of the bark of plants. The Chinese and other Orientals even make them of the woody parts of several plants, such as certain bamboos, and reeds, the stems of the aloes, the fibrous covering of the cocoa-nut, the filaments of the cotton pods, and the leaves of some grasses, such as sparte... But the barks of plants are the most productive of fibrous matter proper for this manufacture. Those of the willow, the linden-tree, the bramble, and the nettle, are frequently used; but hemp and flax are the best; and of these hemp is preferred and employed in all cordage exceeding the size of a line, and even in many of this denomination.
>
> The trade of a Rope-maker is unquestionably very ancient. As early as the fourteenth century, in France, the Rope-makers were formed into a company, and had statutes appointed for their regulation. In this country, where the navy has obtained so much attention, a Rope-maker has, for a long period, been a trade of considerable importance.
>
> Ropes of all kinds are generally made of hemp, twisted or spun, something after the same manner as the spinning of wool; and the places in which ropes are made, are called rope-walks. These are sometimes a quarter of a mile or more in length, in the open air, and have a row or rows

ROPE-MAKING BY MACHINERY.

of trees planted beside them for shade, or are covered with a slight shed to keep the workmen from the inclemencies and changes of the weather.

At the upper-end of the rope-walk is a spinning-wheel, which is turned round by a person, who sits on a stool or bench for the purpose; the man who forms the rope or string, has a bundle of dressed hemp, such as that which lies on the truck in the plate, round his waist. From this he draws out two or more ends, and fixes them to a hook; the wheel is now turned, by which the threads are twisted, and as the spinner walks backward, the rope, or more properly the rope-yarn, is lengthened. The part already twisted draws along with it more fibres out of the bundle, and the spinner gives assistance to it with his fingers, supplying hemp in due proportion as he walks away from the wheel, and taking care that fibres come in equally from both sides of his bundle, and that they enter always with their ends, and not by the middle, which would double them. The arrangement of the fibres, and the degree of twisting, depend on the skill and the dexterity of the spinner. The degree of twist depends on the rate of the wheels motion, combined with the retrograde motion of the spinner.

As soon as he has arrived at the lower end of the walk he calls out, and another spinner immediately detaches the yarn from the hook of the wheel, gives it to a third person, who takes it to the reel, and the second spinner attaches his own hemp to the wheel-hook. In the mean time, the first spinner keeps fast hold of the end of his yarn, to prevent its untwisting, and, as soon as the reeler begins to turn his reel, he goes slowly up the walk, keeping the yarn of an equal tightness all the way, till he arrives at the wheel, where he waits with his yarn in his hand till another has finished his yarn. The first spinner takes it off the wheel-hook, joins it to his own, that it may follow it on the reel, and begins a new yarn himself.

The fibres of hemp are thus twisted into yarns, and make a line of any length: down the rope-walk are a number of upright posts, with long pegs fixed in them at right angles; on these pegs the spinner throws the rope yarn as he proceeds, to prevent its swagging.

As many fibres are made into one yarn, so many yarns are afterwards made into one rope, according to the use and strength required. By this process, which is called laying, it acquires a solidity and hardness which render it less penetrable by water, that would rot it in a short time.

Sometimes the union of several yarns is called a strand, and a larger rope is formed of two or more of these strands; in this manner cables and other ground tackle are commonly made.

Cables and cords are frequently tarred, which is usually done in the state of yarn, this being the only method by which hemp can be uniformly penetrated. The yarn is made to wind off from one reel, and having passed through a vessel containing hot tar, it is wound upon another, and the superfluous tar is taken off by passing through a hole surrounded with spongy oakum; or it is sometimes tarred in skeins or hauls, which are drawn by a capstern through the tar-kettle, and through a hole formed of two plates of metal.

It is a fact, however, that tarred cordage is much weaker than white; it is also less pliable and less durable; but the use of tar is nevertheless

necessary to defend the cordage from the action of the water. Nets are made with small cords; larger cords are used for tying up packages; and ropes of all sizes and dimensions are used for shipping. A ship's cable is sometimes several hundred yards in length, and is worth a considerable sum of money.

Mr. Chapman has lately obtained a patent for making ropes and cordage, the machinery of which consists only of a spindle, divided into two parts, the upper containing apparatus to draw forward the hemp from the spinner, with twist sufficient to combine the fibres, which enabled him to employ women, children, and invalids, and also to appropriate the rope-ground solely to the purpose of laying ropes.

Other patents have been also obtained for improving this art; but we have not room to numerate them.

The master Rope-maker requires a considerable capital to carry on business upon a large scale. A journeyman may earn with ease from a guinea to a guinea and a half a week, or even more if he be sober and industrious.

Yarn for sail-cloth is made of dressed-hemp, and spun in the same manner as rope-yarn is spun. The spinners of this make a good living; women are chiefly employed in it. The person who shapes and sews together the sail-cloth, is called a sail-maker; and is sometimes denominated a ship's-tailor.[1]

From:
Cordage and Cordage Hemp,
J. Woodhouse and P. Kilgour. 1919

One aspect of rope making that is not covered in the above essay is the preparation of hemp before it was sold on as fibre to the ropewalk. This was the subject of much discussion, especially in the US, where water-retted hemp was not generally produced. Attempts to use dew-retted hemp, or even un-retted hemp were tried, but failed.

Dr. O.S. Leavitt wrote an essay in the 1861 *Report of the Commissioner of Patents* in which he advocated a process called 'kyanizing' for ropes. Basically this is a form of chemical preservative, or antiseptic, which lengthens the life of a rope. He writes; "It has been ascertained that either flax or hemp ropes made of the American unretted and kyanized material are superior to those made of Russian hemp, both in strength and durability."[2] Leavitt also mentions pyroligneous acid, a by-product of smoke, which gives the fibres certain longevity.

FIG. 30
LAYING OF A FOUR-STRAND CABLE-LAID ROPE IN THE ROPE-WALK

Many other fibres are also used in rope, mostly abaca *(Musa textilis)*. A 1904 record makes mention of both as follows:

Hemp is practically the only one of the long vegetable fibres used by rope makers. The soft hemps are best for the standard rigging of ships, or for running rigging where a heavy purchase is required, while manila is preferred for light running rigging.[3]

Leavitt also makes comparison:

> This kyanized cordage, made of unrotted hemp, was recommended and used by many in preference to the manilla rope in all situations where it was liable to get wet, and where no one would think of using rope made from rotted hemp. It was found in numerous tests, public and private, to be twenty percent stronger than the Manilla, was smoother, and was less liable to fray in snubbing, qualities rendering it superior to Manilla for running rigging. This cordage was found to have a marked advantage over that from rotted hemp when tarred; it was more flexible and was not liable to what is called burning. A specimen of bolt rope that had lain two years, was found to be as pliable, to all appearances, as when first made. Hemp ropes when worn out are valuable for making paper, which is not the case with abaca. If tarred, hemp is of value for oakum. This comparison can be made not only against abaca, but verses coir, jute and other substances as well.[4]

Hemp cordage on display,
London Cannabis Rally,
June 2002

In the past, great demand existed, especially among maritime nations as Dr. Francis Campbell notes in 1845:

> The great national advantages accruing from the cultivation of hemp will be better understood from the following computations. One hundred and eighty thousand pounds weight of hemp are required to rig completely a first-rate ship of war; and if four acres produce on an average one ton of hemp, a single first-rate man-of-war will require the produce of 320 acres to furnish her with a complete outfit.[5]

Currently other fibres are employed, but hemp is still a preferred material among sailors. Limited production is under way, expected to increase as more farmers gain knowledge of cultivation and processing. One long-range aspect is recycling. There has been in recent time a greater demand among papermakers for recycled hemp products, guaranteeing a secondary market for the ropes as there existed in previous centuries.[6]

1. Anon. *The Book of Trades*. London, Sherwood. Gilbert & Piper, 1835. pp. 235-239
2. Leavitt, Dr. O.S. *The Culture and Manufacture of Flax and Hemp*. Portland, (Or.), The Caber Press, 2001 [Pre-publ. manuscript])
3. Carter, Herbert R. *The Spinning and Twisting of Long Vegetable Fibers*. London, Charles Griffin & Co., 1904. p. 261
4. Leavitt
5. Campbell, Francis. *The Cultivation of Flax and Hemp*. Sydney, Stratham & Forster, 1845. p. 78
6. MacDonald, Ronald G. and John N. Franklin. *Control Secondary Fiber Structural Board Coating*. NY. McGraw Hill, 1969. p. 43

XIII . 25,000 Other Uses

PAUL BENHAIM

*I*t was Jack Herer who first re-inspired the western world with the idea that the hemp crop was far under utilised in the industrial age. In his famous book *The Emperor Wears No Clothes* one will find a plethora of facts and figures and some very interesting ideas surrounding the political and legal history of the hemp plant. The book included the many historical uses of this versatile plant. In fact Herer was renowned for the statement that "hemp has over 25,000 uses", which phrase he took from a *Popular Mechanics* article on the subject. He was once seen as an extreme political activist, now his statements are not only becoming acknowledged, but are truly being realised as hemp begins to touch mainstream industry.

We could find many uses for many crops, but how many of these crops can offer such a variety of products? In recent times our definition for a viable proposition has changed from using mainly economic measurements to a more holistic approach that considers whether an idea can be maintained at all the necessary levels. This must involve everyone and everything connected with the idea. For example, the earth that the seed is planted in, the pesticides required to help the crop survive, the energy needed to sow, harvest and process, the necessity for new or updated infrastructure for primary processes, the energy and materials required for this, and finally the distribution, marketing and use of the end product. Now, if we consider the resources this gives and takes at all direct and indirect stages; we are led to ask: "What involvement does the local community have? Who is benefited by such investment of resources? What is the end product's true value to society?" Only with all this information to hand can we look back and make an informed decision to the true value a crop and its uses have to society.

The twenty-first century is an exciting time. We have many years of recorded information to use. We can learn from our ancestors long, long ago and integrate their ancient knowledge with our new technology, feats of modern engineering and communication. And there is a need for this knowledge now. Can we but help to learn from deforestation? (although old growth trees continue to be hacked for toilet paper or chop-sticks); global warming caused by man-made pollutants? (although our shopping malls are filled with man-made objects that offer little if any true value);

emptying of our earth's resources? (although petrochemicals continue to be harvested from our withering supplies); nuclear power accidents? (although we need to invest in the infrastructure required to take advantage of our abundant natural power sources).

As the world's population increases we have been searching for new ways to feed, clothe and house ourselves. It is anticipated that by 2060 the world population will increase by 100 percent. First world leaders are beginning to recognise the results of industrialisation and new laws such as those that compel manufacturers to use more and more renewable resources and prevent the use of damaging non-biodegradable products are being implemented to suit our needs. Meeting the dramatic increase in demand is not simply a matter of finding more forests to harvest or increasing current crop production with new pesticides or preferred crop varieties, but rather of cultivating a versatile crop offering both high food and fibre yields.

With only 29 percent of the Earth's surface existing above water and only 15 percent of that considered suitable for agriculture, the land will need to become more intensively farmed in a *sustainable* manner for our future survival. We require fast growing crops that offer us oxygen to breathe and raw materials to produce food, cloth, medicine, fuel, paper, building materials and plastics. I am of the opinion that one plant is capable of providing us with many, if not all, of these needs. That plant is hemp. Hemp crops are best used within a new system of co-operative industry. Again, an holistic approach must be observed by allowing others to play their part within the whole picture. With an infrastructure that manages the links of such co-operative groups, a change in the way our human needs are fulfilled in a productive and sustainable manner can be fulfilled.

Hemp seeds and fibre have been utilised by man for thousands of years and only in the last seventy years has hemp cultivation fallen into decline. A number of economic and political factors no doubt played a part in this process. Cheap supplies of wood, cotton, the introduction of synthetics and the outlawing of the crop in America (which spread throughout the world) affected the modern commercialisation of the industry. Between 1940 and 1990 (the largest industrial growth period in history) little breeding or processing technology was put to use on this crop. As our awareness of ecological disasters and reduction in access to renewable forestland continues to grow, so does our interest in hemp.

Hemp produces both seed and fibre. The stem fibre comprises approximately 30 percent long or bast outer fibres and 70 percent hurd (the inner core). Hemp can yield up to twenty tons of dry stem matter per hectare using new Australian cultivars. The long (about 20mm compared to wood fibres that are around 1-3mm) fibres are famous as being one of the strongest organic fibres and are used throughout the textile industry. These long fibres, when mixed with sustainable plantation forest pulp produce a stronger, longer lasting paper. In papermaking, lignin is removed by environmentally unfriendly pulping procedures. The lignin content of hardwood trees such as eucalyptus is

Photograph courtesy of
Juliette Atkinson
www.julietteatkinson.com

Cleopatra's Secret is…
…A recently re-discovered formula that is carefully hand blended to enrich, rejuvenate and restore your skin.
It is prepared using a wide variety of natural extracts and oils, including Hemp Seed Oil.
cleopatrassecret.org

28 percent of the total solid content. The lignin in hemp bast fibre is only four percent, therefore reducing the need for bleaching or other polluting processes required to remove lignins. Hemp can also be used as a reinforcing agent in the paper recycling process. As paper is recycled it loses its strength. Wood based fibre paper can be re-cycled three to four times whilst hemp can double this to around seven times. As well as hemp's use in coffee filters, tea bags, greaseproof paper, speciality art and archive paper, hemp's other uses include medium density fibre boards, geotextiles and pultrusion products.

The core can also be used to produce paper although it contains less cellulose and more lignins. Hemp core is used widely throughout Europe as an animal bedding, with its highly absorbent properties making this one of the most sought after uses for hemp throughout Europe in the late twentieth century. Other uses include composite boards, organic plastics and various building materials, such as those found in hemp houses in France and the UK. In France, hemp is mixed with lime to produce a more breathable plaster and in Austria, quality boards made of hemp are an alternative to 'MDF' board.

The seed can be used for oil production, which in turn is used in human and/or animal food production, its by-products being more nutritional than many other purpose produced products. The oil is used as a base for cosmetics. The Body Shop has taken this product to the public's attention recently promoting the moisturising nutritional benefits of the oil. The omega-3 and omega-6 EFAs work directly on our cells, entering layers of dry skin to replenish their oils.

The whole seed itself has been used in food products for centuries. Hemp seed can be processed to produce a protein powder, and de-hulled to produce a delicious hemp heart. The by-product of this, the husk, is used in animal food containing quality protein, milled to produce flour and soaked to produce milk, butter, ice-cream and other dairy substitutes. Another use of the oil is of longstanding practice-that of a drying oil, where it has been used both in fine arts and in household paint. A recent experiment comparing hemp to linseed oil showed that it is slower drying then linseed, but with a clear, unyellowed finish.

As well as the stalk that produces fibre, and the fruit which is the seed, hemp also produces flowers. These flowers are generally left to fall back to the land completing the cycle of nutrients from deep in the soil back to the top soil, thus creating what is known as the *New Earth* principle. However, recently in Europe the use of the low THC flowers from industrial hemp has become popular in tea, butter and bread making and even as a filler for aromatherapeutic pillows. This market has only recently expanded, but if it continues will mean that 100 percent of the hemp plant has a viable industrial use, making hemp one of the most environmentally friendly crops on the planet.

Being one of the fastest growing plants known to man, hemp outgrows most weeds and does not need any chemicals to ensure its growth. The high THC varieties used for medicinal and therapeutic purposes are particularly strong in keeping pests away.

There are still more uses where hemp can play a practical part in the future of a sustainable planet. This century is no longer the time for hypothesis or further speculation. Now is the time for action and the following ideas are all being put into practical use somewhere in the world (see *www.hemp.co.uk* for up to date information). We are all a part of the wide community and are responsible for our own actions. It is time to question our habits as a consumer as to where and what our energy, money, and time are being invested into.

HEMP AS A PLASTIC

the most seen man-made object at sea (over 70 percent of our planet) is plastic, that may take up to 100 years or more to biodegrade

Plastic is "a: capable of being molded or modeled <plastic clay> b: capable of adapting to varying conditions." Some may say that hemp and plastic are two contradicting terms, however, it is just a habit placed upon us by clever marketing techniques or rather the natural processes of etymology, which have led us to believe plastics are purely petro-chemical based, and hence unsuitable for widespread use within a sustainable system.

In the early 1990s I was saddened by the sight of plastic bottles and plastic bags that were visible throughout the world, particularly in such beautiful spots such as the supposedly pure Himalayan Mountains and tropical islands. It was then that I made a goal to find a plastic that could be made from hemp, the annual, sustainable organic crop of the future.

It was not until 1996 that a conversation was had with a good friend over a glass of hemp wine that led to an opportunity to work with a plastics compounder to trial a mix of hemp fibers with recycled polypropolene. This led to the production of the hemp 'high-fly' plastic flying disc. This was the first commercial hemp plastic product made by the addition of hemp fibres. These hemp fibres were produced to specific length dernier and cleanliness to provide the required properties and blended with a thermoplastic matrix material in a novel compounding process. Less than one percent specialist compatibilisers were added to encourage fibre matrix bonding, enabling the reduction in the amount of plastic required, reaching the companies initial, modest first production goal.

This relatively primitive experiment by Hemp Plastics (UK) Ltd. was a great success, so far as being able to offer a plastic product not wholly produced using conventional petrochemicals. Many discoveries were made during the process of integrating hemp fibres into methods that were originally designed for conventional plastics. This has continued into further research and development that promises an exciting future for yet another use of hemp. Even now Hemp Plastics has developed ways to produce up to 90 percent bio-derived plastic based on the hemp fibres. At the time of writing this raw material was being prepared for mass market. Products being made from this sustainable, annual crop, such as bench chairs for national parks and road signposts are now available.

With each and every choice we make, we choose our dreams and shape reality; a progression which starts from the every day act of consumption/use of products. What is our chair made from? Our computer? Our car? How does our food come packed? And, to look at the whole picture, what other materials and energy were required to make them and where did all of this come from? What is the real cost of cheap fast food compared to seemingly expensive organic foods? When we are offered a cheaper 'made in the Third World' plastic toy - how much does it really cost us? The real cost is only seen when we look at the whole. What is more expensive to our community, an organic apple for which we pay $1 to our neighbour or an apple grown intensively over the other side of the world for $0.50? What are the real costs of fuel, energy, planes, pesticides, and health? That $0.50 soon turns into a real, sustainable cost of well over $1 in monetary value. In these terms, hemp is an ideal alternative to many standard non-sustainable materials.

The hemp plastic story has not ended, however, with 90 percent biodegradability. It was the production of this mix of hemp plastics that led to the discovery of a European company which had been quietly working on the ultimate goal of a truly 100 percent plant based biodegradable plastic that is similar technically to fiberglass. This pure plant material was developed over nine years of research and is produced in an environmentally friendly manner that uses a purely mechanical process from start to finish. With no addition of the resins required for hemp car panels (by 2006, in the EU 80 percent of car interior panels must be recyclable) or hemp plastics for injection moulding, this material is truly a step in the sustainable hemp direction. Hemp Plastics (Australia) Pty. Ltd. are now working in conjunction with their hemp co-operatives worldwide (UK, Europe and North America) and local governments to start work on building the first factory to produce 100 percent hemp plastic by 2002.

This project is being designed with the true ethics of sustainability and yet has proven the economic viability to an array of investors. Who says ethics have to be compromised for success? The uses for such materials is not yet limitless. Being made of 100 percent plant, the material absorbs 250 percent of its own weight in water - so is best not used outdoors! Solutions were developed to overcome this and, with the addition of only a small percentage of dispersing materials the water absorbency can be reduced to less than five percent. With the recent addition of certain natural silicates, organic resins and waxes, a material that is 97-99 percent plant based, organic, waterproof and biodegradable - this form of hemp plastic - is about to show itself in many uses throughout the modern marketplace. The material can be made to very low densities with excellent heat insulation properties having high resistance to pressure as well as being incombustible. Before such materials are sold, franchised or used for virtually 'anything you can think of', the company is keeping itself grounded and proving how just one product will become not just economically viable and sustainable, but can become an example that can be copied world-wide. We need a solid foundation for a

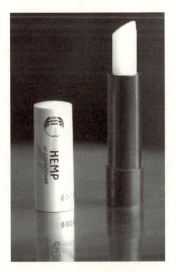

Photograph courtesy of
Juliette Atkinson
www.julietteatkinson.com

sustainable new raw material that can help balance out today's current heavy use of petrochemicals, and hemp seems to offer such qualities.

And what is this first product to be produced by Hemp Plastics (Australia)? The indigenous people of Australia were approached and kindly offered their support in the production of a hemp didgeridoo. With an export market of hundreds of thousands of these pieces of timber every year, the indigenous people are becoming concerned. Concerned over the blatant cutting down of forests by non-indigenous people who place these logs into modern man-made machines to pump out hundreds of didgeridoos daily, to be painted by backpackers, and then sold to unaware tourists who never intend to play the product more than once.

This non-sustainable industry is now being fought, not by traditional activists, but by the positive movement of the hemp industry. Hemp didgeridoos are to be grown on soil, farmed and produced in the sustainable manner hemp is known for. They shall be processed in a non-polluting factory and painted with tradition designs by the indigenous people. This way the consumer is guaranteed that they are not only supporting the local community, but are indirectly preventing the reduction of the forests and are guaranteed an instrument designed and approved by the few remaining elders of this tradition. Modern technology meets ancient traditions.

See *www.hempplastic.com* for updates on this and other hemp and plastic related projects

Back around the other side of the world, in North Wales, home to one of Europe's largest decortication lines, both flax and hemp fibres are being processed to produce 'biomats' that have numerous uses from insulation, car panel lining and mulch mats. The machinery is relatively simple and uses only electricity that is potentially from renewable sources (wind and sun). The by-products are compounded to produce brick logs that are given to the local community to sell as burning logs. In North Wales these logs are slowly replacing the need for major consumption of polluting coal.

Hemp does not stop there. In Australia hemp is being investigated to solve an increasing problem of rising salinity. The fast growing, water loving plant is being implemented in irrigation schemes and as a crop rotation in organic farms. Farmers are starting to realise that chemicals are not always required to make a crop profitable, and the proof is in the pudding. When a crop is seen to grow over ten feet in one hundred and twenty days days, without chemicals, we start to question old habits.

Essential oils are a part of hemp that has been little known or spoken of for many years, but which has been given more attention recently. This is possibly due to the fact that hemp essential oil was once thought to only come from the high THC flowers of the cannabis plant that are outlawed for use in harmless perfumes. The Swiss produced such oil in the early 1990s and have held this product close ever since. It is only recently that experiments with various strains in the UK, Australia, Canada and Austria have shown that low or zero THC industrial grade hemp plants can produce a variety of exquisite fragrances from the whole hemp plant. As the price of this product drops to realistic levels we are now seeing the implementation of this oil into cosmetic and food products.

One acre of land, in one season, can produce a hemp crop with four times the quantity of pulp than that harvested from an acre of trees, or produce organic textiles needing no chemicals. Compare this to cotton, which uses a tremendous 30-50 percent of the world's pesticides, though it is only three percent of the world's crops. Further, hemp yields two tons of human food seed per acre, containing a perfect nutritional balance of omega-3 and omega-6 EFA's and 24 percent highly digestible protein (unlike soya that contains less complete protein). All this, harvested from the same plant that is used for plastics as well.

HEMP AS A FUEL

It is known that Henry Ford's first vehicle was made partly from hemp fibres. Ford stated to a *New York Times* reporter in 1925 that:

> The fuel of the future is going to come from fruit like that sumach out by the road, or from apples, weeds, sawdust- almost anything,...There is fuel in every bit of vegetable matter that can be fermented. There's enough alcohol in one year's yield of an acre of potatoes to drive the machinery necessary to cultivate the fields for one hundred years.

Ford constructed a car out of resin stiffened fibres that are now being rediscovered and improved upon in the high-tech twenty-first century biocomposite universities, such as the one in North Wales, UK. Ford knew the power hemp had in supplying the bodies and fuels of mass transportation vehicles. Would our automobiles be made from hemp today if Ford knew what yields and processing facilities would be available for a season of hemp growing?

Due more to necessity than choice, we once again consider alternative fuels as a potential solution to some of the air pollution problems facing our densely populated cities. It is well documented, though often misrepresented in the mass media, that a fuel called 'biodiesel' can be made from vegetable oils, such as hemp. This biodiesel has the potential to substitute much of the diesel used today in standard, public and heavy goods vehicles with little adaptation of existing engines.

Biodiesel has numerous benefits including reduced pollution, reduced engine wear and improved ignition. Biodiesel is currently produced and sold throughout Europe, North America and Australasia, though only to a few niche markets. To alleviate concerns of performance it should be noted that many modern racing cars use methanol, a type of bio-diesel, as their primary fuel. Increasing anxiety over pollution and recent world interest in hemp growing may soon lead to the introduction of biodiesels to the mass market. This is potentially one of the largest markets for hemp in the long-term and so worth looking at in further detail now.

Rudolf Diesel was the German engineer responsible for designing the engine to run on coal dust, petroleum and vegetable oil. Diesel himself

Henry Ford once asked "Why use up the forests, that were centuries in the making, and the mines, which required ages to lay down if we can get the equivalent of forests and mineral products in the annual growth of fields?"

Hemp	Petroleum
as a source of fuel	as a source of fuel
Ecologically sustainable	Non-sustainable
Cheap	Expensive
Clean	Dirty

147

demonstrated his engine running on a biodiesel made from peanut oil at the Paris Exposition in 1900. Vegetable oils were again used during WWII, as was hemp for ropes and clothes. There is an interesting story that is said to explain the true demise of the hemp industry and the reason has only recently been rediscovered.

The appearance of Diesel's new invention with George Schlichten's hemp decorticating machine (a machine that stood to revolutionise the paper making industry) and Ford's hemp body car that could be run on hemp fuel took the curiosity of an interesting circle of friends that included then Secretary of the Treasury Andrew Mellon (Du Pont's major financial backer) and William Randolph Hearst, made famous for mounting the famous media campaign against hemp. Why? Maybe it was something to do with Du Pont and Hearst having heavily invested in timber and petroleum resources. Hemp was certainly a threat to their empire. It was well known that petroleum vehicles emitted noxious fumes. Diesel was proud of his vegetable oil fuelled engine; in 1913 Diesel died in mysterious unsolved circumstances during an overnight Channel crossing. We can only wonder as to where Diesel would have seen his engine being used - would he have changed from his environmentally friendly vegetable oil fuels to petroleum based diesel? Within a short, but highly effective three month campaign, hemp was seen as a dangerous drug and the hemp industry was practically outlawed throughout the Western world. We can only wonder as to what part hemp would play now in today's society had research and development into the industrial uses of the crop continued throughout the twentieth century.

The Basics of a Diesel Engine

Diesel engines are compression ignition engines. The fuel is ignited inside their cylinders. In gasoline engines the volatile mixture of fuel and air is ignited by a high voltage spark from the spark plugs and the resulting combustion creates the force on the pistons which in turn drives the engine. A diesel engine ignition is achieved through the raising of temperature in proportion to compression. The temperature in the cylinders is raised using the system of glow plugs. Then the upward motion of the pistons compresses the mixture of fuel and air to the point at which it ignites. The tendency of diesel fuel to self-ignite under compression is known as its cetane rating.

It was in 1992 that I met Dylan Maxwell, an ingenious character who was mad about hemp. I learnt much from him, but possibly the most unsuspected lesson for me was the use of hemp oil as a biofuel. He ran his car on recycled chip fat and hemp oil. Nearly a decade later his car still runs well. Today car kits are sold that convert your regular vehicle into a 'Grease Car' that will run on everything from hemp oil to old 'useless' cooking oil. Today we know we can use pure oils, ethanol or petroleum or various proportional mixes of each ingredient as alternatives to more polluting options.

Adding just a percentage of biodiesel to regular diesel results in improving the cetane rating of the mixture, leading to improved ignition, smoother operation by improved lubricity of fuel and reduced pollution, especially particulate exhaust emissions. Biodiesel itself is non-toxic and fully biodegradable.

So, what exactly is biodiesel? Biodiesel is a renewable diesel fuel substitute that can be made by chemically combining any natural oil or fat with an alcohol such as methanol or ethanol. Methanol has been the most commonly used alcohol in the commercial production of biodiesel. In Europe, biodiesel is widely available in both its neat form (100 percent biodiesel, also known as B100) and in blends with petroleum diesel. Most European biodiesel is made from rape-seed oil. In the US, initial interest in producing and using biodiesel has focused on the use of soybean oil as the primary feedstock, mainly because the country is the world's largest producer of soybean oil.

Biodiesel is the name for a variety of ester based oxygenated fuels made from vegetable oils and fats such as hemp. The biodiesel production essentially consists of a chemical reaction known as transesterfication. This involves the splitting of the vegetable oil into glycerine and fatty acids. The fatty acids are then combined with an alcohol to produce esters. The oil is reacted with methanol in the presence of a catalyst to form methyl esters (the fuel) and glycerine (the by-product). The removal of glycerine from the oil, at about 20 percent, is essential and can be used as 40 weight oil (a lubricant), to make industrial explosives, preservatives and sweeteners for the food industry, or, most commonly, as a vegetable soap.

Pure hemp oil can be used in regular diesel engines, but not as successfully as biodiesel (made from processed hemp oil). Mixing ethanol with 15 percent gasoline creates a fuel less volatile than gasoline. Mixes often vary from 20-80 percent biodiesel. There is another option, that of modifying the engine, and this has been done in the form of the Elsbett engine. Developed in Germany, this engine needs to be mass produced to make it economically viable. There are few companies that can take such an engine from this stage to mass production, and none of these companies have an interest in making this happen, yet.

Comparison of Fuels			
	Compressed Natural Gas	Ethanol	Liquefied Petroleum Gas	Methanol
Chemical Structure	CH_4	CH_3CH_2OH	C_3H_8	CH_3OH
Energy content per gallon (Btu)	29,000	80,460	84,000	65,350
Product of :	underground finite reserves	hemp or other grains and agricultural waste	petroleum refining or natural gas processing	natural gas coal or woody biomass

WHY USE (HEMP) BIODIESEL?

- Biodiesel can be produced from organic, annual and sustainable local crops such as hemp where petroleum diesel fuel is a finite resource that is controlled by unstable economics. Wars are rife in unstable economic climates.
- The total use of biodiesel produces approximately 35-50 percent less carbon monoxide emissions, 80 percent reduction in carbon dioxide emissions and almost 100 percent less sulphur dioxide (major cause of acid rain).
- Tailpipe emissions for urban buses that run on biodiesel are nearly 70 percent lower for some particulates.
- Overall ozone deforming potential of biodiesel is less (approximately 50 percent) than regular diesel fuel.
- Combustion of biodiesel alone produces a substantial reduction (90 percent+) in total unburned hydrocarbons (major factor in smog and ozone), and a 75- 90 percent reduction in aromatic hydrocarbons.
- Biodiesel is 11 percent oxygen by weight and contains no sulphur.
- Diesel engine life is increased due to biodiesel being more lubricating than petroleum diesel fuel.
- Biodiesel is safe to handle and transport.
- According to the Canadian Renewable Fuels Association a mix of 85 percent ethanol and 15 percent gasoline could reduce the net emissions of greenhouse gases by as much as 37 percent. Such fuel is available throughout Canada today, and availability will grow with demand.
- Biodiesel has been used in Europe for over twenty-five years.
- Biodiesel biodegrades approximately four times faster than petroleum diesel, is as biodegradable as sugar, less irritating to the skin than a four percent soap and water solution, ten times less toxic than table salt and has a high flashpoint of 300°F compared to 125°F for petroleum diesel.
- An increase in the biodiesel consumption would cause an improvement in world trade balance and reduction in health costs due to improved air quality.
- There is an annual market for 100 billion gallons of biodiesel per year in the US alone according to a 1996 USDA economic study. That is a lot of land for hemp farming.
- One US study has shown that the implementation of a biodiesel system into a small metropolitan area such as Missouri with 100 million gallons of biodiesel production, could generate approximately $8.34million increase in personal income and over 6,000 additional temporary or permanent jobs in the region.
- Biodiesel offers the potential to shift spending from foreign imports to domestically produced energy crops, reducing reliance on any unfriendly countries who wish to trade arms for energy.
- Car emission studies carried out by the Department of Agricultural Engineering, University of Idaho in 1994 have shown that 100 percent ester compared with diesel control fuel shows a 53 percent reduction in carbon monoxide.

In the chart you will see a figure of 32 million kilocalories used to produce a 1.5 ton car. This figure was derived from Stephen Barry et al. from the Chemistry Department of the University of Chicago in 1972. Thermodynamic calculations proved that the necessary quantity required was only 6 million kilocalories. The 26 million kilocalories of excess energy (80 percent of total consumption) are used only to save time. This is an example of an energy intensive industry that requires increased energy to increase production, lower prices, sell more cars and gain more profits. However, this is not sustainable.

The food industry is another interesting example. Energy analysis has shown that food production represents about 15 percent of the total energy budget of the US. This energy is used in farm operations, processing industries, transportation, markets, stores, home refrigeration, freezers, kitchens, stoves and ovens. In 1973 Americans used six times more energy to feed themselves than was necessary for human metabolism. The rate of increase in energy consumption is higher than the population growth and is posing serious considerations for the future of the food industry that supports the populations of developed countries. The only way these methods of production have continued up until now is by means of fossil fuels, which, as we know, are truly finite.

Energy from the sun	3.7×10^{18} Kcal/day
Total world energy consumption	58×10^{15} Kcal/day
Food consumption in France	45×10^{12} Kcal/day
Energy needed to produce:	
aluminium (one ton)	50×10^{6} Kcal
paper (one ton)	10×10^{6} Kcal
steel (one ton)	$.5 \times 10^{6}$ Kcal
cement (one ton)	2.2×10^{6} Kcal
petroleum (one ton)	1.3×10^{6} Kcal
Energy needed to produce a small car	32×10^{6} Kcal
Energy needed to feed a man for 30 years	32×10^{6} Kcal
Energy needs of a man	2,500 Kcal/day
Energy from one litre of gasoline	10,000 Kcal/day
Energy cost for one passenger on a transatlantic flight	6×10 Kcal/day

There are numerous other examples that are fascinating, but on a more basic level, why do our so-called developed countries require from five to ten calories in fossil fuels to produce one food calory if in 'primitive' cultures an investment of one calory brings from five to fifty food calories in return? Whilst we sit comfortably at our full tables, let us remember that our fast, processed food industry is not working. The five main industries that are the largest consumers of energy are aluminium, paper, steel, concrete and petrochemicals. Together they consume 40 percent of all energy used in the industrial sector (US), yet they employ only 25 percent of the total labour force. Highway construction is one of the major consumers of energy due to its use of petroleum based asphalt and concrete, whereas railway system are shown to be much more efficient.

The reason I have gone into some detail about energy analysis is that we must start to look at all processes required to bring to us our food, clothing and housing. We must start to use products made simply from biodiverse crops, produced locally and using sustainable resources.

The principal ways of reducing consumption of fossil fuels and raw materials are: implementation of new energy sources such as nuclear energy, recycling, and conservation. At least 25 percent of the world's energy could be saved by observing a few basic rules of energy conservation and consumption.

HOME GROWN ENERGY

Talk is cheap, especially when by the mid-1980s, over one-hundred corn alcohol production plants had been built and over one billion gallons of ethanol were sold per year in the fuel market. Other home-grown fuels were used out of necessity in places such as the Philippines where a blend of 20 percent sugar cane ethanol was mixed with gasoline and kerosene to take advantage of locally sustainable energy crops. In European countries that have an absence of traditional energy resources, such as Hungary, there are 6.2 million hectares of agricultural land and 1.8 million hectares of forest land that can be used directly or indirectly for home-grown energy resources; add hemp to the equation and many countries can be self-sufficient in their energy requirements.

How are we helping to reduce the increasing carbon dioxide levels leading to the global warming and greenhouse effects we have been warned about for so long? More than a decade has passed and some serious effects are beginning to show; has anyone made the connection yet? Peak oil and natural gas consumptions are about to be met. We have known since 1970 that unless growth in world oil demand is sharply lower than generally projected, world oil production will begin its long-term decline very soon, within this decade. For a full report on the world oil crisis see the *Petroconsultants Report* written for oil industry insiders, cheap at $32,000 per copy.

With recent reductions in growing and harvesting costs and the availability of certain highly efficient strains, we can see promise for the hemp industry, despite early setbacks. With production biomass conversion plants situated near fields to reduce transportation costs (a major factor in energy crops), hemp could well fuel at least part of our future.

Biomass conversions can be met in two ways. Firstly, by biological processes that are essentially microbic digestion and fermentation. High moisture herbaceous plants, such as hemp, are most likely to be suitable for this form of biological digestion. Microbial fermentation can produce methane that can be converted to methanol - a potential fuel.

Secondly, by pyrolysis (application of high heat in the absence of air or reduced air), which converts organic materials such as hemp biomasss into usable fuels with up to 95 percent 'fuel-to-feed' ratios, making it the most efficient process for biomass conversion. This process can produce natural charcoal (same heating Btu value as coal), condensable organic liquids (pyrolytic fuel oils), non-condensable gasses, acetic acid, acetone and methanol. Pyrolysis has been used since the dawn of man. When some means is used to collect the smoke, the process is called wood distillation. The ancient Egyptians practised this method for use in their embalming industry. Pyrolysis was used to produce charcoal in the 1800s, supplying fuel for the industrial revolution until it was replaced by coal. The wood distillation industry finally faded in the 1930s due to the advent of the low priced petrochemical industry. Charcoal is still produced in this way in both the UK and US for activated carbon purification systems.

According to a report issued by the American Natural Resource Defense Council in 1997, the world energy industry produced 5.2 billion tons of coal, 26.4 billion barrels of petroleum and 81.7 trillion cubic feet of natural gas. When these carbon-based fuels were consumed, their combustion resulted in emissions of 6.2 billion tons of carbon into the atmosphere. Nearly 80 percent of that carbon came from fossil fuels produced by one-hundred-and-twenty-two companies. 22 percent of the world's carbon pollution comes from fuels produced by just twenty private companies, according to the report.

Hemp biodiesel is not the only potential solution to our energy crisis. Alternative technology vehicles that use new fuel cell technology are the base to much excitement in the electric vehicle field. Research and development over the last ten years or so has increased dramatically with the first hybrid electric vehicles now being available on the mass market. The future is still uncertain in this field, however it seems most likely that fuel cells will take hold due to their ability to promote energy diversification, offering a transitional state to renewable energy sources, an easy stepping-stone. The hemp revolution that was first introduced to us by those forward thinking pot-smoking hippies is now being taken up by the more serious high powered industries as we realise there is no better choice than hemp for a variety of other uses: Hemp is for Victory.

Photograph courtesy of
Juliette Atkinson
www.julietteatkinson.com

Hemp biodiesel is available in the USA today. In quantities it can be sold for less than $1.00/ gallon. Not bad for amateurs. This biodiesel is being used to run a hemp car around the US on an educational tour - showing the many other uses of hemp that many of us seem to forget.

Some Other Uses

- As a lubricating oil-the US Navy employed hemp oil in WWII.
- As a drying oil-hemp oil dries more slowly but more clearly than linseed oil. Some artists prefer it, as its clear finish does not yellow.
- As a pesticide-either planted around crops, or in dried or powdered form.
- The leaves of hemp can be used as livestock feed, as can the seeds or the cake left over from pressing the seeds.
- In rugs hemp makes an ideal lasting fibre.
- In cosmetics, The Body Shop is already selling $40 million a year of hemp based skin care products.
- Many building materials now incorporate hemp hurds.
- Animal bedding.
- Cat litter. Its absorbency makes it an ideal material.

PART THREE

METHODS

...Behold, I have given you every herb bearing seed,
which is upon the face of the earth...

Genesis 1:29

ML Upton

XIV. Botany

J.P. DARIEN

$\mathcal{H}$emp, *Cannabis sativa* L., is an annual, dicotyledonous herb of the Cannabinaceae family. It is dioecious, with the staminate, or pollen-bearing flowers, and the pistillate, or seed producing flowers born on separate plants;[1] the male flowers before the female. Earlier writers, *e.g.* Berti, Flint, Sinclair, and Durno, have reversed the sexes, assuming the seed bearing plants to be male: somewhat ironic was this assumption to prove, as hemp had been initially used by Camerorius in 1694 to reveal the sex of plants.[2] Monoecious individuals, with male and female on the same plant exist, but are of rare occurrence. Recent breeding efforts have produced monoeicious varieties, but there is a tendency to revert to the dioecious state in subsequent plantings.

ROOT

Marcandier's (1758) description is as follows: "The root of hemp produced by cultivation is six inches long, or there about, of a whitish colour, ligneous, undivided, and running to a point, having fibres only on two lines, diametrically opposite to one another, when it is not straitened for want of room; and thick in proportion to the stalk it bears."[3] Dr. Campbell (1845) records a male plant whose root descended 14 inches (35cm) perpendicularly;[4] Dr. Bócsa (1998) states: "As long as the roots are not obstructed by the water table or by a hard layer of soil, the root can reach a depth of 2-3 metres (6-10 feet)." Lateral development is noted by Dragla (1993), "if the soil conditions are unfavorable." [5]

STALK

Dewey (1913) notes: "It is a rigid, herbaceous stalk, attaining a height of 1 to 5 meters (3 to 16 feet), obtusely 4-cornered, more or less fluted or channelled, and with well-marked nodes at intervals of 10 to 50 centimetres (4 to 20 inches). When not crowded it has numerous

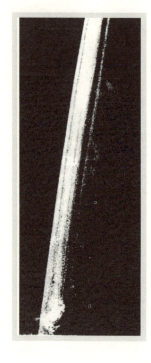

spreading branches, and the central stalk attains a thickness of 3 to 6 centimeters (1 to 2 inches), with a rough bark near the base. If crowded, as when sown broadcast for fiber, the stalks are without branches or foliage except at the top, and the smooth fluted stems are 6 to 20 millimeters ($1/4$ to $3/4$ inch) in diameter." [6] It can grow up to 25 feet, in warm and well-watered conditions.

Berti (ca. 1657) cites a stalk that was $3^{7}/_{8}$" (9.8cm) in diameter,[7] and Smith (1839) records stalks in France that were as thick as a man's wrist, over 3" (7.6cm).[8]

Dr. Bócsa recommends a thickness not to exceed 10 mm (0.4") and a length of at least 150 cm (5"); such measurements are classified as first grade.[9] Du Hamel in 1747 describes the stalk:

> The stalks of Hemp are hollow within, or only filled with a soft pith. This pith is surrounded by a tender, brittle, woody substance, which is called the reed: over this reed we find a thin bark or rind, composed of fibres extending in a parallel direction along the stalk: this bark adheres pretty strongly to the reed; and the longitudinal fibres of which it is composed, are joined together by a vesicular or cellular web; the whole being covered by a very thin membrane, which Botanists call the epidermis.[10]

Dewey further relates: "The hemp stalk is hollow, and in the best fiber-producing types the hollow space occupies at least one-half the diameter. The hollow space is widest, or the surrounding shell thinnest, about midway between the base and the top of the plant."[11] Commercially, this is the most important part of the plant, and much care is given both to its growth and knowledge of its structure.

LEAF

The leaf is palmate (hand shaped), with an odd number, (5-13) of serrated, lanceolate 'fingers'.   Leaves grow in pairs, opposite, along the stem, one per branch; the largest of the leaves attains a size slightly larger than the size of a man's hand. Near the top, branches grow singly, the attachment to the stem of the first such single branch is known as the 'GV node'.[12] Leaves are a rich green colour, and contain a high amount of the plant nutrients.

Hemp leaves are covered in 'hairs', much like mint. These are known as trichomes, (depicted in figure 8 of plate 5 on page 162)

FLOWER

Boyce describes both sexes of the cannabis flower as follows:

> In male hemp the flowers are panicled axillary and terminate. They have 5 nearly equal sepals, 5 drooping stamens, and oblong, tetragonal anthers disposed, ordinarily, in light green clusters. When mature, in some ten days to 2 weeks from time of blossoming, these turn yellow and, it not harvested, the plant dies and rapidly loses its nature.
>
> Female hemp has sessile axillary flowers, too small to be noticed excepting by close observation. The calyx is elongated and extended on but one side. The crowns are ovary bearing, with 2 styles and their stigmas.
>
> A small, round capsule with 2 valves contains one little grain of seed, at first white and then the covering green, turning to brown.[13]

FRUIT

As this is a dry, indihescent fruit, it is most commonly called the seed. It is technically a nut, or 'achene'. One seed is contained within each, surrounded by a pericarp. It ranges in size from 2.5 - 5 mm (0.08 - 0.16") in width, and from 2 - 3.5 mm (0.08 - 0.14")[14] in diameter.

A study of the seed's embryology was undertaken in 1862 by Guglielmo Gasparini in Naples; one of his plates is here on page 163 (plt. 6), along with the three plates from Robert Wissett's 1808 work, *A Treatise on Hemp*, which also contain a study of the seed.

CANNABIS SATIVA L.

Throughout this book it may be noted that all hemp, even that grown for medicinal purposes, is referred to as *Cannabis sativa*. It would only be fair to note that there are a number of other binomials by which hemp has been named, and still are by some authorities.

The first use of *Cannabis sativa* is by Dioscorides in ca. 70 AD; Linnaeus followed this in 1753. Other names have included: *C. afghanicus, C. americanus, C. chinensis, C. domestica, C. erratica, C. e. palvdosa, C. floritera, C. fœmina, C. gigantea, C. indica, C. macrosperma, C. ruderalis , C. silvestris* and *C. sterilis*. Of these, only *C. indica, C. ruderalis* and *C. afghanicus* are currently recognised; they are applied to the low growing, high THC producing types. Further, some taxonomists recognise subspecies, and thus apply trinomials, e.g., *C. sativa indica*.

A study undertaken in 1974 was published by Harvard University which concluded, "all strains inter-cross and produce fertile hybrids";[15] this and other studies set the tone among most researchers for recognising only one binomial.

VARIETIES

Breeding has been worked on by several scientists; Lyster Dewey in the US; Dr. Ivan Bócsa of Hungary; and Nikolai Vavilov of Russia, who noted that hemp has hundreds, if not thousands, of varieties.[16] Ecofibres of Australia has also committed vast resources to hemp husbandry, working on hemp for warmer climates. Below is a short list of the more well known cultivars.

Monoecious

Bialobrezeskie – Polish variety with a good seed yield

Bemiko – a cross of Fibrimmon 21 with Fibrimmon 24

Drepovskaya 6 – high fibre, good seed yield

Felina 34 – used for fibre and seed, maturing late September in France

Ferimon 12 – used for paper pulp in France

Fibrimmon 21 – German variety used in France in the 1950s

Futura 77 – late maturing French variety

Irene – recent (1994), late blooming, Romanian variety

Odrodomnaya Bernburger – provenance includes German 'Bernburger'

Secveini 1 – Dreprovskaya 4 x Fibrimmon, very good fibre, excellent seed yield, matures 105-110 days

Zulortanskaya – Russian late maturing variety

Dioecious

Arlington - Kymington x Chington, stalks slender and elastic

Chameleon - a new Eastern European fibre variety which has been used in genetic modification experiments. GM free planting of this was used in trials by BioRegional in 2003, results of which were made available on the internet.

Chington - developed in 1913 using Chinese seeds, noted for uniformity and quality of fibre

Ermakovkyan Mostiage - central Russian; early maturing variety

Ferramington - developed from northern Italian stock, maturing slightly earlier than other varieties

Fibrumoltu 151 - developed in 1965; Romanian

Fibriko - very good fibre content, strongest of all Hungarian varieties

Kompolti – oldest known variety in Europe, very high fibre content, negative period 110-115 days

Krasno-derskaya – used in the Caucuses

Kymington – Kentucky favourite, introduced in 1912

LKCSU – a variety used in Poland after WWII

Lovrin 110 – medium fibre content of good quality, maturing in 110-115 days

Smyrna – a preferred seed growing variety, ripening in 100-110 days, used in late nineteenth/early twentieth centuries

USO – large seed variety, favoured by Canadian seed growers

Finnola – a frost resistant variety, produced in Finland but used in warmer countries such as the UK for seed

Fig 1   Fig 5   Fig 2.

Pl÷1.

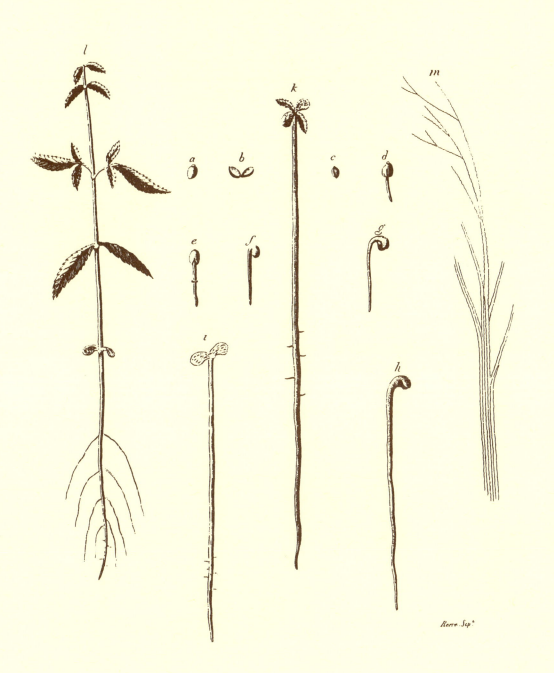

Recce.Scp.

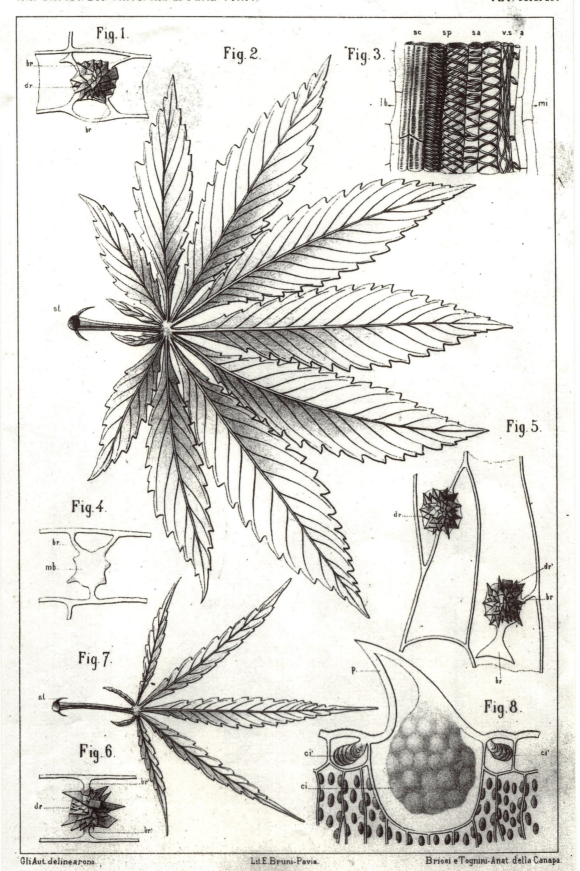

Fig. 1.
Fig. 2.
Fig. 3.
Fig. 4.
Fig. 5.
Fig. 6.
Fig. 7.
Fig. 8.

Pl—3

Pl. 2

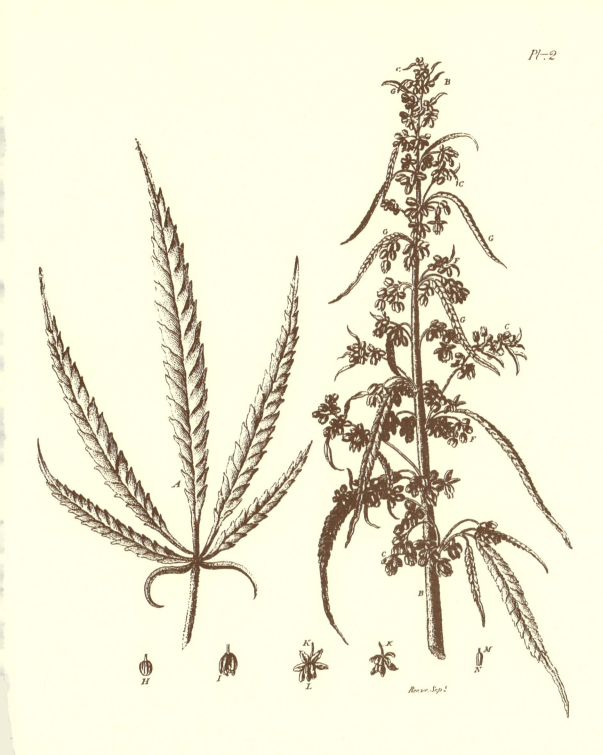

Ree.ve. Scp.

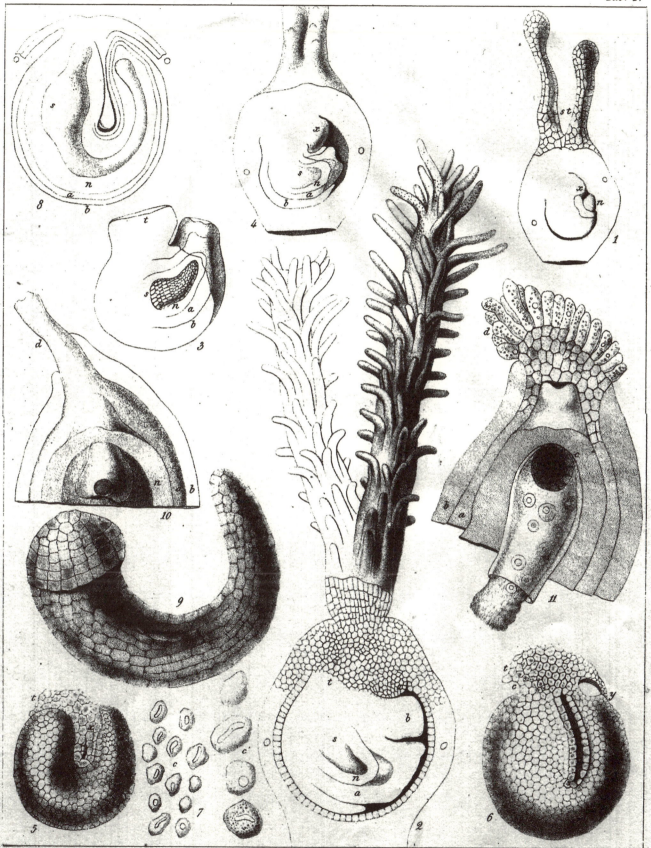

Polonio dis.

Morghen inc.

Formazione dell'uovicino nella canape

EXPLANATION OF PLATES:

Plt. 1: [**This and Plts. 2 & 3 from Wissett, 1804**] These on the foldout
a – the Hemp-seed
b – the Shell which encloses the Kernel
c – the Kernel
d – the Radicle coming forth from between the Lobes
e,f,g,h – the same in different stages of its growth
i – the seminal leaves
k – the Leaves of the Plant beginning to appear; and the lateral Roots beginning to shoot out
l – a Stalk of Hemp, in more advanced Stage of Growth
m – a small Piece of the bark of the Hemp-plant, macerated, dissected, and viewed through the Microscope

Plt. 2: (Male Hemp) foldout
A – represents a detached Leaf with its Stipules
B, – represents the Top of the Stem of a Male Hemp-Plant
C, F, G, - represents the cluster of Flowers, the Leaflets, and the Sipules, which grow on the Stalk
H – an unexpanded Flower-bud,
I – a Flower-bud, beginning to expand
K – full blown or expanded Flowers, exposing to view the Stamina, L
M, N – a stamen
N – the Anthera

Plt. 3: (upper Part of a Stalk of Female Hemp) foldout
D, E, O, P, Q, - the Clusters of Seed-buds, the Stipules, and the Leaves, H

Plt. 4: [**This and Plt. 5, from Briosi and Tognini, 1896**] p.161
Fig. 1. Male plant in flower, 1/10th natural size
Fig. 2. Female plant in flower, 1/10th natural size
Fig. 3. Tip of female plant, photographed when the fruits were almost ripe, 1/6th natural size.
Fig. 4. Portion corresponding to a rib of transverse section of a very young stem at an internode; rmi = pith radii between bands; lii = interior pseudo-phloem; t = tubes.
Fig. 5. Portion of transverse section in the hypocotyle axis of a completely developed plant; a,b,c,d,e = zones of greatest thickening; fls = secondary phloem fibres.

Plt. 5: p. 162
Fig. 1. Calcium oxalate druse surrounded by cellulose membrane and kept suspended in the middle of a cell of four cellulose strands. Mag. = 1135:1
Fig. 2. Very large female leaf of 11 segments. 1/2 natural size.
Fig. 3. Portion of longitudinal and radial section of a stem's xylem from a leaf with 7 segments. lb = phloem; mi = pith, vs = squashed tracheae. Mag. = 135:1
Fig. 4. Druse as in fig. 1, treated with hydrochloric acid; the crystals have dissolved, and only the membrane which wrapped them remains. Mag. = 1125:1

Fig. 5. Two more druses of Calcium oxalate. The upper is adhering to a transverse cell wall; the lower is held by two chords from adjacent walls. Mag. = 1125:1

Fig. 6. Another druse which has formed in one of the transverse walls of the cell. Mag. = 1125:1

Fig. 7. Medium sized male leaf of 7 segments. $^1/_2$ natural size.

Fig. 8. Portion of a radial section of upper epidermis of the edge of the leaf, which shows a large hair [p] with its cystolith [ci], and two collateral epidermis cells with two small cystoliths [ci]. Mag. = 545:1

Plt. 6: From Gasparini, 1862 p. 163

[n = nucleus, s = embryo sac, e = embryo, t = trophosperm, x = lateral protrusion of the trophosperm at the base of the egg, a = internal membrane superimposed on the nucleus, b = external membrane, o = ovary]

Fig 1. Normal egg, very young, as it begins to curve inside the ovary for .25mm, its nucleus protrudes naked, and is surrounded at the base by two winding circular ledges, the beginning of two membranes, which will remain open. The two styles also have collecting hairs protruding.

Fig. 2. Further developed carpel, almost 4mm in length, from the base to the tips of the stigma, with collecting hairs, and its ovary cut in half with its eggs, all the parts are distinctly visible; the trophosperm in continuation with the endocarp, and the protrusion, which later, lengthening, enters the concavity of the egg; the embryo sac inside the nucleus is enclosed in the internal membrane, and this in turn to the external membrane, both open.

Fig. 3. Egg further developed, .33mm in length, cut along its centre, revealing the embryo sac inside the nucleus enclosed in the second membranous envelope, this in turn in the exterior membrane.

Fig. 4. Another egg more developed; .25mm in length in its ovary, cut lengthwise; its nucleus enclosed in the second membrane, open at the tip, bulging over the edge of the external membrane. The embryo sac was formed from the cellular substance within the nucleus.

Fig 5. An ordinary whole egg, elongated, the same at .25mm., part of the sperm at the base of the egg.

Fig. 6. Another whole egg, somewhat more developed, 1mm. in length. The cells [c] of its base extend in those of the troposperm [t], the extremity of the micropyle projected into the trophosermic material, and has in relation to [y] the endostoma outside the exostoma. Some of the cells in the trophospermic production inside the concavity of the egg have been released.

Fig. 7. Some cells involved in the trophospermic production in figs. 5 & 6, inside the concavity of the egg, seen in isolation and with a magnification of 235x, when the embryo is now a round cellulosic mass. Nearly all contain a nucleus of various shapes and sizes.

Fig. 8. Egg only just larger that that in fig. 6, cut down the centre, leaving the embryo sac whole, to show the number, shape and position of the parts. At the tip of the embryo sac [s], a dark dot indicates the young, round and multi-cellular embryo within; the nucleus [n] underneath the two membranous envelopes, O-O epicarp and endocarp cut at that point.

Fig. 9. Embryo sac of a larger egg than those in figs. 3 & 4. It is still solid cellular tissue, later becoming membranous; the base of cells [c], different from the ramaning in shape, size and location, have separated themselves from the end of the nucleus to which they are adhered.

Fig. 10. Modification of the tip, which extends itself as an appendage [d], which inserts itself in the trophosperm. This has been observed numerous times, this fig. is taken from an egg more developed than in fig. 8, where the embryo was starting to become bilobate, and at the heart its bud was sprouting.

Fig. 11. Tip of the micropyle of the same egg as in fig. 8, cut along its centre and observed at a greater magnification; [e] growing at the internal tip of the embryo sac [s], full of lumpy substance [c]; the nucleus [n] has a depression or opening at the tip; endostomic cells [d] distinctly evident.

1. Dewey, Lyster H. "Hemp", pp. 285-346 in *USDA Yearbook* 1913. Washington, GPO, 1914
2. Martin, John H. and Warren H. Leonard. *Principles of Field Crop Rotation.* London, Collier-MacMillan, 1967. [2nd ed.] p. 940
3. Marcandier, M. *Traité du Chanvre.* Paris, 1758. p. 2
4. Campbell, Dr. Francis. *The Cultivation of Flax and Hemp.* Sydney, Statham & Forster, 1845. p. 87
5. Dragla, Peter. "Hemp Farming", pp. 14-15 in *Hemp Pages 1999 – 2000.* Forestville, (Ca.), 1998
6. Dewey
7. Berti, G.A. *La Coltivazione delle Canape.* N.p., ca. 1657
8. Smith, Rev. Daniel. *Natural History for Sunday Schools.* Vol. XII. NY, T. Mason & G. Lane, 1839. p. 46
9. Bócsa, Dr. Ivan and Michael Kraus. *The Cultivation of Hemp.* Sebastopol, (Ca.), Hemptech, 1998. p. 24
10. Du Hamel, as quoted in Wissett, Robert. *A Treatise on Hemp.* London, J. Harding, 1804. p. 187
11. Dewey
12. Bócsa and Karus. p. 32
13. Boyce, S.S. *Hemp.* NY, Orange, Judd Co., 1900. p. 13
14. Bócsa and Karus pp. 36-37
15. Schultes, R.E. and W.M. Klein. "Cannabis, an example of taxonomic neglect", pp. 337-367 in *Botanical Museum Leaflets* 23'(9). Harvard, 1974
16. Vavilov, Nikolai Ivan. *The Law of Homologous Series in the Inheritance of Variability,* USSR, 1951. p. 85

XV. Cultivation

KENYON GIBSON

*H*emp cultivation is of long established practice; only in recent times has it been discouraged or made illegal. Thus the literature concerning its culture is vast, and any discussion of the raising of hemp crops would not be complete without a look at the practices of centuries past, as well as the latest, most up-to-date methods. A recent work by Dr. Ivan Bócsa and Michael Karus, titled *The Cultivation of Hemp*, will give a very thorough view of this topic. As the interest in marijuana cultivation is quite vast, there have been a good number of books and articles written on the cultivation of *Cannabis sativa* from such a perspective; however, much of that material, geared towards producing a more bushy, leafy variety, will no doubt be of limited use to the industrial hemp farmer.

Many works on cannabis cultivation have been written over the years for the hemp farmer. In 1804 Robert Wissett of the East India Company wrote, or rather compiled, a treatise, in which he compared many of these works. In 1900 Samuel Boyce in the US wrote a book geared for the American farmer, which included many innovations, and in 1913 the US government published a lengthy article in the *USDA Yearbook* which gave more up-to-date methods, along with a general history of the plant. The following is written along the lines of Wissett's work, with each step of the cultivation process described by a number of authorities, sometimes in complete agreement, while at other times differing in their advice.

SOIL

"Most sorts of soil are or may be made fit with good manuring, to sow Hemp upon,"[1] claims the author of *England's Improvement* (1691); "Hemp requires a fat, deep, brown Soil", writes D. Flint of Scotland (1750),[2] recommending "Grounds lying upon the Coast, enriched with Sea-ware, and other Weeds from the Sea." Wissett quotes an example cited in the *Board of Trade* (1801) as follows: "Soonamooky – The Resident says, he has seen Ganja, Cannabis sativa, grow luxuriantly on a sandy soil, manured with dung from the stables. This happened on his own grounds: the horses had been there from February."[3]

A French writer (1747) opines: "the best situation for Hemp-ground is generally thought to be along the side of a stream, or of a ditch so full of water, that the water may constantly be nearly on a level with the surface, but without overflowing it. In some of the provinces of France such lands are called Courties or Courtils, and are highly esteemed by the cultivators of Hemp."[4] In Australia, Dr. Francis Campbell (1845), notes hemp growing on the sandy banks of a river and advises "...rich, dark, vegetable soils, and the deep mellow sandy loams."

Prints from:
La Coltivazione della Canape,
by **G.A.Berti, ca. 1657**

Writing in the US, Samuel Boyce (1900) notes:

> Flat lands, or bottoms, or alluvial, adapted to hold moisture, but which may
> be readily drained, are best for hemp, especially when lying along streams,
> and not much elevated above the surface of the water. A regular supply of
> moisture, too much rather than too little, and a soil well filled with the
> humus of decaying animal and vegetable matters, are most favorable. But

all soils can be made suitable for hemp, provided expense is not considered. If uplands are used, the plowing should be very deep, the earth made mellow and friable, and an abundance of humus incorporated to hold moisture in case of periods of drought where irrigation cannot be provided. Irrigated plateau lands, containing proper proportions of sand, mold and humus are good. In fact, bottomlands are better adapted to hemp than to most other crops, because hemp requires a larger amount of moisture, and in case of periods of drought, it can then send its long and strong taproot far down for it. With the addition of an abundance of moisture, any soil well adapted to a perfect growth of any crop can be made serviceable for hemp.[6]

Lyster Dewey, writing for the US Department of Agriculture (1913) observes:

In eastern Nebraska, hemp has grown on a deep clay-loam prairie soil underlain with lime rock. In some of the fields there are small areas of gumbo soil, but hemp does not grow well on these areas. In California, hemp is cultivated on the reclaimed lands of alluvial deposits in the lower valley of the Sacramento River. This is a deep soil made up of silt and sand and with a very large proportion of decaying vegetable matter. These rich, alluvial soils, which are never subject to drought, produce a heavier growth of hemp than the more shallow upland soils in Kentucky. In Indiana, crops of hemp have been grown in the Kankakee Valley on peaty soils overlaying marl or yellow clay containing an abundance of lime these lands have been drained by large, open ditches. There is such a large proportion of peat in the soil that it will burn for months if set on fire during the dry season, yet this soil contains so much lime that when the vegetation is cleared away Kentucky bluegrass comes in rather than sedges. It is an alkaline rather than an acid soil.

The large amount of peat gives these soils a loose, spongy texture, well adapted to hold moisture during dry seasons. Water remains in the ditches 6 to 10 feet below the surface nearly all summer, and the hemp crops have not been affected by the severe drought, which has injured other crops on the surrounding uplands. In south-eastern Pennsylvania, and in Indiana, Wisconsin, and Minnesota, the best crops, producing the largest yields of fiber of the best quality, have been grown on clay-loam upland soils. In some instances, however, the upland crops have suffered from drought.
Soils Suited To Hemp. Hemp requires for the best development of the plant, and also for the production of a large quantity and good quality of fiber, a rich, moist soul having good natural drainage, yet not subject to severe drought at any time during the growing season. A clay loam of rather loose texture and containing a plentiful supply of decaying vegetable matter or an alluvial deposit alkaline and not acid in reaction should be chosen for this crop.
Soils To Be Avoided. Hemp will not grow well on stiff, impervious, clay soils or on light sandy or gravelly soils. It will not grow well on soils that in their wild state are overgrown with either sedges or huckleberry bushes.

These plants usually indicate acid soils. It will make only a poor growth on soils with a hardpan near the surface or in fields worn out by long cultivation. Clay loams or heavier soils give heavier yields of strong but coarser fiber than are obtained on sandy loams and lighter soils."[7]

Dr. Ivan Bócsa of Hungary recommends:

Very rich black soils (mollisols) degraded black soils, brown rendzina soils, and brown steppe soils. These soils have a favourable water balance, good water permeability, and an excellent nutrient-accumulation potential. The "brown" soils and the transitions to black soils are also suitable, provided the soil is deep enough…The ideal soil acidity for hemp is between pH value of 5.8 and 6.0."[8]

SUCCESSIVE SOWING

The question of how many times a crop can be grown on the same land is asked often. Ultimately, none should monopolise. Hemp does have a reputation for long-term successive planting, but a more practical balance must be observed.

A number of eighteenth century British works even recommend the re-use of the same acreage for hemp as producing better quality in the hemp, such as Mills Husbandry (1792) and The Lincoln Report (1799). The former states: "…it is said, that the Hemp which grows on an established Hemp-ground is softer and more silky than that which is raised elsewhere," while the latter records: "The quality of the Hemp is best from old Hemp land: it is worth 2 shillings more per stone than from other lands." The Suffolk Report (1797) contains a description of "a piece at Hoxne which has been under this crop for seventy successive years."

Boyce gives an account of this practice in France: "M. Charpentier asserts that, contrary to most plants, hemp may be grown continually upon the same soil without any material deterioration."[9] Speaking of farming in Illinois, he goes on to say: "Hemp was then grown upon the same land for 31 years in succession without fertilizers beyond the return of the foliage and the ashes of the boon, hurds, burned as fuel to run the machinery."[10]

Dewey records similar observations: "The amount of plant food actually removed from the soil by hemp is so small as to demand little attention in considering soil exhaustion. The depletion of the humus is the most important factor, but even in this respect hemp is easier on the land than other crops except clover and alfalfa. The fact that hemp is often grown year after year on the same land for 10 to 20 years, with little or no application of fertilizer and very little diminution in yield, is evidence that it does not exhaust the soil."[11] One of the factors of hemp farming is that when only the fibres are taken away, allowing the leaves, root and parts of the stem to replenish the soil, most of the nutrients are returned.

The choice of companion crops is also a factor, as several authors note; Wissett: "in years when Hemp is pulled early, a few turnips are sown for a stubble crop"; Mills: "these thrive well after hemp"; and Brulles : "The most advantageous time to begin the culture of hemp on any land, is immediately after a crop of turnips."[12] Wissett quotes in his book Durno (ca. 1800) as follows:

> In the northern parts of Europe, as Poland, Prussia, and Russia, the most infallible mode of ascertaining when the soil is of a proper degree of strength, is by raising previous crops of other grain. On a vigorous soil, in a good state of cultivation, the usual rotation of crops is; Winter-wheat; 2nd. Winter-rye; 3rd. Barley; 4th. Oats; and then Hemp. Such a soil will bear a crop of Hemp without being manured: if manured after the first, it will give a second. But on a soil of less strength, a crop of Hemp is taken immediately after the winter crop of rye; the land being ploughed up once, either in the intervening autumn or spring, harrowed and manured in the spring, and then ploughed over a second time for sowing. To make the most of this poor soil, a winter crop of rye is sown immediately after the Hemp has been drawn, without any further manure.[13]

Boyce favours cow-peas, comparing the height of hemp grown after this as opposed to corn as being 2-4' (.6-1.2m) higher.[14] Dewey makes careful observation of what plants were used:

> In Kentucky, hemp is commonly grown year after year on the same land without rotation. It is the common practice in that State to sow hemp after bluegrass on land that has been in pasture for many years, or sometimes it is sown as the first crop on recently cleared timberland. It is then sown year after year until it ceases to be profitable or until conditions favour the introduction of other crops. On the prairie souls in eastern Nebraska and also on the peaty soils in northern Indiana, more uniform crops were obtained after the first year. On some of the farms in California hemp is grown in rotation with beans. Hemp is recommended to be grown in rotation with other farm crops on ordinary upland souls suited to its growth. In ordinary crop rotations it would take about the same place as oats. If retted on the same land, however, it would occupy the field during the entire growing season, so that it would be impossible to sow a field crop after hemp unless it was a crop of rye. The growing of rye after hemp has been recommended in order to prevent washing and to retain the soluble fertilising elements that might other wise be leached out during the winter. This recommendation, however, has not been put in practice sufficiently to demonstrate that it is of any real value. Hemp will grow well in a fertile soil after any crop, and it leaves the land in good condition for any succeeding crop. Hemp requires a plentiful supply of fertilizing elements, especially nitrogen, and it is therefore best to have it succeed clover, peas or grass sod. If it follows wheat, oats, or corn, these crops should be well fertilised with barnyard manure. The following crop rotations are suggested for hemp on fertile upland soils:

First Year	Second Year	Third Year	Fourth Year	Fifth Year
Hemp	Corn	Wheat	Clover	Grass and Pasture
Hemp	Sugar Beets, Potatoes, or Onions	Wheat	Clover	Grass and Pasture
Corn	Peas or Beans	Hemp	Barley or Oats	Clover

Hemp leaves the ground mellow and free from weeds and is therefore recommended to precede sugar beets, onions, celery, and similar crops, which require hand weeding. Beans grown before hemp and the vines returned to the land and plowed under have given good results in increased yield and improved quality of fiber on alluvial soils at Courtland, California. Clover is sometimes plowed under in Kentucky to enrich the land for hemp. It must be plowed under during the preceding fall, so as to become thoroughly rotted before the hemp is grown.[15]

PREPARATION

Dr. Bócsa advises: "It is wise to choose tillage methods that retain precipitation, incorporate the nutrients into the soil, sustain porosity, and keep a smooth surface."[16]

All writers encourage thorough preparation, with plowing several months previous and final ploughing somewhat before sowing. Du Hamel writes in his treatise:

The first and most considerable ploughing or stirring is given to the Hemp-ground in the months of December and January, and is called the winter ploughing or stirring. Some use for this purpose the common plough, laying the ground rough in furrows: others use the vineyard-hoe, likewise forming furrows, that the ground may be the better mellowed by the winter's frost. Some even dig it with the spade, which is certainly the best method, but more tedious and laborious; while, on the contrary, ploughing it is the most expeditious, but the least profitable. In the spring, the ground is thoroughly prepared for the receiving of the seed by two or three ploughings or stirrings; and a fortnight or three weeks should intervene between each of these ploughings, making them gradually slighter, and laying the ground smooth and even. In these spring-stirrings, as in the winter one, either the plough, hoe, or spade may be used. If after all these ploughings or stirrings, any lumps or clods of earth remain, they should be broken by the hand with mallets; for the whole Hemp-ground should be as level, and of as fine mould, as the beds of a garden.[17]

Comparative Demands for Plant-Food From: *Hemp,* by Samuel Boyce, 1900				
	Nitrogen	Potash Acid	Lime	Phosphoric Acid
Hemp Plant	1.74	.34	1.90	.15
Hemp Seed	2.61	.97	......	1.75

His preference for the use of the spade is borne out by the fineness of Italian hemp, for which the soil is prepared by spade. Of this method G. Berti (ca.1657) states: *'Questa è la più bella cultura'* (this is the finest method of cultivation).[18]

FERTILISATION

Generally, manure or nitrogen rich fertilisers do well for hemp, although some authorities state that an excess of this element produces weak stems. Du Hamel's account is as follows:

> All the manures that render the earth light are proper for Hemp; and accordingly the dung of horses, sheep, pigeons, and poultry, or the scouring of the ponds in villages, when it has had time to ripen, are preferable to cow-dung. Marle is not, to my knowledge, used for the manuring of Hemp-grounds. It is best to dung the Hemp-ground every year; and before the winter-ploughing, that the dung may have time to rot during that season, and that the spring-ploughings may the more thoroughly mix it with the earth. Pigeons'-dung is the only one which, in order to derive the greater advantage from it, is put in the ground during the spring-ploughings. It is to be feared, however, that, if the spring proves dry, the pigeons'-dung may burn the seed, which it would not do, if laid on during the winter: but in this case, a greater quantity of dung should be used, or less advantage must be expected from it.[19]

Sir Joseph Banks (1802) relates the following statement from his travels in Italy: *'Canape cresce dappertutto, ma la Canape à vendere ne in cielo, ne in terra, ma nel letame'.* (Hemp grows everywhere, but marketable hemp is not to be found without fertilisation, whether in heaven or on earth).[20] Charles Dodge of the US Department of Agriculture (1895) gives a record of Japanese fertilising techniques as follows:

> An application of 200 pounds of bone-meal in November has the effect to warm the soil and hasten germination where hemp is sown early, and to stimulate the hemp to a quick, early growth, before it comes to assimilate the coarser foods, and to give an increase of a foot to a foot and a-half in the growth Boyce makes detailed notes of this and the effects on growth. The hemp plant produces four to six tons of dry matter per acre, of which three to five tons is refuse, and if the machinery is run by water-power all of this refuse may be returned to the soil. If so done, it is spread as evenly as possible by a manure spreader, some two inches deep, before plowing. The result is to add to the humus in the soil, to improve its mechanical condition, and to hold moisture. Of itself this refuse, largely of woody matter, does not contain the fertilizing elements of the fibrous material in the bark; these come out in the stepping, and should be run upon the land. The results of some experiments now making show that where the soil contains a large amount of humus and decaying animal foods, furnishing an abundance of nitrogen, the hemp plant grows very much faster and

taller. If two crops a year is to be grown, a different manurial condition would be required than if the whole season were to be given to the production of one crop. With an abundance of nitrogen and moisture, the nitrogen dominates the growth, and the hemp stalk is far more hollow, the growth more rapid, and the distance between the leaf joints greater.[21]

An American account supports their conclusions:

The amount of fertilizing elements required to produce the plants for one hundred pounds of cotton lint, and of flax and hemp fibres, is given by the USDA Year Book in 1897 as follows:

Per 100 Pounds	Fiber	Nitrogen	Potash	Phosphoric Acid
Cotton	747	20.71	13.06	8.17
Flax	687	19.06	7.29	6.76
Hemp	597	6.27	10.13	3.32

This shows that hemp requires less than one-third of the nitrogen and less than one-half of the phosphoric acid that does cotton, which requires 41.94 pounds of fertilizers, flax 33.42 pounds, and hemp 19.72 lbs.

The amount of manures should be liberal, and be spread upon the ground as early in winter as possible, that the rains may soak the nutritive matter into the soil. If we wish to use poudrette or guano, these should be applied after the last plowing, only a short time before planting. These fertilisers produce a more immediate effect and insure a more rapid and uniform germinating of the seed.

The amount and composition of manures all produce their effects upon the character of the hemp plant... none are more important that the provision of a deep, mellow soul with all abundance of humus and moisture-holding manures, high in nitrogen, to insure a quick germination and rapid growth.[22]

This same author, who urges that steep-water be let run back on the land, as well as foliage waste and the ashes from the hurds be used as fuel, cites nitrogen as the most important element for a tall, rapid growth, and favours cotton seed as fertiliser:

The best manure is cottonseed, put into the ground in autumn, at the rate of 1,000 pounds per acre. The next is compost of cottonseed and farm manures of equal proportions, with an addition of 10 per cent of acid phosphate, applied according to the condition of the soil. The only other addition to the compost of 1,000 pounds cotton seed, 1,000 pounds barn manure and 200 pounds of acid phosphate, would be 250 pounds of sulphate of ammonia.[23]

Dewey further advises:

An abundant supply of plant food is required by hemp but most of it is merely borrowed during development and returned to the soil at the close of the season. The amounts of the principal fertilizing elements contained in mature crops of hemp, as compared with other crops, are shown in the accompanying table.

Crops	Nitrogen	Phosphoric Acid	Potassium
	Pounds	Pounds	Pounds
Hemp (yielding 1,000 pounds of clean fiber)	62.7	33.2	101.3
Corn (50 bushels and 1_ ton of stover)	74.0	11.5	35.5
Wheat (25 bushels of grain, 1_ ton of straw)	48.0	8.0	24.0
Oats (50 bushels of grain, 1_ ton of straw)	48.5	8.0	34.0
Sugar beets (20 tons of roots)	100.0	18.0	157.0
Cotton (yielding 400 pounds of lint)	29.2	22.5	35.3

The data in the table indicate that hemp requires for its best development a richer soil than any of the other crops mentioned except sugar beets. These other crops, except the stalks of corn and the tops of beets, are entirely removed from the land, thus taking away nearly all the plant food consumed in their growth. Only the fiber of hemp is taken away from the farm and this is mostly cellulose, composed of water and carbonic acid.

The relative proportions by weight of the different parts of the hemp plant, thoroughly air dried, are approximately as follows: Roots 10 per cent, stems 60 per cent, and leaves 30 per cent. The mineral ingredients of these different parts of the hemp plant are shown in the following table:

Ash ingredients of the leaves, stalks, and roots of the hemp plant, carbonic acid excluded, 100 parts dried material in each case.

Ingredients	Leaves	Stalks	Roots
Lime	4.992	0.949	0.713
Magnesia	.585	.194	.291
Potash	2.858		
Soda	.024	1.659	1.829
Phosphoric Acid	.947	.447	.531
Sulphuric Acid	.226	.040	.047
Chlorine	.017	.019	.014
Silica	10.224	3.343	3.502

The foliage, constituting nearly one-third of the weight of the entire plant and much richer in essential fertilizing elements than stalks, all returns to the field where the hemp grows. The roots also remain and, together with the stubble, they constitute more than 10 per cent of the total weight and contain approximately the same proportions of fertilizing elements as the stalks. The leaves and roots therefore return to the soil nearly two-thirds of the fertilizing elements used in building up the plant. After the hemp is harvested it is spread out on the same land for retting.

In this retting process nearly all of the soluble ingredients are washed out and returned to the soil. When broken in the field on small hand brakes, as is still the common practice in Kentucky, the hurds, or central woody portion of the stalk, together with most of the outer bark, are left in small piles and burned, returning the mineral ingredients to the soil. Where machine brakes are used the hurds may serve an excellent purpose as an absorbent in stockyards and pigpens, to be returned to the fields in barnyard manure.

The mineral ingredients permanently removed from the farm are thus reduced to the small proportions contained in the fiber. These proportions, calculated in pounds per acre and compared with the amounts removed by other crops, are shown in the following table:

Mineral ingredients removed from the soil by hemp, wheat, corn, and tobacco, calculated in pounds per acre.

Ingredients	Hemp Fiber: in 800 Pounds	Wheat: in 20 Bushels	Corn: in 50 Bushels	Tobacco: including Stalks: in 1,000 Pounds
Lime	7.872	1.63	0.22	68.00
Magnesia	1.128	2.43	3.61	8.67
Potash	.968	5.45	8.06	69.73
Soda	.096	.13	6.22	6.80
Phosphoric Acid	2.080	9.12	11.85	8.13
Sulphuric Acid	.232	.08	(2)	8.40
Chlorin	.016	.35	(2)	1.06
Silica	.736	.41	.71	5.86
Total Ash	13.128	19.60	30.67	176.65

The best single fertilizer for hemp is undoubtedly barnyard manure. It supplies the three important plant foods, nitrogen, potash, and phosphoric acid, and it also adds to the store of humus, which appears to be more necessary for hemp than for most other farm crops. If other fertilizers are used, it is well to apply barnyard manure also, but it should be applied to the preceding crop, or at the latest, in the fall before the hemp is sown. It must be well rotted and thoroughly mixed with the soil before the hemp seed is sown, so as to promote a uniform growth of the hemp stalks.

Uniformity in the size of the plants of other crops is of little consequence, but in hemp it is a matter of prime importance. An application of coarse manure in the spring, just before sowing, is likely to result in more injury than benefit. The amount that may be applied profitably will vary with different soils. There is little danger, however, of inducing too rank a growth of hemp on upland soils, provided the plants are uniform, for it must be borne in mind that stalk and not fruit is desired. On soils deficient in humus as the result of long cultivation, the increased growth of hemp may well repay for the application of 15 to 20 tons of barnyard manure per acre. It would be unwise to sow hemp on such soils until they had been heavily fertilised with barnyard manure.

Commercial fertilisers.- On worn-out soils, peaty soils, and possibly on some alluvial soils, commercial fertilisers may be used with profit in addition to barnyard manure. The primary effect to be desired from commercial fertilisers of hemp is a more rapid growth of the crop early in the season. This rapid early growth usually results in a greater yield and better quality of fiber. The results of a series of experiments conducted at the agricultural experiment station at Lexington, Ky., in 1889 led to the following conclusions:

1. That hemp can be raised successfully on worn bluegrass soils with the aid of commercial fertilizers.
2. That both potash and nitrogen are required to produce the best results.
3. That the effect was the same, whether muriate or sulphate was used to furnish potash.
4. That the effect was about the same, whether nitrate of soda or sulphate of ammonia was used to furnish nitrogen.
5. That a commercial fertilizer containing about 6 per cent of available phosphoric acid, 12 per cent of actual potash, and 4 per cent of nitrogen (mostly in the form of nitrate of soda or sulphate of ammonia) would be a good fertiliser for trial.

The increased yield and improved quality of the fiber on the fertilized plants compared with the yield from the check plants, not fertilized, in these experiments would warrant the application of nitrogen at the rate of 160 pounds of nitrate of soda or 120 pounds of sulphate of ammonia per acre, and potash at the rate of about 160 pounds of either sulphate or muriate of potash per acre.

On the rich alluvial soils reclaimed by dikes from the Sacramento River Courtland, Cal., Mr. John Heaney has found that an application of nitrate of soda at the rate of not more than 100 pounds per acre soon after sowing and again two weeks to a month later, or after the first application has been washed down by rains, will increase the yield and improve the quality of the fiber.[24]

CLIMATE

Temperature and humidity have a noticeable effect on hemp, as Du Hamel notes: "in hot, dry seasons, the fibres are harsh: on the contrary, they are supple, and sometimes tender, in cold, wet seasons."[25]

Boyce compares two plantings made in the US as follows:

> Within an abundance of moisture and special plant-food, hemp grows much more rapidly in climates of a high mean temperature. A crop of hemp planted in Mississippi, April 18, 1894, grew fifteen feet, and was ready to harvest for fiber in eighty days. Another crop planted upon the Sacramento River bottoms in California, upon similar and nearly equally favourable soils, was fourteen and a-half feet high and ready to harvest for fiber in 115 days, the only apparent difference in conditions being the mean temperature of May, June and July, which was nearly ten degrees higher in Mississippi than in California.[26]

Dewey records the following:

> Hemp requires a humid temperate climate, such as that throughout the greater part of the Mississippi Valley. The best fiber-producing types of hemp require about four months free from killing frosts for the production of fiber and about four and one-half months for the full maturity of the seeds.
>
> Hemp grows best where the temperature ranges between 60° and 80° F., but it will endure colder and warmer temperatures. Young seedlings and also mature plants will endure with little injury light frosts of short duration. Young hemp is less susceptible than oats in injury from frost, and fields of hemp ready for harvest have been uninjured by frosts, which ruined fields of corn all around them. Frosts are injurious to nearly mature plants cultivated for seed production.
>
> Hemp requires a plentiful supply of moisture throughout its growing season, and especially during the first six weeks. After it has become well rooted and the stalks are 20 to 30 inches high it will endure drier conditions, but a severe drought hastens its maturity and tends to dwarf its growth. It will endure heavy rains, or even a flood of short duration, on light, well-drained soils, but on heavy, impervious soils excessive rain, especially when the plants are young, will ruin the crop.
>
> In 1903, a large field of hemp on rich, sandy-loam soil of alluvial deposit, well supplied with humus, near Gridley, Cal., was flooded to a depth of 2 to 6 inches by high water in the Feather River. The hemp had germinated but a few days before and was only 1 to 3 inches high. The water remained on the land about three days. The hemp started slowly after the water receded, but in spite of the fact that there was no rain from this time, the last of March, until harvest, the last of August, it made a very satisfactory crop, 6 to 12 feet in height. The soil, of porous, spongy texture, remained moist below the dusty surface during the entire growing season.
>
> The total average rainfall during the four months of the hemp-growing season in Kentucky is 15.6 inches, as shown in the table on page 305, and this is distributed throughout the season. When there is an unusual drought in that region, as in 1913, the hemp is severely injured. It is not likely to succeed on upland soils in localities where corn leaves curl because of drought before the middle of August.

In 1912, and again in 1913, crops of hemp were cultivated under irrigation at Lerdo, Cal. The soil there is an alluvial sandy loam of rather firm texture, but with good natural drainage and not enough clay to form a crust on the surface after flooding with water. The land is plowed deeply, levelled, and made up into irrigation blocks with low borders over which drills and harvesting machinery may easily work. The seed is drilled in the direction of the fall, so that when flooded the water runs slowly down the drill furrows. Three irrigations are sufficient, provided the seed is sown early enough to get the benefit of the March rains. The fiber thus produced is strong and of good quality. [27]

Dr. Bócsa recommends a temperature range for optimal growth at between 19° and 25° C (66°-77°F). As to precipitation, he gives the figure of 500-700mm (20-28") of precipitation, with 250-300mm (10-14") as necessary during the vegetative period.[28] It is this stage that the demand for water is at its peak, and a hemp crop must have adequate rainfall or irrigation to produce the best quality; French author M. Marcandier (1758) exhorts: "This labour and attention in the person who cultivates Hemp, often turns out to his advantage, and is well rewarded."[29]

SOWING

Hemp is generally sown in the spring, with certain variations as to location. Berti, in considering a Mediterranean climate, gives the dates as March 20-25, *'poco piu, o poco meno, conforme corre la stagione'* (a little earlier, a little later, depending on the season).[30] Eighteenth century British authorities give a range of dates from March to May:

> Your ground being cultivated in autumn, will, by the winter frost, be ready to receive your seed by the latter end of March or the beginning of April. The moon being on the wane, or declining, is a fit season to sow your seed.
> - *England's Improvement*
> Hemp should never be sown sooner than the beginning of April.
> -*McDonald's Essay*
> The best time for sowing Hemp is between the 1st and 29th of May, according as the season is favourable. When it is sown, it should be carefully guarded against birds, till firmly rooted in the ground.
> - *Taylor's Instructions*
> It is sown about the middle or end of May.
> - *The Lincoln Report*
> The whole month of April is the proper season for sowing of Hemp.
> - *Complete English Farmer*
> It may be sown from the first week of April till near the end of May; but the sooner the better, both for the Hemp and the seed. - *A Treatise on Hemp*

Abbé Brulles (1790) cites a later date for France: "The season for sowing varies, according to the soil, weather, and convenience of the cultivator, extending from the 25th of March to the 15th of June."[31]

Durno notes: "In Russia, Prussia, Poland, and c. Flax and Hemp are generally sown at the same time …between the 15th of May and the 19th of June."[32] Dr. Campbell cites the date of 18th December for a planting in Australia, with the plants making their first appearance on Christmas morning.[33] Boyce recommends winter sowing in parts of the US: "South of lat. 35° hemp may be planted any month in the year. The growth will be slow in December and January above ground, but the top-root will be taking a firmer hold in the warmer earth below, and the crop will be a decided improvement over one sown in March and April."[34] He notes that in Florida, hemp and winter grains are best sown in November or December. Winter sowing is directed also by Pliny *(Nat. Hist., Lib. Xix., cap. 9).*

Much agreement exists as to the necessity of fresh seeds. Boyce states "...clean, bright, plump, glossy seed one year old, per acre, is best, while if two years old, or uncertain in character, it should be tested before sowing."[35]

Quality is also a consideration, and here one must consider the purpose of the crops. Thus a thin sowing is made for seed plants, while a thick sowing is made for fibre plants. This is especially important for the latter purpose, as plants that grow close together will not branch but near the tops, thus allowing the fibres to grow longer.

For seed, Boyce gives a figure of two quarts to the acre, or one bushel. For fibre, many advise 3 - 3½ bushels per acre.[36] Growers differ as to whether broadcast or drill sowing is best; some arguments are based on the machinery available at the time. As to depth of sowing, Boyce advises an even depth of 1"- 1½",[37] while Dewey writes: "Hemp seed should be sown as uniformly as possible all over the ground and covered as nearly as possible at a uniform depth of about three-fourths of an inch, or as deep as 2 inches in light soils."[38]

After germination hemp requires little care; the main concern is as already discussed, proper irrigation. Birds have been known to attack seedlings and mature crops, and there are occasional instances of insect pests and pathogens that have harmed hemp, which are discussed in the next chapter. Generally, hemp is a crop that requires less care than most, and is even used to eliminate weeds and other pests from fields; centuries of observations corroborate this:

> Weeds are smothered by the growth of the hemp plant. - Berti, ca. 1657
>
> Hemp does not need weeding. It is so swift a grower, and such a poison to all the weeds, that it over-runneth, choaketh, and destroyeth them. - Anon, 1691
>
> Hemp requires no weeding; and, indeed, the leaves and dust of it is of such a nature as to kill almost every weed. - McDonald, 18th century
>
> This plant is never overrun with weeds, but on the contrary, has the remarkable property of destroying their revelation. The cause of its producing this effect is attributed by some cultivators to a peculiar poisoning quality residing in its roots…It is said that this plant has likewise the peculiar property of destroying caterpillars and other insects which prey upon vegetables; it is therefore very usual, in those countries where hemp is much cultivated, for the peasants to secure their vegetable gardens from insects, by encircling the beds with a border of hemp, which in this

> The time of sowing is from the middle to the end of April; but it will bear being sown in all May. It is often found that the early-sown seed yields Hemp of the best quality.
> **Rev. Mr. Mills**

manner proves a most efficient barrier against such predators.
- Rev. Daniel Smith, 1839

Hemp...so completely covers the ground that not a weed can grow against it. - Peter Robert, 1890

It is said that plants of hemp even keep off insects from other plants planted close beside them. - G.F. Scott Elliot, 1907

If a field has become troublesome with weeds, no crop will eliminate them as quickly as that of hemp. - J. Woodhouse and P. Kilgour, 1919

Following the establishment of the plant stand, one of the most important ecological advantages of hemp soon becomes evident. Due to hemp's early growth and the density of the crop, strong weed suppression is virtually guaranteed. Even thistles and crouch grass are killed off by hemp.
- Dr. Ivan Bócsa and Michael Karus, 1998

HARVESTING

Reaping is in three to four months. Fibre hemp is ready before seed hemp, which will be only the female plant. In some instances, crops have been harvested for both, with the male plants pulled first; or, when monoecious varieties are sown, all the plants reaped together.

In the male, the signs of maturity are the yellowness of the leaves and the whiteness of the stalks,[39] the fading of the flowers, and the falling off of the *farina fœcundus*.[40] If the male plants are pulled first, it is important to let the pollen do its work; some leave a position of male plants to mature, or shake the male plants before cutting in to release their pollen; monoecious varieties excepted. The signs of maturity for the female are the same, with the addition of the seeds beginning to turn brown, and the capsules beginning to open.[41]

For fibre, it is best to take the male plants first; Boyce gives the following advice:

> When in full blossom the hemp is in best condition for fiber. The oil is still in the bark, while it has become sufficiently mature to stand the action of the chemical changes by the putrefactive fermentation in warm, soft water, and the harsh methods of crushing and breaking the hemp stalks to separate the wood from the fibrous material. If a soft fiber is desired, such as is highly susceptible of a subdivision into fine fibrillæ or laces and lawn tissues, the hemp may be harvested some ten days earlier, or at the first general appearance of the indications of bloom upon the male stalks. When delayed until the male stalk dies and seed begins to ripen, the fiber becomes drier, grows harder, the stalks begin to lose their natural form, and the fiber becomes 'dead'.[42]

The female also loses fibre quality if reaped too late, as Du Hamel notes:

> If the female Hemp is suffered to stand too long, the rind becomes too woods; the consequence of which is, that the fibres obtained from it are coarser and harder than those from the male. When the Hemp-growers

perceive that the seed is properly formed, they pull up the female Hemp, and arrange it in handfuls in the same manner as the male.[43]

Mills even recommends pulling before the seed is ripe,[44] whereas Du Hamel opines: "On the other hand, Hemp must not be pulled too green. When this is the practice, the fibres are, it is true, more supple, but the ropes made therefrom are not so lasting as when obtained from riper plants."[45]

An experiment in France that took place in 1759, where some hemp was pulled before it was ripe, produced fibre that was whiter in colour.[46] Boyce gives further observations about this balance:

In harvesting hemp, if we wish a very fine, high-priced fiber, the harvesting is done before the seed is ripe. If the hemp is left growing too long the male stalks languish, while the fiber upon the female, or seed-bearing stalks, becomes coarse and hard; while if the hemp is harvested too early, and before the male has blossomed, the fiber will be very fine, but too soft.[47]

Lastly, there is some discussion as to whether hemp ought to be cut, or pulled up by the roots. Modern machinery will cut, leaving roots intact, which may be the best method, as this leaves behind nutrients in the soil.

---

1. Anon. *England's Improvement*, London, 1691
2. Flint, D.A. *Rules and Directions for Raising Flax and Hemp in Scotland, after the Flanders and other Approved Methods*. Edinburgh, 1750. p. 20
3. Wissett, Robert. *A Treatise on Hemp*. London, J. Harding, 1808. p. 37
4. Du Humel (1747), as quoted in Wissett, p. 36
5. Campbell, Francis. *The Cultivation of Flax and Hemp*. Sydney, Statham & Forster, 1845. p. 81
6. Boyce, S.S. Hemp. NY, Orange Judd & Co., 1900. pp. 58-59
7. Dewey, Lyster H. 'Hemp', pp. 286-343 in the *USDA Yearbook* 1913. Washington, 1914, GPO
8. Bócsa, Dr. Ivan and Michael Karus. *The Cultivation of Hemp*. Sebastopol, CA, Hemptech, 1998
9. Boyce, p. 23
10. *Ib.*
11. Dewey
12. All as quoted in Wissett
13. Durno, in Wissett
14. Boyce, p. 62
15. Dewey
16. Bócsa and Karus, p. 87
17. Du Hamel, (1747) in Wissett, pp. 43-44
18. Berti, G.A. *Coltivazione della Canape*. Ca. 1657. p. 11
19. Du Hamel (1747) in Wissett, p. 44
20. Wissett, p. 33
21. Dodge, Charles. "Hemp Culture", pp. 215-222 in the *USDA Yearbook* 1895. Washington, GPO, 1896
22. Boyce, pp. 25-26
23. *Ib.*, p. 75
24. Dewey
25. Du Hamel, (1747), in Wissett, p. 191
26. Boyce, p. 59
27. Dewey
28. Bócsa and Karus, p. 75
29. Marcandier, M. *Traité du Chanvre*. Paris, 1758, p. 52
30. Berti, p. 12
31. Abbé Brulles, in Wissett, p. 79

32. Durno, in Wissett, p. 77
33. Campbell. p. 82
34. Boyce, p. 80
35. *Ib.*, p. 78
36. *Ib.*, p. 93
37. *Ib.*, p. 88
38. Dewey
39. Guenet, François. *Chanvre.* N.d., n.p.
40. Ince, Mehmed. *Kenevir.* N.d., n.p.
41. Guenet
42. Boyce, p. 88
43. Du Hamel, in Wissett, p. 112
44. Mills, in Wissett, p. 195
45. Du Hamel, in Wissett, p. 112
46. Mills, in Wissett, p. 195
47. Boyce, p. 28

XVI. On the Culture and Preparing the Hemp in Russia

JOHN QUINCY ADAMS

*I*n Russia, when the season is mild, the hemp seed is sown about the 1st June, old style. The richer the soil of the land employed for it, the better. A chetwirt of seed, (100 chetwirts are equal to 73 quarters, Winchester measure,) is sown on a piece of land of 80 fathoms (English feet) long and 60 fathoms broad.

The land is first ploughed and harrowed, and, about 200 single horse loads of dung being spread upon it, it is left for six days, when it is again ploughed, and the seed sown and harrowed the same day. In about four months the seed becomes ripe, and the hemp is then pulled up with the roots; if it be allowed to remain too long in the ground, it is apt to become harsh. It is bound into heads or bunches of four handfuls each; these are hung upon sticks placed horizontally, thus: x-0-0-0-0-0-x and allowed to remain so for two days. It is then made into cut or thrashed hemp as may be agreeable. The cut hemp is made by chopping off the heads containing the seed. These are put into the kiln, and, after remaining there for eighteen hours, the seed is beaten out.

If thrashed hemp is to be made, the heads or tops must not be cut off, but the bunches of hemp placed entire in the kiln; and, if the weather be warm, it will be sufficiently dry in three days, when the seed must be thrashed out of the heads. In either case, three days after the seed is separated from it, the hemp must be put to steep or rot, either in a stream or a pond, and that the hemp may be entirely immersed, it is put under wooden frames upon which stones are placed, or, where they are not to be had, earth is substituted, after the frames are covered with planks.

The clearer and purer the water, the better will be the color of the hemp. Where the water is warm, the better will be the color of the hemp. Where the water is warm, three weeks steeping will be sufficient; but, if cold, as in rivers, springs, &c. five weeks or longer may be necessary. At the expiration of this period, a head of the hemp is taken out and dried; if, on beating and cleaning it, the husk comes off, the hemp may then be taken out of the water; but, if the husk still adheres to it, it must be allowed to remain some time longer. This trial must be repeated from time to time, till the husk separates, when the hemp must be taken out of the water, and suspended to dry, as directed before, on its being taken off the ground.

The hemp is now made into the two sorts, distinguished by the names of Spring and Winter hemp, the former being dry, and rather of a withered appearance, the latter more moist, and of a fine brownish green color, containing more of the vegetable oil, and, therefore, the most apt to heat, though, if not shipped at St. Petersburg or Riga before September, there is not much risk of its heating any more on board the ships, especially on short voyages, as to England, and are the best fit for cables. If it be intended that the hemp should be early ready for the market, it is made into Winter hemp by the following process: On being taken out of the water, it is left suspended in the open air for about a fortnight, when it is put into the kiln for twenty-four hours, after which it is broken by means of a hand-mill, and the husk is then beaten off by striking the heads obliquely with iron and wooden instruments, of the shape of a large two-edged knife; lastly, to unravel it, it is drawn through a wooden comb, or card, with one row of wide wooden teeth, fixed perpendicularly.

The hemp is then laid up or suspended in sheds, and is fit to be sorted, bound into bundles, and loaded into the barks.

The hemp to be prepared as Spring hemp, is allowed to remain suspended and exposed to the weather the whole Winter, until it be dried by the sun in the Spring, when it is broken and cleaned in the same manner as the Winter hemp.

As the greatest part of the Summer elapses before it can be made fit for the market, none of this hemp reaches St. Petersburg until the following Spring, that is, two years after it was sown.

The hemp is sown in the same manner as linseed, rye, or wheat. Land of a sandy soil may also by employed for it, but it must be strongly manured; other wise it will be too short and a flat country should always be preferred.

One chetwirt of seed commonly yields 25 loads (upwards 36 pounds English) of hemp, and twelve chetwirts of hemp seed.

Transmitted by the Hon. J. Q. Adams, Minister at St. Petersburg, March, 1810.

XVII. Pests and Pathogens

KENYON GIBSON

Lyster Dewey in the 1913 *USDA Yearbook* stated that: "Hemp is remarkably free from diseases caused by Fungi."[1] While he is not far from the truth, there are some fungi, and other enemies as well, that must be taken into account. The earliest writing dedicated to examining hemp pathogens was penned by an American preacher, Lewis David von Schweinitz, in which he named and described a fungus, *Sphaeria cannabis,* in 1832. Leaf diseases were next examined in Europe, with *Ascochyta cannabis* described in 1846; in 1860 two insect pests were named - *Aphis cannabina* and *Psyche cannabinella.*

Harrison Garman wrote about the broomrapes (*Orobanche*) in 1890, those being some of the most serious pathogens to attack hemp. Many occasional papers have been published since, while a recent publication, *Hemp Diseases and Pests - Management and Biological Control,* by J.M. McPartland, R.C. Clarke and D.P. Watson (2000), presents a comprehensive, exhaustive look at the subject, listing organisms found even remotely harmful to hemp. These include species that are not known to naturally affect cannabis, but that have been deliberately innoculated onto hemp, and mentions many isolated examples, some gleaned from the pages of *Sinsemilla Tips.* Their work is an indispensable reference tool to the hemp farmer, and to its pages I refer those needing a complete text on hemp's pathogens.

Arranged, according to type of organism, are these natural enemies to hemp and remarks as to their prevention and cure.

VIRAL ORGANISMS

Alfalfa Mosaic Virus, Arabis Mosaic Virus, Cucumber Mosaic Virus, Hemp Mosaic Virus and Hemp Streak Virus. Most viruses are spread by insects, thus insect control is doubly beneficial. THC and other cannabis constituents inhibit most viruses, so hemp has built-in protection.

Hemp plant infected with Broom-rape. From: *The Broom-Rapes,* **Harrison Garman, 1890**

BACTERIA

Bacteria Blight, Bacteria Wilt, Crown Gall, Phytoplasmas, Striatura Ulcerosa, Wildfire and Wisconsin Leaf Spot, Xanthomonas Blight.

FUNGI

Hemp's most common type of pathogen; prevalent on many hosts, beneficially on grapes, where it is the cause of 'noble rot'. Its effect on hemp is not welcome; it can be a devastating pest. Symptoms include discolouration and cankers. The causes of this are among the most studied fungi, *Botrytis cinererea*, one of the first such species described in 1729. Controlling dampness is a key factor in prevention, as well as maintaining a proper balance in the levels of nitrogen, phosphorous and calcium.

Grey Mould is caused by several species - *B. cinerea, B. infestans, B. felisiana, B. vulgaris, Polyactis infestans.*

Hemp Canker is one of the most common pests, and cases of it have been reported recently. Water soaked lesions and cankers develop, affected plants may wilt; caused by *Sclerotinia sclerotiorum, S. libertiana, S. kauffmanniana, Whetzelinia sclerotiorum, Peziza sclerotiorum,* and *P. kauffmanniana*

Yellow Leaf Spot is manifested by small lesions from white to brown in colour attacking lower leaves, which become pockmarked and weakened. It is caused by *Septoria graminum, S. neocannabina, S. cannabina, S. cannabis;* this last has yellow spots, marbled with black. Alternating crops is recommended if a field is affected or humid.

Brown Leaf Spot and Stem Canker exists world-wide. Lower leaves develop spots, growth is stumped; caused by *Phyllosticta cannabis, Depazea cannabis, Ascochyta arcuata, A prasadii, A cannabina, Phoma exigua, P. glomerata, P. herbarum, P. piskorzii, P. nebulosa.*

Downy Mildew is another enemy of ubiquitous occurrence, having expanded its range in recent years. Once proposed to be used against marijuana crops, capable of causing "complete devastation."[2] Symptoms are yellow spots of irregular size and angular shape, contorted leaves; caused by *Pseudoperonospora cannabina* and *P. humuli.*

Fusarium Stem Canker generally appears several weeks into the growing season surface lesions, chlorosis, swelling and cankers are signs of this; caused by *Fusarium sulphureum, F. graminearum, F. lateritium, F. sambucinum, F. avenaceum, F. culmorum.*

Fusarium Wilt is another pathogen with a large-scale, destructive potential that was touted to eradicate cannabis. Arthur McCain, a US scientist, had the support of President Richard Nixon for such a scheme. McCain's claim was that it would "in several years spread throughout the country with devastating results."[3] While President Jimmy Carter showed more sense than to let this continue, interest resumed after he left office. The obsession with destroying hemp has led some to use genetic engineering to create even more harmful strains of wilt. Reckless as this obviously is, one might take into account the state of mind of the anti-cannabis people, and the belief of President Ronald Reagan that "trees caused pollution."[4] Symptoms start on lower leaves and include dark irregular spots, leaf chlorosis, curling, wilting and yellowing; caused by *Fusarium oxysporu* and *F. vasinfectum*.

Powdery Mildew, Charcoal Rot, Brown Blight and Texas Root Rot are also known to affect *Cannabis sativa* in one form or another.

NEMATODES

Nematodes are known to attack hemp. *Meloidogne haplii* has in recent field trials been introduced to hemp, but has not been observed to attack hemp under natural conditions. In studies with *M. chitwoodi,* it was shown that hemp caused a recession in this nematode; a finding of economic value, as this is a highly prevalent and damaging species to other crops. Of the nematodes that can infest hemp, Southern Root Knot Nematode is perhaps the most harmful, a fair weather fiend, occurring generally south of the Mason-Dixon line (39° latitude),[5] with symptoms including stunting, chlorosis, and midday wilting.

PARASITIC PLANTS

Dodder, a non-chlorophyll-producing relative of morning glory, is a pest that insinuates its roots into a host to draw nutrients. Of the five that have ever been reported to prey on hemp, *Cuscuta campestris* is the most serious. The other four, *C. europea, C. pentagona, C. epilinum,* and *C. suaveolens* are marginal problems, the last having only been mentioned once in 1914. All species of dodder twine around the stems. Their seeds may get mixed into hemp seeds.

Broom-rape was considered by Dewey as "...the only really serious enemy to hemp."[6] It may also be the most well studied - two investigations were made in Kentucky, published in 1890 and 1903,[7] with a previous *Monograph of the Orobanche* having appeared in 1824. It is a widespread family, attacking mainly Leguminosae, Compositae, Labiatae and Umbelliferae. Branched Broomrape (*Orobanche ramose*), Person's Broom-rape (*O. aegytiaca*) [possibly a subspecies of Branched Broom-rape] and Tobacco Broom-rape (*O. cernua*) are the species known to attack hemp.

Crop rotation, soil sterilisation and setting hemp seeds in water at 140°F (60°C) for ten minutes are recommended.[8] Boyce underscores soil conditions, stating:

> We have said that hemp can be raised for many years upon the same land, because the fertilizers applied easily restore in most part the elements which hemp takes from the soil. However, there usually comes a time when, from neglect to completely recuperate the conditions of the soil by rotation and the application of manures, the condition becomes inimical to a luxuriant growth of hemp. The soil has become exhausted, and a parasitic plant of the genus Orobanche, chokeweed or broom-rape, fastens upon the root of the hemp plant in such a manner and in such numbers as to sap its vitality.[9]

ARACHNIDS

Spider mites and the hemp russet mite are known to attack hemp. Damage may be hard to detect, and measures need to be taken at once, as mites can multiply rapidly. C.E. Faber, a marijuana grower in the US, notes that one female, at a constant room temperature, can give rise to more than 13,000,000 mites in one month.[10]

INSECTS

"Insects rarely attack the hemp; in fact, it is in its nature, peculiar odor and medicinal composition a preservation against the attacks of insects upon other plants growing near it."[11] While this observation, made by Boyce is true, there are several species of aphids which affect hemp, going for the undersides of leaves and turning them yellow. Certain wasps, lady beetles and other insects prey on aphids, although ants may guard aphids. Certain sprays, such as those used for roses, are effective, as are fungi and planting of aphid repellent plants such as *Mentha* spp. and *Allium sativa*.

Whiteflies like the undersides of leaves, and thorough examination can be the best prevention. Avoid planting near eggplant, sweet potato, tobacco or cotton, as they attract whitefly. Birds, paralytic wasps, lady beetles, and predators mites are effective natural controls.

The European Corn Borer (*Ostrinia nubilalis*) is one of the more serious pests, voracious and omnivorous. Larvae eat leaves, and bore holes; eggs are laid on the undersides of leaves. Control includes sanitation, crop rotation with red clover (*Trifolium pretense*), lady beetles, wasps, and some fungi. Other lepidoptera include: Hemp Ghost's Moth (*Endocylyta excrescens*), Hemp Dagger Moth (*Plataplecta consangui*), Death's Head Moth (*Acherontia atropos, Sphinx atropos*), and Cutworms, (*Agroits/Spodoptera* spp.). These last are mentioned by James Lane Allen (1900) as hemp's only enemy;[12] they are listed often as leaf eaters, but are also borers. In one instance termites have been recorded in Africa.

BIRDS

> The farmers endeavour to frighten the birds away with scarecrows, and cause their children to watch the Hemp-grounds. But these precautions are found to be insufficient; for this is a very laborious task when the Hemp-grounds are large, especially if the pigeons, which are so greedy after it, be hungry. I have seen strong men, and even dogs, so wearied out with fatigue, as to be forced to give up the task. Happily, this troublesome work does not last long; for when the Hemp has put forth a few leaves, it requires no further tending.[13]

This early nineteenth century account holds true today. Any graminivorous bird may be a culprit; whatever the species, one remedy exists that is time tested, natural, and enjoyable: falconry. Fight birds with birds, as US government ornithologist Dr. H.C. Merriam advised in

1886,[14] estimating that a single trained hawk would protect two-hundred acres. This is not only a time honoured and environmentally sound practice, of but one which is used of necessity in conjunction with modern technology at most large airports.

MAMMALS

On occasion deer have been known to forage in fields, forcing some growers to fence in their plots. The two-legged variety, however, can be a more serious pest, ravaging both industrial hemp and marijuana fields. As awareness of hemp takes root, people have learned that one is not the other, and industrial hemp growers have been left alone. Posting signs to the effect that hemp and *not* marijuana is being cultivated has proven to be of value in dealing with this kind of pest.

1. Dewey, Lyster H. "Hemp", pp. 286-343 in *USDA Yearbook*. 1913. Washington, GPO, 1914
2. O'Reilly, Daniel. *Common Sense*. Freedom Club Information Pamphlet, 2005
3. McPartland, J.M., R.C. Clarke and D.P. Watson. *Hemp Diseases and Pests*. Wallingford, CABI Publishing, 2000 p, 109
4. O'Reilly
5. Boyce, Samuel. *Hemp*. NY, Orange Judd Co., 1900
6. Dewey
7. Both offprints of the Kentucky Agricultural Experiment Station, authored by Harrison Garman
8. Guenet, François. *Chanvre*. N.d., n.p
9. Boyce, p. 28
10. Faber C.E "A Guide to Growing Cannabis under Fluorescense", pp. 1-29 in *Seven Rare Classics*. Berkeley, Ronin Publishing, 2000
11. Boyce, p. 28
12. Allen, James Lane. *The Increasing Purpose*. London, Macmillan, 1900. pp. 10-11. Allen may have been observing the Bertha Armyworm, a relative of the Cutworm.
13. Wissett, Robert. *A Treatise on Hemp*. London. J. Harding, 1808 [2nd ed.]
14. *Forest & Stream*, 21 October, 1886

XVIII. Processing

KENYON GIBSON

*A*fter hemp is harvested it is processed, usually for seed or fibre. The former requires but little further work, i.e., their removal and, if used for oil, their pressing. Fibre and ethanol production are both more involved, although ethanol production is relatively simple, and information on this process is easy to obtain. The latter purpose involves a number of steps, which have been undertaken by quite simple means. However, there is quite an art to producing fine fibres or even course fibres, used for rope. There is a spirit in these details, and much attention has been given to the perfection of these processes, especially the retting. It is this step that is the most crucial, and may yet need to be relearned and given careful observation. Usually, this is the first step; although some agriculturists have proposed letting the stalks dry first, a practice which has been largely rebutted, primarily because the drying of the gum only causes it to harden around the fibres. Drying was practised at times, not out of preference, but because the female hemp was harvested later, and it seemed easier to ret them all at once. Not only does this shortcut allow the male hemp to harden, but then there is also the disadvantage of having to separate the two in the retting tanks, as they are of different thickness.

Another step sometimes undertaken before retting is defoliation, but this is considered unnecessary: Marcandier notes a practice of striking dried bundles against a wall or tree, but claims that this "multiplies toil and labour."[1] In 1938 Minnesota farmers discovered this for themselves, as they tried to comply with new government regulations and remove all foliage from their crops.[2]

As there are different kinds of retting, it is necessary to enumerate and describe each type: dew-retting, snow-retting, water-retting, stem-retting, chemical-retting, and boiling. Of these, dew-retting may be the most common, as it is a matter of simply leaving the harvested stalks on the ground some time, turning occasionally. It is, without a doubt, inferior to water-retting; for which reason many nations chose to buy Russian water-retted hemp than to purchase their own dew-retted, even when the former was twice the price.

WATER-RETTING

The basic object of all retting processes is to separate the fibres from the stalk, but includes also the conditioning of the fibres, and is not just a purely mechanical exercise, but a matter of judgement and experience. One needs to take into account the size of the hemp, the water temperature, the air temperature, the flow of the water, and other factors. Wissett (1804) quotes the *Encyclopædia Britannica:* "The length of time 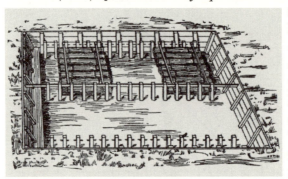 required for steeping Hemp is various; a complete knowledge of it can only be obtained by practice."[3] Generally the length of time involved is a function of temperature. The following is a letter from Mr. Fawkener, Secretary to the Lords of the Privy Council for the Affairs of Trade, to the Court of Directors of the East India Company in 1803.

> It appears certain, that the process of watering or retting Hemp in India has material influence upon the quality of its fibre. In a hot climate, where the whole time in which the process is performed does not amount to one-fourth of what is necessary in a cold one, it is evident, that it must be infinitely more difficult to ascertain, with accuracy and precision, the actual moment when the bark is sufficiently rotted, and the fibre still uninjured. In Europe, it is probable that the period of this process may be continued for some days too long, with less damage to the fibre than will happen in as many hours in India. I am therefore directed to call the attention of the Court of Directors to this point, and to recommend to them to give orders to the English Hemp-dressers, in order to ascertain the best mode of practice for retting in the different seasons in which the Hemp-harvest of India may be collected.[4]

Wissett cites the retting time for hemp in Bengal as being forty to fifty hours,[5] and quotes another source: "in very cold weather, 18-20 days may be necessary."[6] *Matthews' Textile Fibres* in 1938 advises a temperature of 30°-35°C (84°-93°F). The size of the stalks is also part of the equation, with the slenderest generally requiring most soaking.[7]

Wisset gives the advice of many as preferring stagnant water to running water.[8] Stagnant water works more quickly, and is said to produce softer fibres.[9] However, this results in discoloration, though easily bleached out. Du Hamel even advises letting hemp wait till the next year to ret, rather than retting in cold water; however, there arises to this the objection of letting the stalks harden.[10] Ultimately a slow running stream, or a retting pond with a controlled flow is considered ideal, on which Boyce elaborates:

For this a pool of a size to hold two to ten or twelve tons of hemp will be required, although these pools are usually four or five feet deep, ten to twelve feet long, and five to eight feet wide. The sheaves of hemp are packed with the butts alternately one way and the other, until the pit is full or all the hemp is used up. It is then weighted down by stones and the pit filled with water. The same water may be used over several times, until all the hemp is steeped. The method is wasteful, the steep-water not being utilised, while the stench at the retting season of many of these stagnant pits is something unbearable. Nor is the product of much greater value than by the more primitive method of spreading the hemp upon the ground.

The best results are obtained when hemp is grown upon a large scale and the hemp retted by being steeped in running water. Quite often the hemp is placed in crates holding a ton or more of stalks, and then weights of stones placed upon them to hold the hemp under water for five to eight days, according to the temperature of the water.

Part of the more modern practice is to dig pools five to seven feet deep, which will hold ten to twenty-five tons of hemp, and into which, if the pits are so situated, a small stream of water may be conducted and the overflow allowed to run out upon the land as a fertiliser. The illustration, Fig. 4, (depicted opposite) shows a pit make of upright posts and cross bars for holding down the hemp, and in Fig. 5 (depicted below) is seen a pit in which stones are used to weight and hold down the stalks when in place.[11]

A later practice is to place the hemp in the water for four to five days and then take it out and dry it, returning it again to the retting- or steeping-place for from four to six days more. This gives a better fibre, of a creamy white color, and a more evenly retted product. Some growers ret twice, which he claims ..."gives a more even result, with less injury to the fibre".[12] He also makes note of the practice of breaking the hemp first, which saves space and labour.[14]

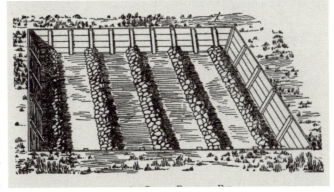

Boyce mentions the use of a crate[15] which was a French technique. The crate was lowered into the water by pulley;[16] this method not only saved time, but allowed more control and made for a more even and exact retting. What actually happens in the water is twofold; first, the loosening of the gum by action of the water; second, putrefaction. Boyce states: "...the effect of the fermentation is to generate an acid which corrodes and burns the fineness of the fibers."[17]

Dewey states that the solution of the gums is accomplished chiefly by certain bacteria. "If the retting process is allowed to go too far, other bacteria attack the fiber. The development of these different bacteria depends to a large extent upon the temperature. Processes have been devised for placing pure cultures of specific bacteria in the retting tanks and then keeping the temperature and air supply at the best for their development."[18] The French had achieved a certain expertise in this undertaking, making precise observation of the chemical reactions as follows: "...special fermenting agents transform pectic matter primarily into pectin and pectic acid, which, being gelatinous, adheres to the fibres and imparts a luster."[19] Bonnétat in 1907 names *Bacillus amylobacter* as an organism in this process;[20] Allen in 1926 specifies *Granulobacter pectinovorum*[21]; McPartland et al. in 2000 list these bacteria as *Clostridium acetobutylicum, C. butyricum, C. pectinovorum, C. pectinovorum var. parvum,* and *C. felsineum.*[22] Both aerobic and anaerobic bacteria are known to produce enzymes, which dissolve pectin around fibre.[23] Safarik in 1988 discusses the use of pectolytic enzymes, which can decrease the time involved and increase the quality of the fibres. The wastewater is then used to feed plankton, which are then fed to fish, thus enriching the environment and utilising 100 percent of the stalks.[24]

A 1923 study examines this process, using flax as a fibre, which, being similar to hemp, provides a close, if not perfect, parallel. It concluded as follows:

> The rapidity and order with which the different tissues in the flax stem are retted depends on the digestibility or solubility of the cementing substances that bind the tissues together, their accessibility, and the relative amounts of them present in the different tissues. The tissues of flax stems that lie in the cortex may be divided into the fiber bundles, the phloem parenchyma lying between the epidermis and the fiber bundles. Retting takes place first in the cambium layer where the pectin is quite soluble and where because of the very thin cell walls the layers of pectin or cementing substance are correspondingly thin.[24] It is true, however, that the cambium layer, located on the inside of the stem, is somewhat more accessible to the attack of the bacteria than the tissues lying to the outside in the cortex. The stems are partially protected from the outside by the waterproof nature of the cutin in the outer wall of the epidermis. The areas where the leaves drop off are waterproofed by the formation of leaf scars where suberin is deposited. At harvest time the waterproof covering on the outside of the stem is complete with the exception of the stomatal openings.

Flax Plant (Linum usitatissimum)

> Part of the stomata, as microscopic examination shows, are closed and made water-tight by the formation of cork cambium. The retting liquid and bacteria, however, can find their way through the epidermis, as the flax stems, which have been paraffined at both ends, will ret. The closing up of the ends, however, does distinctly retard retting, indicating that the bacteria enter more readily through the epidermis than at the stem ends. The variables in the retting process itself are the nature of the retting

Below and opposite page:
Hemp processing machinery
From:
Monthly Journal of Agriculture,
May, 1847

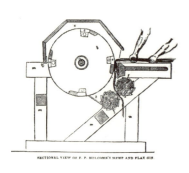

SECTIONAL VIEW OF F. F. HOLCOMB'S HEMP AND FLAX GIN

bacteria, the temperature of the water, the rate of water circulation, the water quality (whether hard or soft), and the duration of the ret. Of these factors the one that causes most trouble is the duration of the ret, or making the decision as to when retting is completed. A study of the process of disintegration of the flax stem as retting proceeded was undertaken in order to find out what changes in the flax stems were closely associated with the completion of retting.[25]

FLAX PLANT (Linum Usitatissimum).

JAPAN-RETTING

Another form of retting is steam-retting, practised in Japan. This is actually a combination of steaming, drying, wetting and fermenting as Dodge describes:

> In Japan hemp is ready for harvesting about one hundred and twenty days after sowing, or about the 20th of July. In harvesting, the plants are pulled; leaves and roots are cut off with a sickle, and the stems sorted into long, medium, and short lengths and bound in bundles. These bundles are steamed for a few minutes in a steaming bath specially constructed, and dried in a sunny situation for three days, when they are fit for keeping to be manipulated according to the condition of the weather, if favorable or unfavorable. If good, settled weather is anticipated, three bundles of the stems above mentioned are made into one bundle, exposed to the sun by turning upside down once a day for about three days, then dipped into water and exposed again to the sun for number of days, until they are completely dried, when they are kept in a dry place for future work. For preparing the best quality of hemp fibers, the drying process takes thirty days, and for second and third qualities, fifteen and twenty-five days, respectively, are required. For separating hemp fibers from the stalk, the bundles treated as above mentioned are immersed in water and moderately fermented by heaping them upon a thick bed of straw mats in a barn specially built for the purpose. The number of hours depend much upon the temperature at that time; in short, the fermentation requires great skill. When the stalks are fermented to a proper degree, the fibers are separated by hand and immersed in water, the outer skin is scraped off by hand tools specially constructed, and dried in well-ventilated places by hanging the fibers on bamboo, without exposing to the sun.[26]

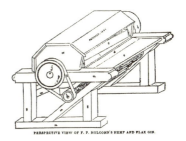

PERSPECTIVE VIEW OF F. F. HOLCOMB'S HEMP AND FLAX GIN.

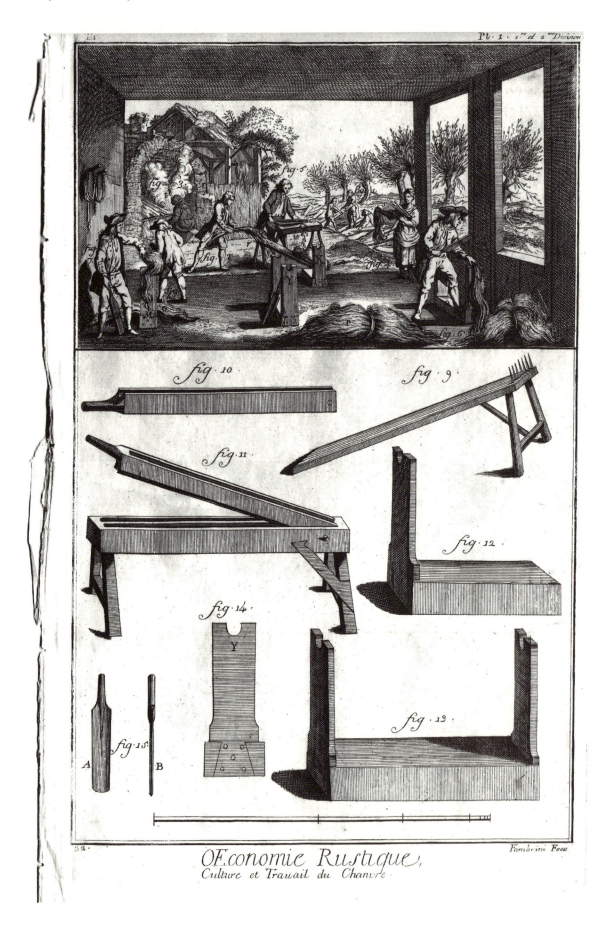

OEconomie Rustique,
Culture et Travail du Chanvre.

Dewey gives a slightly different account of this method:

> In Japan, where some of the best hemp fiber is produced, three methods of retting are employed- dew retting, water retting, and steaming, the last giving the best results. Bundles of hemp stalks are first immersed in water one or two days to become thoroughly wet. They are then secured vertically in a long conical box open at the bottom and top. The box thus filled with wet stalks is raised by means of a derrick and swung over a pile of heated stones on which water is dashed to produce steam. Steaming about three hours is sufficient. The fiber is then stripped off by hand and scraped, to remove the outer bark. The fiber thus prepared is very strong, but less flexible than that prepared by dew retting or water retting.[27]

SNOW-RETTING

Snow-retting is a variant of dew-retting, practiced mainly in Russia and Sweden and Livonia. Stalks are left on the ground till spring. Dewey recommends "alternate freezing and thawing or light snows melting."[28]

HOT WATER-RETTING

Retting in hot or boiling water has also been tried, as Du Hamel in the eighteenth century documents:

> I have also tried the boiling of Hemp in water, in hopes of bringing it speedily to the same condition as it is when taken from the usual place of steeping: but when, after having been boiled upwards of then hours, it was taken out of the water in order to be dried, it was not at all fit for peeling. It is true, that while it yet remained hot and wet, its bark separated easily from the reed; but then it peeled off like a ribbon; the cellular web, which connects the longitudinal fibres, and makes them adhere closely to each other, not being at all destroyed, so that they could not be separated, nor was it possible to divide them into fine threads.[29]

A later writer (ca. 1790) gives a more favourable account:

> On the continent a new process for steeping Hemp has been suggested by Mons. Breulles... the utility of which, he asserts, has been confirmed by many experiments. It consists in heating water in a vessel or vat to the temperature of 72 to 75 degrees of Reaumur, dissolving in it a quantity of green soap, in the same proportion to the Hemp as 1 to 48. The water employed for the purpose should be about forty times the weight of the Hemp: then throw the latter into the water so as to slot on the surface, covering the vessel and extinguishing the fire. Let the Hemp remain in this situation two hours, when it will be found to be sufficiently steeped. The advantages derived from this method are various, independent of the saving of time and expense.[30]

Dr. Campbell (1845) also positively records such a method:

> But the process first suggested, I believe by Mr. Lee, is so much superior to every other method, both in point of cheapness and cleanliness, that it ought justly to be universally adopted where steeping is at all thought requisite. It is extensively used on the continent of Europe with both flax and hemp; and is mainly this, the plants, whether green or dried, are steeped 3 or 4 hours in hot water, in which soft soap is dissolved, and then taken out and dried. This method has the advantage of saving time and labour, and is as effectual in separating the fibre from the woody matter as watering and grassing for weeks.[31]

He makes mention also of a process of macerating hemp, in "water, heated to one hundred and sixty degrees of Fahrenheit, it forms an entirely new staple of that invaluable fibre; it becomes silky - more delicate and beautiful than the finest flax; and that when the process is properly carried into execution, this new article will supersede cotton."[32]

This page, opposite page and page 203
From: *USDA Yearbook,* 1913

COLLECTING SEED AND RETTING STALKS.
Fig. 1.—Beating off seed from an entire shock of seed hemp. Fig. 2.—Homemade hemp seed-cleaning machine. Fig. 3.—Spreading fiber hemp for retting.

CUTTING HEMP.

Boiling of hemp is also used at a later stage, as Boyce (1900) recommends;

In France it is the practice to partly rot the hemp in the water, and after drying the stalks and breaking them to remove the hurds, boiling off the fiber, as is done with silk. One method of "boiling off" the fiber before spinning consists in first passing the partly water-retted hemp through a softening machine consisting of sixteen sets of fluted rollers, set in a circular manner and made to move with a forward and back, or reciprocal motion. The fiber is then macerated in a nearly boiling solution of carbonate of soda and soap, then washed, first in cold water and then in water containing a small amount of muriatic acid, and again steeped in water containing soda without soap, to remove the acid; it is then placed in a solution of one part of acetic acid and one part of water and afterward in water alone, and dried and again softened. The process is too long, but is well rewarded in producing an exceedingly fine, soft, valuable fiber, highly adapted to the manufacture of fine linen, lawns and laces.[33]

ACID AND OTHER FORMS OF CHEMICAL-RETTING

Chemicals were used in the retting process as early as 1766, as a paper by Andreas Kilian of Freiburg, Austria attests: "...hemp is first soaked in water for twenty-four hours, and then covered with a lye made from ashes. Next, it is heated, and then for several days subjected to the action of a number of other lyes. After that it is well washed, then thoroughly wrung or mangled, in order to remove all traces of moisture freed of its last humidity by means of a press."[34] A 1926 report goes into the technical aspects of heat-retting flax:

> When flax stems are sterilized in water at 115 degrees C much of the pectin in the cambium layer is dissolved, and the cortex is so well loosened from the wooden core that the loose-core test is of no value at all as a positive indicator that retting is completed. The pectin in the tissues of the cortex is less soluble than that in the cambium layer and is not much affected by the solvent action of the hot water. It is not entirely because of a difference in accessibility that the cortex is retted after the cambium layer, as at the exposed surfaces of cut stems where all tissues are equally exposed to the attack of the bacteria, retting is not materially hastened in the cortex.[35]

Boyce mentions use of acids and alkalines alternately: "Another process of retting consists in placing the hemp in tanks of convenient size, holding five to ten tons of stalks, which are filled with water first impregnated with acid, and then emptied and refilled with water containing alkaline preparations, or vice versa."[36] A 1912 record mentions the "use of dilate sulphuric acid or hydrochloric acid, which allow the completion of the process in a few days."[37]

Presently many processes are being studied, including steam explosion sound wave technology,[38] and enzyme-retting.[39]

KYANISING

There have been some attempts to use hemp for textiles and cordage without retting. (See chapter XIX on machinery). The US Navy tried repeatedly in the nineteenth century, but decided firmly against using un-retted hemp.[40] Leavitt (1862) advocates this process, which he describes as the use of chemical antiseptic substances, named after a Mr. J. Kyan of England.[41] Leavitt lists corrosive sublimate, arsenic, sulphate of iron, sulphate of copper, and chloride of zinc as having been employed for this purpose. Chloride of zinc, he notes, was used both by the British and by Americans, who used it on un-retted hemp cordage in Kentucky.[42] These assertions, however, are not borne out by any long-standing practice, and while he demonstrates some value to kyanising as a preserving process, un-retted hemp has never been accepted to any great degree.

He does, however, put forth a convincing example of un-retted, kyanised hemp surpasing Manilla hemp. George Schlicten in 1916, exhibited a decorticating machine that produced hemp fibres[43] which sold for a premium and brought him great acclaim, but left no lasting record of this achievement. Leavitt also mentions pyroligneous acid, which is a by-product of smoke, and present in hemp that has been dried over fire. This acid unites with the gluten of hemp, thus preserving it. As his example is of water-retted hemp, it does not in any way support an argument for omitting the step of retting. It does, however, note an advantage in smoking hemp for preservation.

BREAKING HEMP.

WASHING

After most forms of retting, washing is of a necessity, as Mills (1792) exhorts: "Some injudiciously neglect to wash their Hemp when it is taken out of the water; because, say they, the filth brought out of the water with it will afterwards fall off; but in the drying of the Hemp this filth gives it a bad colour, and the dust which arises therefrom is extremely prejudicial to the health of the workmen."[44]

Boyce cites washing as advantageous, but in a general way; it is the farmer's 'ancient injunction' that is not only more specific, but touches on an issue which needs to be addressed - the health of the worker.[45]

Certain fibres, perhaps most notably, cotton, give off dust that has been proven to be an occupational hazard: hemp is not exempt from this. There exists a suspicion that fungi and bacteria find their way into the lungs when handled, and thus "the dust, which is extremely prejudicial,"[46] must be dealt with, despite any extra cost. For this reason alone washing is not to be neglected; the matter of colour is also, however, of note and will not only give a more saleable product, but, more importantly, save on bleaching.

DRYING

After washing, the fibres are dried; which may be accomplished by heating, or laying on the open field (grassing). For heating over a fire, many accounts are given of kilns and ovens in which this is accomplished. It is a careful process, and the right material must be used in the fire. Quite often it was hemp hurds; Mills recommends coke as the very best fuel that can be used.[47]

SWEATING

Wisset records that in India drying was not always practised, which saved time and labour. A mention occurs of 'sweating' in various writings; perhaps the earliest is in a 1724 treatise printed by the Honourable Society for Improvement in the Knowledge of Agriculture. There it says: "…you ought to let it sweat for six weeks or two months, that it may work the more kindly." Wissett later records this step which, as practised in Russia, took place in this manner:

> They tie up the plants in bundles, about the size of a man's thigh at the knee. These bundles are placed upright, supported by a stake in the centre, and then are left one day to drain. The next day they are spread abroad to dry; after which they are made up in heaps, and covered over with straw or hawlin of any kind to make them sweat; and when they have sweated enough, they are laid again in small heaps, so that the air may dry them in the shade by blowing through them; after which they are most effectually dried by fire…and be it observed, that the Livonians say, it is in this operation of sweating that their good or bad quality of the Hemp depends.[48]

Quoting Frushard, he cites the use of sweating in curing of tobacco and preserves; Savary he also quotes, as recommending sweating as necessary.

BRAKING, SCUTCHING, HECKLING & SORTING

When dry, the next step is to remove the fibres. Peeling, or more often, braking, is the method. On occasion, this is done without drying, or even before retting, but usually after the stalks are retted and dry. Dewey gives the following description:

> Breaking [sic] is a process by means of which the inner, woody shell is broken in pieces and removed, leaving the clean, long, straight fiber. Strictly speaking, the breaking process merely breaks in pieces the woody portions, while their removal is a second operation properly called scutching. In Italy and in some other parts of Europe the stalks are broken by one machine, or device, and afterwards scutched by another.[49]

Marcandier (1758) recommends seeping hemp fibres after braking, with the possible addition of the ley of ashes in warm water, from one to four days, after which it is rinsed thoroughly. The fibres are then scraped clean. To soften hemp, it is beaten, as depicted by the illustration on p. 198.[50] However, beating it is more economically accomplished by more mechanical means. Heckling is a further step, which one description being quite to the point: "This last process is familiar to all who are interested in political matters. It consists of being drawn on hard points difficult to traverse and of a very fine and sharp character. Sometimes oil is used in this process, which may have an affect on the quality of the fibre."[51]

The fibres, when finally processed, must be sorted, a step that demands some skill. Dr. Campbell points out its importance, giving as example, "the Russian hemp industry, on which so many other countries depended; and could do so with continence, as this last step of sorting was there finely tuned."[52] At present, a grading system is most necessary; hopefully, with proper attention paid to the steps outlined in this and the previous chapter, there will again be fine grades of hemp available, with a system in place to designate origin and quality.

1. Marcandier, M. *Traité du Chanvre*. Paris, 1758. p. 55
2. Lupien, John C. *Unravelling an American Dilemma: The Demonization of Marihuana*. Malibu, Pepperdine Univesity thesis, 1995
3. *Encyclopædia Britannica*, as quoted in Wissett, Robert *A Treatise on Hemp*. London, J. Harding, 1808. p. 173
4. Mr. Fawkener, in Wissett. p. 180
5. Wissett. p. 194
6. *Ib.*
7. Mausberger, Herbert R. *Matthews' Textile Fibers*. NY, John Wiley & Sons, 1947, [5th ed.] p. 312
8. Wissett. p. 188-190
9. *Ib.*
10. Du Hamel (1747), in Wissett. p. 188
11. Boyce, S.S. *Hemp*. NY, Orange Judd Co., 1900. pp. 30-31
12. *Ib.*
16. Bonnétat, L. *Plantes Textiles*. Paris, Librarie Hachette & Cie, 1907. p. 16
17. Boyce, p.
18. Dewey, Lyster. "Hemp", pp. 286-343 in *USDA Yearbook*, 1913. Washington GPO, 1914

19. Bonnétat, p. 16
20. *Ib.*
21. Allen, Paul W. *The Retting of Flax and Hemp.* Portland, (Or.), The Caber Press, 1997 [repr. ed.] p. 6
22. McPartland, J.M., R.C. Clarke and D.P. Watson. *Hemp Diseases and Pests.* Wallingford, Oxon, CABI Press, 2000. p. 168
23. Bonnétat, p. 16
24. Safarik, P. "Application of Enzymes in Flax and Hemp Technology", pp. 483-491 in *Progress in Biotechology,* vol., 4, 1988
25. Allen
26. Dodge, Charles Richard. "Hemp Culture", pp. 215-222 in the *USDA Yearbook* 1895. Washington, GPO, 1896
27. Dewey
28. *Ib.*
29. Du Hamel (1747), in Wissett, p. 93
30. Wissett
31. Campbell, Francis. *The Cultivation of Flax and Hemp.* Sydney, Statham & Forster, 1845. p. 93
32. *Ib.*
33. Boyce, p. 96
34. Schaefer, Gustov. "Hemp", pp. 1779-1788 in *CIBA Review #49.* Basle, 1965
35. Allen
36. Boyce, p. 32
37. Sadtlor, Samuel P. *Industrial Organic Chemistry.* Philadelphia, Lippincott, 1912 [4th ed.]. p. 306
38. Much new research is being conducted. *The Journal of Industrial Hemp,* published biannually by the Haworth Press in Binghamton, NY, and the *Journal of Natural Fibers,* edited in Poznan, Poland, cover the latest developments in the industry.
39. Enzyme-retting is still under development in Australia and Canada. There are expectations of this producing fibre in twenty-four hours, which would facilitate the growth of the hemp textile industry.
40. *Ib.*, p. 223
41. Leavitt, Dr. O.S. *The Culture and Management of Flax and Hemp.* Portland, (Or.), Caber Press, 2001 [Reprint of 1865 ed.]
42. *Ib.*
43. Herer
44. Wissett, p. 184
45. Boyce
46. Wissett
47. *Ib.*
48. *Ib.*
49. Dewey
50. Marcandier, as quoted by Wissett, p. 244
51. Elliott, G.F. Scott. *The Romance of Plant Life.* London, Seeley & Co., 1907. p. 306
52. Campbell, p. 92

XIX. Tools and Machinery

KENYON GIBSON

*H*emp can be processed with the simplest of tools as its history shows. Invention, born of necessity, has advanced those implements from knives, mallets and spinning wheels to harvesting machines, decorticators and high-tech weaving factories. Harvests were at first sown and pulled by hand; later drills and blades were used, but well into the twentieth century, horses still harvested almost all hemp. Boyce writes of harvesting in the US:

> The hemp is cut close to the ground by a self-raking combined reaper and mowing machine, preferably the old style heavy, substantially made Champion, cutting four to four and one-half feet wide, rear cut No. 4, and using but two of the four rakes used in cutting grain ...With three heavy, quick-stepping mules or farm horses, and a driver who understands his work, an average of ten acres per day may be cut.[1]

Dewey was to later describe the process. with machines replacing the horse:

> The most satisfactory hemp-harvesting machines now in use are the self-rake reapers, made especially for this purpose... A machine is needed which will cut the stalks close to the ground, deliver them straight and not bruised or broken, with the butts even, and bound in bundles about 8 inches in diameter. A modified form of the upright corn binder, arranged to cut a swath about 4 feet wide, is suggested. Modified forms of grain binders have been tried, but with rather unsatisfactory results. Green hemp 8 to 14 feet high can not be handled successfully by grain binders; furthermore, the reel breaks or damages a large proportion of the hemp. The tough, fibrous stalks, some of which may be an inch in diameter, are more difficult to cut than grain and therefore require sharp knives with a high motion. A hemp-reaping machine is also needed that will cut the hemp and lay it down in an even swath, as grain is laid with a cradle. The butts should all be in one direction, and the swath should be far enough from the cut hemp so as not to be in the way at the next round.[2]

In the 1930s the John W. Deere Company of Illinois manufactured a dozen or more harvesting machines that were modified small grain binders, having extended their platforms further than normal to account for the height of the hemp.

Dr. Ivan Bócsa in 1998 mentions the use of a cutter made by this same outfit: the Kemper cutter, which cuts the plants into pieces 50-60 cm (20-24") long and ejects the stalks into the field.[3] This process of chopping is practised where fibre hemp is not the goal as in western Europe. For fibre hemp, a mower must be used; bar mowers equipped with rollers are employed to cut and partially decorticate stalks, in preparation for retting. Rotation mowers have proved impractical, as stalks get entangled in rotary parts.

Braking machines have been given much attention; the first American patent is for one invented by Thomas Jefferson, and by 1895 there were nearly three-hundred patents for braking machines in the US.[4]

An objective of inventors was to devise a machine that would process raw un-retted hemp. In 1819 an Italian published a record of his invention, *Istruzione pei Villici sulla Maniera di Prepare il Lino e la Canapa senza Macerazione*. He included detailed drawings (see left), which sparked interest and arguments as to the feasibility of processing un-retted hemp. Given the financial incentives to processs raw hemp, he was not the first in history to attempt such a feat, nor was he the last. In February 1847, an article appeared in the *Monthly Journal of Agriculture* claiming that, "the hemp trade has been brought to perfection." The author, James Anderson of Louisville, extolled a machine that braked, cleaned, and heckled un-rotted hemp.

Boyce writes further on this in 1900:

> Before the hemp stalks are retted they may be run through a hemp-breaking machine (see opposite), consisting of ten to twenty or more sets of cast-iron rollers fluted lengthwise, some six inches in diameter, and having fifteen or seventeen flutes to each roller for the first three sets, twenty-one or twenty-three for the next five sets, and twenty-seven to thirty-one for the rest. If but ten sets of rollers are used, it will be necessary to pass the hemp stalks in small handfuls twice through the machine; with twenty sets twice the amount can be broken. This machine, which can be built upon an oak frame of four by eight inch stuff, and the rollers, cast by any iron founder, can be set up by ordinary mechanics and run by common laborers under the direction of a superintendent...
>
> In a ranch of five hundred acres the use of two of these breaking machines would be required, and the capacity of unretted straw five tons a day each and of retted straw seven tons, requiring ten horse power and the service of four men to each machine. The hurds from the hemp furnish all the fuel, and are moved by endless carrier to such points as desired, and are fed under the boiler with a large door by a large hand scoop made of seven or eight tines two and one-half feet long.[5]

US Patent #1,308,375 was awarded in 1919 to George W. Schlichten.[6] His machine was called the Schlichten's Decorticator, a dream he realised after twenty years of research. Using $400,000 of his own money, he invented a machine which enabled the separation of the fibre from the tough stalks of hemp and other fibre crops. Other decorticators had been invented, but none came close to Schlichten's machine. Dried stalks were fed in one end, and the green leaf vegetation was stripped off to be used as cattle feed. The stalks were then crushed, breaking the hurds out of the machine, while the fibres were brushed and combed, the long fibres massaged so that they separated, leaving a sliver of the highest quality, ready for spinning. Other machines required the hemp to have an additional combing stage before the spinning stage. As the hemp did not have to be retted in the fields, the fibres were not discoloured, which meant that a superior paper stock could be produced. The hurds were also clean and in one place, thus they were also very economical as a raw material to be processed into paper.

These facts came to the notice of Edward W. Scripps, by way of Harry Timken, a leading machinist of his time, who called it "the greatest invention in the world."[7] Timken invited Schlichten to plant hemp on his ranch in Imperial Valley, California, with the idea that he would invest in Schlichten's company. By August 1917 he was processing this hemp, just as the US was entering WWI and paper costs were becoming very expensive. Schlichten was convinced that with the amount of hurds his machine would produce processing hemp stalk, he could make better paper and at half the cost of wood pulp.

On 3 August 1917, Schlichten met with Scripps' partner, Milton McRae and his chief assistant Edward Chase, to describe his machine and its benefits. They were impressed by his presentation and Chase was ordered to travel to Imperial Valley to investigate the full possibilities of the decorticator. He reported back to Scripps on 28 August fully satisfied with its potential. On 5 September, Timken wrote to Scripps. encouraging him to go forward with the project. However, Scripps suddenly lost interest, as he thought it easier to make up the increased paper costs from wood pulp by doubling the price of his newspapers. This understanding was made known to Chase and McRae who two weeks later suddenly reversed their opinion and persuaded Timken not to go ahead with the project.

Unknown to Schlicten, the minutes of this meeting had been passed on to Scripps. Schlicten had done a good job of creating a machine that used hurds in on unretted state, preserving their natural glues for the paper making process. In his pitch he pointed out the advantages of hemp to wood, and that cutting down the forest was a crime. These remarks, leaked to Scripps, were clearly not in line with the policies of the day; the decorticator was abandoned, and Schlicten slipped into obscurity. It is fitting to note that many of the decorticators 'invented' in the 1930s and 1940s are merely copies of his.[8]

Scutching is a process that has not been as readily designated to mechanical means as other steps have been. *Matthews' Textile Fibres* in 1947

At that time many inventions were proposed; most dramatically, the machine for extracting fibre designed by Benedict Roezl, an illustrious orchid hunter, who severed his left hand while demonstrating his apparatus in Cuba, which he replaced with an iron hook.

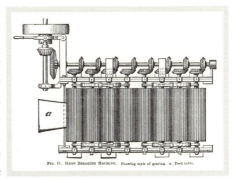

FIG. 11. HEMP BREAKING MACHINE. Showing style of gearing. a. Feed table.

stated that: "Power crimping roller machines and beating blades are still used to free the fiber from the woody core; but so far the industry still awaits a modern scutcher, especially one that will handle the long fibers obtained from the canes over 8 ft in height. The short canes can be scutched over a flax turbine machine."[9]

AN IMPROVED HEMP AND FIBER BREAKING MACHINE.

From:
Scientific American,
June, 1892

Final processing, into textiles, paper, oils, fuels, etc. all require their own devices, too numerous to describe in detail here. In many cases, machinery is being redeveloped to better utilise hemp; paper pulpers, fibre spinning machines and knitting mills are those most in need of fine tuning to be able to use hemp.

As the hemp industry grows, so must the related industries, as Dr. Bócsa stated in 1994, "technical innovation is needed, we need better machines for harvesting and for the entire processing chain."[10] Since then there has been much improvement, with companies such as Hempline of Canada designing new machinery, but there is still a long way to go. The hemp industry of the future has the challenge of inventing, or re-inventing, the wheels-within-wheels that are necessary to keep up with demand.

1. Boyce, Samuel. *Hemp*. NY, Orange Judd Co., 1900. p. 88
2. Dewey, Lyster L. "Hemp", pp. 286-343 in the *USDA Yearbook 1913*. Washington, GPO, 1914
3. Bócsa, Dr. Ivan and Michael Karus. *The Cultivation of Hemp*. Sebastopol (Ca.), Hemptech, 1998
4. Anderson, James. "Industrial Resources of the West", p. 140 in *Monthly Journal of Agriculture* 1847, vol. II.
5. Boyce, pp. 105-106
6. Robinson, Rowan. *The Great Book of Hemp*. Rochester (Vt.), Park Street Press, 1996
7. Rosenthal, Ed. *Hemp Today*. Oakland, The Quick American Archives, 1994. pp. 47-62
8. *Ib.*
9. Mausberger, Herbert R. *Matthews' Textile Fibers*. NY, John Wiley & Sons, 1947
10. Bócsa and Karus

PART FOUR

THE MANY FIELDS OF HEMP

All the world's a stage,
And all the men and women merely players:
They have their exits and their entrances;
And one man in his time plays many parts....

William Shakespeare
As You Like It

XX. Not just for the Birds

KENYON GIBSON.

Silence descended as a man asked a question about a law that was being considered: "The birds will sing just the same?" Outside, the subjects of this discussion, ignorant of what was being debated, frolicked in the bliss of a summer day. The fluttering, the whurring of their wings and their calls to one another could be heard by the passers-by. There were robins, finches, sparrows, bluebirds and meadow larks spending themselves in motion, while doves and flocks of starlings, rustling like silk, played upon the lawns outside of the large imposing buildings, inside of which senators listened to arguments that would effect the fate of their nation's wildlife.

But of these creatures the men in the room took no notice. Even the one who raised the question did not pause to take stock of their activities. This was American Sen. Prentiss M. Brown, and the date was 12 July, 1937. Three months earlier, on 15 April, 1937 many of the same people had assembled for discussion of the law that was at hand that day in July – the Marihuana Tax Act. At the April session, for which there is no record of the aforementioned Brown having attended, Raymond G. Scarlett of the William G. Scarlett Corp. of Baltimore, Maryland, had given the following testimony:

> Mr. Chairman, our company handles a considerable quantity of hemp seed annually for use in pigeon feeds. That is a necessary ingredient in pigeon food because it contains an oil substance that is a valuable ingredient of pigeon feed, and we have not been able to find any seed that will take its place. If you substitute anything for the hemp, it has a tendency to change the character of the squabs produced: and if we were deprived of the use of hempseed, it would affect all of the pigeon producers in the United States, of which there are upwards of 40,000. It has a tendency to bring back the feathers and improve the birds. We are not interested in spreading marihuana, or anything like that.[1]

Hemp is, in fact, so much a part of the diet of birds that one bird is named after it: *Carduelis cannabina*; Hämpling in Swedish; Hämfling in German; the Linnet in English. This bird, to many ornitholigists a familiar sight, is a medium sized finch found in Palearctic regions - Europe, North

Africa and parts of Asia. Formerly abundant, it has been recently declining in numbers. Like so many other finches and seed eating birds, the Linnet knows a good meal when it sees one. It has a brain, perhaps more advanced than that of certain mammals.

This propensity for hemp seed has not gone unnoticed by bird-keepers and ornithologists, and thus copious record of hemp as a source of nutrition for birds is at hand; John Ray recommends it for laying hens in 1690;[2] in the late nineteenth century Sulphur-crested Cockatoos (*Cacatua galerina*) were fed exclusively on this seed while displayed at the Tower of London;[3] miners on the west coast of the US fed their canaries (*Canarius serinus*) hemp so they could sing effectively, for which they were granted special license;[4] in the 1950s one British breeder fed his male Bullfinches (*Pyrrhula pyrrhula*) hemp seed in order to darken their plumage;[5] another British breeder, P. M. Soderberg (1956) recommended hemp for Yellow Buntings (*Emberiza icterica*) and lovebirds (*Agapornis* spp.).[6]

Robert Stroud (the Birdman of Alcatraz) in his famous work, extols hemp seed: "Fresh hemp seed is one of the most valuable bird foods known. Because this seed is rich in the reproductive vitamin, an unlimited supply of it should be kept before hens making eggs."[7] Stroud, writing from his cell, goes along with the very mistaken belief that "the shells of hemp seed are rich in the drug Hashish." As accurate as he is generally, this is an example of error made, due to misinformation he was not in a position to correct, reflecting the misconception that existed in his day.

Currently cannabis for birds is available and widely used. There was a shipment from Canada that was impounded while on route to the US in 1999, but this was an isolated incident, regarded as an exercise in futility and harassment. The seed was destined for legitimate purposes, and would quite possibly have ended up in New York's Central Park, (where birds are fed hemp by local birders), or on the adjacent grounds of the American Museum of Natural History. Londoners also provide hemp for their feathered friends, scattering it from Trafalgar Square to Richmond Park where it attracts a wide range of species.

Giving hemp to birds is of a long-standing practice, especially in the case of pigeons and doves. Pigeon breeders have long known the value of hemp to members of this order, the Columbiformes, both in captivity and in the wild. Julius Caesar's pigeons, used extensively to deliver messages for his troops, may well have been raised on hemp, which Romans at that time ate as a delicacy. Whether the Romans shared this with their 'captives' we do not know, but a US Army officer, Wendell Levi, is on record as to what was fed to the pigeons.

Levi's name is synonymous with pigeon keeping, which vocation he practised in the US Army Signal Corps. He is most recognised for his book *The Pigeon*, in which he is quite specific about hemp. He notes that breeders call it 'pigeon candy,' that it is high in fibre (about 18 percent), and also high in fat, (about 30 percent).[8] The high fat content he deems undesirable for year round feeding, but cites Carr and James (1931) as having a positive reaction to hemp as food all year round: "Hemp seems to be a remarkably well balanced grain and all squabs receiving this grain made good gains both before and after weaning."[9] Levi prefers hemp in the autumn, and notes that this seed not only has a beneficial physical effect, but psychological as well. He recommends feeding in the middle of the day during moulting season, and advises scattering it upon the ground, which is contrary to his advice for all other seeds, noting the "avidity with which the seed is devoured", and that "birds may be seen diligently searching for hours for a possible additional grain. This keeps them in the sun light and active."[10] His notes conclude with the observation: "It is a great assistance in taming birds and in training them for shows, as all fears seem to be set aside when they know that hemp seed is being offered."[11]

Earlier pigeon breeders give similar comments. Moore (1735), whom he cites as the writer of the first English language treatise on the subject, recommends hemp, stating: "hemp-seed are food that pigeons are very fond of."[12] Fulton and Lumley (1895) also advise hemp. "If a bird appear low spirited, nothing will cheer it up more than a little good hemp-seed mixed with some dry raw rice."[13]

Prepared Mocking Bird Food, 35c. per jar.	By mail	60c.
Parrot Food,	15c. per pint.	"	30c.
" Seed,	15c.	"	30c.
Bird Bitters,	25c. per vial.	"	30c.
" Eye Water,	25c. "	"	30c.
Pigeon Food,	20c. per quart.	"	40c.
Mite Exterminator	25c. per box.	"	30c.
Moulting Pepper,	25c. "	"	30c.
Aquarium Cement,	25c. "	"	40c.
Fish Food,	10c. "	"	15c.
Chicken Cholera Pills,	25c. "	"	25c.
Poultry Powder,	25c. "	"	40c.
Nestling Food,	25c. "	"	30c.
Nesting Hair,	10c. "	"	12c.
Orange Color Food	25c. "	"	30c.
Ant Eggs,	15c. per oz.	"	18c.
Phenolated Brassica Oil,	25c. per vial.	"	30c.
Mexican Salve,	25c. per box.	"	30c.
Sunflower Seed, bulk,	15c. per pound.	"	30c.
Unhulled Rice,	15c. "	"	30c.
Hulled Millet Seed, bulk,	15c. "	"	30c.
Yellow " "	10c. "	"	25c.
White " " "	15c. "	"	20c.
Russian Hemp " "	10c. "	"	25c.
Japanese Rape " "	15c. "	"	30c.
Sicily Canary " "	15c. "	"	30c.
Maw Seed, " "	30c. "	"	40c.
Patent Cuttle Bone, with Fastener, large, 10c.	"	15c.
" " " " " small, 8c.	"	10c.

Pricelist
Philadelphia Bird Food
Company, ca. **1920**

Mention of the pigeon tribe in the wild eating hemp is made by James Lane Allen in his 1900 novel *Reign of Law: A Tale of the Kentucky Hemp Fields*. In this account he cites both the Mourning Dove (*Zenaidura macroura*) and the now extinct Passenger Pigeon (*Ectopictes migratorius*), as well as the House Sparrow (*Passer domesticus*), the Crow (*Corvus* spp.), the Blackbird (*Agelius phoeniceus*) and the Quail (*Cornix virginianus*).[14] That such birds should esteem hemp is not surprising, as these and most game birds are known to feed on wild hemp, a fact that causes hunters and birdwatchers to decry the useless eradication programmes.

Other types of birds that frequent hemp are tits (Paridae) and woodpeckers (Picidae). The former is mentioned, ironically, in a German pamphlet of 1943, *Die Lustige Hanffibel*, which states: "The seed, of high value, provides sowing material and is the favoured meal of the titmouse, because when it eats hemp seed, its song is loud and full of love." The Syrian Woodpecker (*Picoides* [major] *syriacus*) is cited by Dr. Lester Short as one whose diet includes hemp: P. Sorauer notes the Lesser Spotted Woodpecker (*Dendrocopos minor*) along with the Magpie (*Pica pica*).

There is also record of use of hemp as avian medicine. Many falconers in fact give it to their raptors in times of sickness, a practice that has long-standing precedent, dating back to the sixteenth century writings of Raja Rudradeva of Kumaon; other falconers have also advocated this, including the Anglo-Indian practitioners Lt. Col. D.C. Phillott and Major E.L.S. Ewing.[15] The falconry community has not only an interest in hemp as a part of holistic raptor medicine, but in a much wider sense as a factor in the environment as it is such a food for gamebirds. In 1971 James Vance wrote an article for *Outdoor Life* titled "Marijuana is for the Birds", in which he demonstrated how the loss of hemp, due in part to government

Thrushes: Feed them with raw meat and some bread chopped together with bruised hemp seed. Bread and hemp seed is as good food for them as can be given.

Wood-lark: Bread, egg, and hempseed, which will cause them him to thrive extraordinary upon the first taking of your wood-Lark, thus you must do, you must put into your cages two pans, one for minced meat, and another for oatmeal and whole hemp-seed. Then having boiled an egg hard, take the crumb of white bread, the like quantity of hemp-seed pounded in a mortar, and mingle your bread and it with your egg minced very small, and give it him.

Sky-Lark: When they feed alone, give them bread, hempseed, and oatmeal. Let the bread be mingled with egg, and the hemp-seed bruised.

Gold-Finch, or Christmas-Fool, so called in Norfolk. You must take the young ones with the nest at ten days old, and feed them after this manner; take some of the best hempseed, pound it, and mix it with the like quantity of white bread, with some flower of canary-seed, and taking up the quantity of a white pea upon a small sheet, feed them there with three or four bits at a time, making fresh every day.

Nicholas Cox, 1674

eradication programmes, had led to a depletion of the gamebird population in some parts of the US.

Yet another use of hemp is recorded by Walter Scheithauer in his book *Colibris*, who records hummingbirds employing hemp as nesting material. He records a Sylph, an Inca and a Rufous-tailed Hummingbird using it this way.

Birds are not the only creatures that Sen. Brown needed to be concerned about. Fish also have a liking for hemp, of which Marcandier (1758) noted: "fishes love this plant and fly to it."[16] Anglers corroborate this, such as E. Marshall-Harding who stated in *Angling Ways* that "...the general opinion seems to be overwhelmingly in favour of the use of hemp by fishermen of the Thames and many other waters."[17] Thirty years later, angler Ted Lamb epitomised their love of cannabis by writing "if any bait possesses the 'magic' qualities of being able to draw fish from afar and bring them avidly on the feed it is hemp seed."[18] Sen. Brown had started to ask about the ecological ramifications of tampering with a useful plant species, but there was no-one there with enough sense to protect America and its wildlife from such tampering by the agents of special interest groups, among whom was Harry J. Anslinger, who replied: "There is some question about that."[19] Thank you very much Mr. Anslinger, there certainly is.

1. Herer, Jack. *The Emperor Wears no Clothes.* Van Nuys, CA, AH HA Pub., 1998 [11th ed.]. p. 190
2. Guenet, François, *Chanvre.* N.d., n.p.
3. Bennett, Edward Turner. *The Tower Menagerie.* London, Chiswick Press, 1829
4. Hegaard, Mina. *Showtime Magazine,* October 1998. p. 53
5. Keeling, Clinton. Personal Communication.
6. Soderberg, P.M. *Foreign Birds for Cage and Aviary.* London, Cassell & Co., 1956. p. 13
7. Stroud, Robert. *Stroud's Digest on the Diseases of Birds.* Neptune, (N.J.), T.F.H. Publications, 1964 [rep.ed.] pp. 205-206
8. Levi, Wendell. *The Pigeon.* Columbia, (S.C.), R.L. Bryan Co., 1941. p. 334
9. *Ib.*
10. *Ib.*
11. *Ib.*
12. *Ib.*
13. *Ib.*
14. Allen, James Lane. *The Reign of Law: A Tale of the Kentucky Hemp Fields.* NY, Macmillan, 1900. pp. 13-14
15. Gibson, Kenyon (ed.). *One Thousand Years of Falconry.* London, The Eryr Press, 2004
16. Marcandier, M. *Traité du Chanvre.* Paris, 1758
17. Marshall-Harding, E. *Angling Days.* London, Herbert Jenkins, 1948. [2nd ed.] p. 79
18. Lamb, Ted. *The Bait Book.* Newton Abbott, David & Charles, 1979. p. 61
19. Herer

XXI. The Economics of Hemp

KENYON GIBSON

*W*all Street in lower Manhattan is one of the world's busiest locations. The course of history is to a good degree determined by the decisions made in the offices and trading floors of this city-within-a-city. Millions of daily transactions are noted and reported on with great energy, as they serve as a pulse of the world's financial state. What exists today is a function of an earlier Wall Street, where much the same energy prevailed, and a newly born nation traded stocks on paper, or at times, made deals on a handshake, a man's word being then valued at more than it is today. The sun's rays shined a brighter light on this bustling stage, unobscured by the skyscrapers that now so darken the few smaller buildings that remain from a bygone era. Wider streets were also a feature then, as actual commodities were exchanged and transported to the docks in the same area in which they were bought.

Some commodities were more pivotal in their role than others, and a young nation, facing the demands of defence and expansion, took heed to maintain a constant supply of the more essential. One early American made note of his nation's needs, advising: "Hemp is of first necessity to the wealth and the protection of the country."[1] This was Thomas Jefferson, who was involved firsthand in this industry, and had invented a machine for processing hemp, which was to be the nation's first patent.

Much hemp was then grown in the US, but much was imported as well, mainly from Russia, arriving in Boston, New York and Charleston by the shipload. The trade in this article certainly did not start on Wall Street; it began trading many thousands of years before in the Orient, where it was used extensively. Hemp may in fact have been used in the acquisition of Wall Street; historical record shows that the Dutch traded hemp cloth for Manhattan.[2] Thread, paper, oil, and other products came from this crop, an easily cultivated annual that could be harvested in three months from planting. Its strength and versatility made it useful to every nation, and it was prized wherever it went. The Greeks and Romans sailed their ships by hemp, as did all maritime powers until the twentieth century. The Italians refined the fibres to produce fine cloth, an export of considerable value. Europe recognised other uses, such as oils for painting, nuts for food, and fibres for papermaking; banknotes and stock certificates

217

were for centuries made of hemp. From the eighteenth to the twentieth century the country that produced the most hemp was Russia, known as the 'grand mart'[3] for this staple. At that time it was the world's most traded commodity;[4] every nation in Europe grew hemp, but not always enough to furnish navies and clothe their people. Many turned to Russia for their supplies, going to great lengths to acquire it.

The two biggest customers for Russian hemp were Britain and the US; in 1803 the former obtained 1,313,912 lbs., the latter 315,432 lbs.[5] Napoleon, not content to see such a valuable commodity unloading on the docks of Belfast and London, used his clout to prohibit the Russian sale of hemp to the British; little as this policy served the Russian interests, it was not easy to enforce. France took military action against the Americans[6] for helping the British obtain hemp, and Napoleon sent his armies into Russia, partly in retaliation for their double dealing. As war time prices of hemp and related fibres surged, there was added temptation to engage in this business. From 1807 to 1808 the price rose from £53 per ton to £118 per ton.[6] Such fluctuations were still to be found in the twentieth century as the following table shows.

Price of Hemp and Related Fibres From: *Cordage and Cordage Hemp*, by J. Woodhouse and P. Kilgor, 1919			
Type of Fibre	**1915** £	**1916** £	**1918** £
P.C. Italian Hemp	55	90	190
F.S.P.R.H. Russian Hemp			170
China Hemp			154
Manila (Fair)	37	53	100
New Zealand Hemp	32	86	99
Mexican Sisal	28	77	97
Java Sisal		95-100	99
Mauritius		70	95
Maguey	30	70	74

Hemp has always proved itself to be easy to cultivate profitably, it was lucrative not only in war but in peace as well. A sampling of opinion from different years shows this to be the case:

In hemp countries, when the season is favourable, they have immense returns; insomuch, that the profit arising from 5 or 6 acres is found sufficient to feed a family. - McDonald, 1784

In Russia, Prussia and Poland, it is generally understood that flax and hemp render more profitable crops than any other sort of grain. - Abbé Brulles, 1790
After deducting all expenses of land and rent, here is a clear profit exceeding the whole of an acre of the best wheat. - W. Tonge, ca. 1795

The value of hemp for fibre, birdseed and oil would seem to make its cultivation a very profitable one. - Gilbert Hicks, 1895

These records do not take into account the discoveries in the early part of the twentieth century in regards to employing the hurd (the unused centres of the stalk) for cellulose. Occasionally, these were put to some use, such as charcoal, or as fuel, as one 1808 record notes: "The offal is called Hemp-sheaves, which is good fuel, and sells at two-pence per stone."[7]

This, however, is but a poor example of the use to which hemp hurds, long regarded as waste, could be put; business, science and government were much in agreement over this realisation, and as researchers developed ways to use hurds, which account for around 75 percent of the weight of the stem, many businessmen started to invest in what *Popular Mechanics* dubbed the 'New Billion Dollar Crop' in 1938. The Massilon Co, Amhempco, Atlas Hemp Mills, the Central Fiber Corp, Hemlax Fiber & Co. and Cannabis Inc. were but a few of the many businesses putting money into this 'Billion Dollar Crop'. Lawmakers also took note, and a bill was passed to promote the study of 'new markets and new uses for the abundant crops.'[8] Not everyone, however, was welcoming this act, and private interest groups in Washington had the bill stricken from the record; President Calvin Coolidge, however, took an interest in the proceedings, and had it reinstated,[9] seeing the economic need for this research.

One cannot fail to notice some discrepancy in all this, especially as the 1930s were a time of great financial hardship. The financial interests of the US population weighed in balance against the financial interests of a few businesses and wealthy individuals, and the latter won. This came at a time when Nazi infiltrators were in the US working hard to promote munitions, as they believed that the US would come into the war on their side. War, as profitable as it is, has been known to increase profits by as much as 600 percent for some companies; the temptation to instigate a war therefore is tremendous. This love of money, the root of all evil, gives rise to terrorism and fear. Hearst falsely claimed terrorism as the reason for the explosion on the USS *Maine* in 1898 so he could instigate a war, and, going quite a bit further, it is now known that in 1961 several top Republicans in the US planned to stage terror attacks in the US so as to bring the public to a state of fear and demand a war. The plan, known as Operation Northwoods, included phony hijackings to be made to look like the work of 'terrorists', and went so far as to use real Cubans to kill Americans in order to have a scapegoat. Cleverly thought out, it included attacking the Commonwealth so as to drag the UK into the war.[10] President John F. Kennedy opposed this; he was not long afterwards assassinated. Less than a year later the Vietnam War was started when President Lyndon B. Johnson misled the world in order to sanction a war which greatly benefited Brown & Root, a Texas firm which has since merged with Halliburton. That war, which many US soldiers claimed could have been easily won, lasted ten years, and may well have been artificially prolonged as was WWII when certain parties held back oil from the troops. The influence of warmongers all along has done much harm to the American working class, who, as a group, were meant to be used in the promotion of war, but not accorded any share in the profits.

Among those who *did* share in the spoils of war was Andrew Mellon, who not only financed General Motors, but was Secretary of the Treasury from 1921-1932, a position he used to further his own interests. Harry J. Anslinger, his nephew-in-law, was appointed head of a bureau that answered only to Mellon.

Hemp Imported From Russia into the United Kingdom
From: *A Treatise on the Culture of Flax and hemp*, by Francis Campbell, 1845

	Tons of Hemp	Acres	Average Cost
1825	21,829	87,316	£545,725
1826	17,900	71,600	448,500
1827	28,670	114,680	706,750
1828	25,214	100,856	630,350
1829	18,746	74,984	468,450
1830	25,250	101,000	631,250
1831	27,000	108,000	675,000
1832	29,700	138,800	737,500
1833	26,326	105,304	658,150
1834	35,029	140,116	875,725
1835	34,332	137,328	758,300
1836	29,301	117,204	731,525
1837	38,610	154,440	965,250
1838	36,473	145,892	911,825
1839	49,778	199,112	1,284,450
1840	34,218	136,872	855,450

Anslinger took a great interest in hemp, and, being made aware of its potential as a source of cellulose for fibres, chemicals and paper pulp, worked to create a tax law that would be prohibitive of hemp. Once accomplished, hemp farmers and businesses were shut down. Chemical and fossil-based fuel businesses got larger, and the prescient efforts of the Ford Motor Co. to run cars on ethanol were abandoned.

One aspect of this is that hemp was not developed as a biomass fuel, nor was diesel; both are eco-friendly alternatives to oil, and as such, were in competition with Mellon and his associates. The economy of a nation can be put to great risk by dependency on a single product, especially when imported; a rise in the price of a barrel of oil leads to inflation, rising interest rates, and falling markets; unemployment, lending scarcity and repossessions accompany this progression, although on the other side of it there are parties who gain enormously. Thus the price of energy can be the key to either prosperity or chaos. Like a lever, it can be manipulated to suit the needs of a secondary market, the derivatives. An inside control over the price of oil can create price fluctuations made to give options traders a behind-the-scenes gain. The US public has been made painfully aware of this as the investigation into Enron's trading in energy futures progresses. On a global level, such actions could throw the world into chaos.

America's reliance on foreign oil has grown in two ways: first, in the percentage of oil imported, which is currently around 60 percent, up from 40 percent in 1980. Second, in the amount of ways that oil is used - heating, transportation, energy, plastics, chemicals and more. The possibilities of disaster become evident to anyone with a brain. While this goes on, many in the mainstream press ignore it; even still, all of the public is not fooled all of the time. In 2000 concerns over this state of affairs were expressed by Samuel Heslop, who in his Oxford Brookes thesis wrote that military and financial tensions in the Middle East are a byproduct of not developing natural energy supplies. His writing was then a bit like the facts spoken by the boy in the tale of the naked emperor, only in this day and age certain parties in business, government and the media drown out the truth and the emperor runs around with a silly grin. Perhaps that story today would end with the boy getting arrested for subversion as the emperor's friends and advisors saw their illegal profits threatened.

> Hemp is growing in certain countries, and the market is expanding dramatically.
> **Daniel O'Reilly, 2002**

Hemp can not only clothe an emperor, it can provide economic opportunity for the people. As a renewable energy source it can make a difference in the way a nation does business. It may not, as some claim, solve all of a nation's energy needs, but it will reduce an unhealthy dependency. This sobering realisation is part of the hemp industry's *raison d'être*. Current studies have shown that cars not only do well on alcohol based fuels, but could run for a lot less money. Estimates place the cost of ethanol at $1 per gallon (12p/lt.), which would not only be a direct savings to drivers, but would reduce inflation by easing transport and raw material costs. A plethora of other products are made from hemp, and world-wide many businesses have been recently created which deal in hemp. Most notable of all such entrepreneurs is Anita Roddick, who has boldly displayed the cannabis leaf at The Body Shop. This company, which started on an original investment of £4,000 in 1976, has now grown to a world-wide franchise operation with a market capitalisation of £376,000,000; arguably, 'one of the best investments ever made.'[12] In 1998 their hemp-based products reached sales of $40,000,000 in the US alone. While this is certainly a lucrative market, Roddick does not only see hemp as a financial gain to her shareholders, but has a global vision in which local communities share in the wealth, reduce pollution, and are able to employ their residents. 'Trade not aid' is her philosophy, combining common sense and business in a long-term strategy.

> The US leads the world in the number of hemp clothing outlets. However, much of the apparel for sale is still made outside the US. Made in the USA can be seen on few brands, most notably Minawear, Swirlspace and Satori, all of California.
> **Yves de Saussure, 2006**

Other companies which are devoted to hemp and share similar goals are Minawear in California and Ecofibres in Australia. Minawear started in 1999 with a few items of clothing, and has steadily grown to the point of issuing catalogues. Public acceptance of hemp has grown considerably in that time frame, and Minawear has been able to reach a clientele all over the US as well as some amount of overseas trade. Phil Warner of Ecofibres is quite clear on his country's needs in the realm of finance and agriculture; coming from a background of both, he has set Ecofibres on a course of steady growth for the future. Warner sees a degradation of regional Australia, with a lessening of services, dismantled infrastructure adding burdens to cities, the urbanisation of surrounding

the hemp shop

Logo of the UK's oldest and largest dedicated hemp retail outlet, founded by Bobby Pugh, whose initiative has been the cornerstone of many hemp projects, including Mother Hemp and Hempiness.

agriculture, and the increased distance in transport weakening the economy as a whole. Growing hemp would counteract this, as a commodity that creates local employment in processing, reducing the pressure on government handouts. This vision is not just national, but worldwide, as Warner points out; there will be an increase in fibre use as population expands. Competition for agricultural land will fall to food and fibre, the two most common applications, and any crop that can produce both will be the more necessary, giving it an edge over single use crops.[13] His insight is all the more apt as hemp's use for fuel and paper as fossil fuels are running out and timber already needs replenishing.

Farmers in Australia and many other countries are able to get in on this just as consumer awareness is growing. However, US farmers are restricted from what some consider their birthright. In Pennsylvania, Mrs. Jane Bolmer, a widowed mother who farms on four-hundred acres of land in Lancaster County, has witnessed dramatic losses from tobacco. "Most of us are selling tobacco at a loss," she notes. "Twenty years back we had 30,000 acres of tobacco; this year we will see 12,000." Speaking of hemp, she has more a hopeful tone: "It would fit right in as a replacement for tobacco."[14]

Her concerns, and those of farmers nationwide, have not yet been met in the US, though Canada has recently legalised hemp, where farmers have been harvesting since 1998. There have been some start up hitches, such as the unusual act of impounding Canadian birdseed coming into the US, and the business failure of Consolidated Growers and Processors.

This firm, formerly listed as CGPR on the NASD-BB, started out with a huge amount of self-publicity. Registered in Delaware, it issued fifteen million shares, which traded briefly as high as $3, but with little volume. Some of their ideas were not in harmony with the hemp movement, such as their willingness to genetically modify hemp seeds.[15] Their demise was seen by many as due to inexperience and bad practices; farmers who dealt with CGPR were left with unsold hemp.[16]

Most businesses dealing with hemp are small; Ecofibres and The Body Shop are leaders in what is still an emerging industry. Some of these will undoubtedly join the ranks of Ecofibres and The Body Shop, some will be local successes, and some, like CGPR, will cease to exist.

The worldwide market is emerging, and in some areas the figures are skyrocketing; *U.S. News & World Report* describes growth as "Booming. . . sales rose from less than $3 million in 1993 to $75 million in 1997." Companies such as Mercedes and BMW are using hemp fibres in their cars and trucks; food companies and grocery retailers are including lines with hemp, such as Sainsbury's (UK); many beers are brewed with hemp, which, incidentally, is 'cousin' to hops. In New York City, Denis Cicero stocks hemp food items in his restaurant, Galaxy Global Eatery, which has weathered not only present economic crisis, but the threat of hemp foods being made illegal, against which he has spent large sums of his own money on fighting in the courts along with John Roulac of Nutiva. Cicero's restaurant has grown to serve internet custom as well as the established walk-in business,with a range of items including a successful cookbook.

However, everyone does not benefit unless legislation is enacted to legalise hemp in countries where it is prohibited. For the US, this would be an economic loss and a bitter irony; it has recognised the economic value of hemp perhaps more than any other country, as Thomas Jefferson wrote in 1776: "The great value of this industry is evident."[19] Writing in 1900, Samuel Boyce observed:

> The hemp industry is the last of the great sources of the employment of capital and labor to feel the revivifying influences of more modern inventions; but the writer is confident in the belief that the same labor which has been given to other agricultural products and textile manufactures will place hemp at the head.[15]

Jack Herer almost a century later asserted: "Experts today conservatively estimate that, once fully restored in America, hemp industries will generate $500m- $1b per year."[16]

These three Americans pay homage to a principle that Adam Smith had laid down in *Wealth of Nations:* that the real wealth of a nation lay in its agriculture. Dr. Francis Campbell in 1845 quoted economist Don Jos Volcarel as follows: "It must be acknowledged that England has opened the eyes of other nations. These islanders have discovered at last, after many schemes, that it is agriculture alone which forms the source and origin of their greatness."[17]

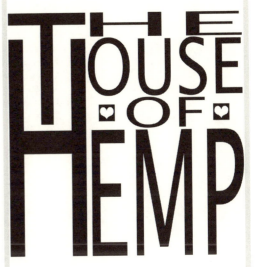

This attitude toward the soil as the basis of the economy may seem an outdated way of thinking; however, it is yet more pertinent today, as both pollution and over-population make farmland that much more of a precious asset. Nations are increasingly under pressure to minimise pollution, as its destructive efforts are felt; they cannot afford to continue to poison the soil with pesticides or burn petrochemicals.

The *Wall Street Journal* took note of the growing hemp movement and its ecological philosophy, featuring Herer on its cover in May 1991, which brought the movement to the attention of the mainstream public. In this article, Chris Conrad, founder of the Business Alliance for Commerce in Hemp (BACH), described how tactics changed at one point: "We realized that smoking pot (while) dressed in tie-dyes in front of the White House wasn't getting us anywhere."[18] The article also cited use of hemp by Kimberly-Clark, cancer specialists advocating THC, and hemp's "many commercial possibilities." At the turn of the twentieth century, one American businessman published his own treatise in support of hemp, in which he had asserted: "Carried on intelligently, hemp culture is one of the most productive industries known."[19]

John Hanson, a British paper maker, echoes these sentiments: "The economics of hemp are both exciting and contemporary. None more so than today, now that global warming is at last recognised by governments."[20] He is certainly not alone, as George Soros has placed money in hemp - his bet is on pharmaceutical cannabis, useful for treating a wide number of ailments. Recently GW Pharmaceuticals (UK) has been listed on the AIM, with a capitalisation of £175m. Successful clinical research trials since then have made this company a rising star in a world of falling share prices.

Should hemp succeed, it is not only good news to those investing in Ecofibres, The Body Shop, Minawear or GW Pharmaceuticals, but to the whole planet as well. Such dividends constitute real wealth, achieving a harmony of ecology and economy that is long overdue.

As we go forward into the new century, will we develop strong local and national economies, or will we allow certain forces to continue to steal our money? That answer is up to all of us to sort out. As for the emperor, he must get hold of the economy or his subjects will sell him down the river.

1. de Saussure, Yves. *Cannabis for Health, Energy, Medicine, Paper and 25,000 Other Uses.* London, The Eryr Press, 2002. p. 6
2. Walton, Frank L. *From Tomahawks to Textiles.* NY, Appleton-Century, 1953
3. Wissett, Robert. *A Treatise on Hemp.* London, J. Harding, 1808. p. 28
4. Rosenthal, Ed. *Hemp Today.* p. 155
5. Horner, John. *The Linen Trade of Europe.* Belfast, McCaw, Stevenson & Orr, 1920. pp. 506-507
6. Crosby, Alfred W. Jr. *America, Hemp, Russia and Napoleon.* Columbus, Ohio University Press, 1965
7. Wissett
8. Lupien, John C. *Unravelling an American Dilemma: The Demonization of Marihuana.* Malibu, Pepperdine University thesis, 1995
9. *Ib.*
10. Operation Northwoods is the plan that GOP members drew up in the 1960s; it was intended to make war by false terror, much like the Reichstag Fire, which was proven to be an act committed by the Gestapo. It was very involved, resembling in many details 9/11. For well researched reading on Operation Northwoods, the recent book by Ian Henshall and Rowland Morgan, titled *9.11 Revealed: Challenging the Facts Behind the War on Terror* (ISBN 1-84529-140-9) will also contain information on this form of rogue government activity. Websites on this subject are legion, see: *www.nineeleven.co.uk www.911research.vote7.net www.st911.org www.rense.com www.911review.com www.questionsquestions.net www.fromthewilderness.com www.physics911.net www.bilderberg.org*
11. Slingsby, Helen. *The Times*
12. Cheavens, Suzanne and Martin Zonoria. *MF Magazine,* p. 35
13. Warner, Phil. *Personal Communication.*
14. Macklin, William R. *The News-Times.* 29 April, 1999
15. Boyce, Samuel. *Hemp.* NY, Orange Judd Co., 1900. p. 52
16. Herer, Jack. *The Emperor Wears no Clothes.* Van Nuys, (CA), AH HA Publ., 1998. [11th ed.] p. 17
17. Don Jos Volcarel, quoted by Campbell.
18. *Wall Street Journal,* May 1991. pp. 16-17
19. Boyce
20. Marcandier, M. *A Treatise on Hemp.* Lyme Regis, John Hanson, 1996. p. 90

XXII. Cellulose

KENYON GIBSON

$\mathcal{P}$aper; clothing; cellophane; ethanol; these can all be made from one substance, cellulose. This is one of nature's most common and most useful compounds. It is the "...predominating constituent of plant tissues...the structural basis of the vegetable world."[1]

The formula for cellulose is given as $C_nH_{2m}O_m$; there is no one 'empirical' formula. From this it is seen that cellulose is somewhat basic; for the initial conversion to sugars, one cellulose molecule need only lose two hydrogen atoms and one oxygen atom. Water, thus removed by dehydration leaves sugar, which in turn can be reduced to alcohol. It was this simple set of equations to which Ford Motors paid attention in the 1930s, making alcohol based fuels at their Michigan facilities.

An element not found in cellulose, sugar, or alcohol is sulphur. This is noteworthy, as without sulphur, which is found in fossil based fuels, there are no sulphur based compounds to be formed on combustion: hence, no acid rain. Sadly, alcohol fuels were put on the back burner so corporations with an interest in oil could sell their way of life to the world. Other cellulose applications continued to be in great demand, most notably wood pulp. As hemp bast fibre is 75-80 percent cellulose (the cellulose content increases with age), hemp was used a great deal over the years. The hurds, which also contain cellulose, could well be used to make paper; this was successfully demonstrated in the early twentieth century, before some folks decided they might as well not be used to make paper, or, for that matter, anything. Instead, trees were cut down for their cellulose, which required greater processing, as wood contained greater amounts of lignin that had to be washed out with sulphur based chemicals, then bleached with chlorine based chemicals. There are some differences between tree cellulose and hemp cellulose, such as size - hemp fibres are longer, an obvious advantage.

Not only does cellulose break down into simpler compounds, but it can also be merged into more complex ones, such as nitro-cellulose. A host of other compounds derived from cellulose are produced everyday, such as ethyl cellulose for plastics and coatings; cellulose acetate for film products; cellulose acetate butyrate for coatings; cellulose propionate for plastics, and carboxymethylcellulose for detergents.

COTTON PLANT (Gossypium).

In the manufacture of clear cellulose film, wood chips (about 50 percent cellulose) are pulped, mixed into a vat with caustic soda, pressed into sheets, shredded, and then churned in a tank with carbon disulphide and caustic soda. This mix is further passed on to be blended, homogenised, filtered, ripened and de-aerated before passing through an acid bath, a wash, a de-sulphurant, bleach, further washing, and plasticising agents. This, and many other cellulose based products, including synthetic textiles, could be made with hemp hurds or fibres. Why do some companies want to chop down trees?

It would be impossible to avoid contact with cellulose on this planet; most animals in fact digest cellulose (a carbohydrate) in their diets, a fact which at least one scientist was keen to exploit. With a certain tablet, Dr. A.M. Chakrabarty envisioned people "eating hay like cows." Jeremy Rifkin noted in his book *Who Should Play God?* a bizarre twist to this experiment; the intent to test it out on welfare recipients.[2]

Hopefully this will not be; cellulose is a very diverse and useful compound, and used sensibly, can be part of an ecologically balanced lifestyle. While hemp is not the only source of cellulose, it does have advantages over other sources; it takes four times as much land to produce a ton of paper from trees as it does from hemp, according to a US government study.[3] While cotton fibre has a higher percentage (91 percent) of cellulose than hemp fibre, hemp's yield per acre is greater than cotton's; hemp fibre alone, which is roughly one-quarter of the stem, will yield as a general rule 100 lbs/ac (111 kg/ha), per foot; thus a 12 foot stalk gives 1,200 lbs/ac (1,321 kg/ha). Of that, 77 percent or more will be cellulose; thus, 924 lbs/ac (1,017 kg/ha) while roughly three times that weight will be hurds, which are 35 percent cellulose, yielding yet another 1,260 lbs/ac (1,375 kg/ha), thus a total of 2,184 lbs/ac (2,392 kg/ha). Cotton produces up to 1,000 lbs/ac (1,100 kg/ha); 91 percent of this being cellulose, the yield is 910 lbs/ac (1001 kg/ha). In addition:

a) Cotton requires from six - seven months to mature
b) Other parts of the cotton plant are of little or no use
c) Cotton has many pathogens, requiring a substantial use of pesticides
d) Cotton can only be grown in warm weather
e) Cotton is a more intensive crop

While these facts about cellulose are obvious to any scientist, they do not always follow the best path, especially if having so readily available a source of cellulose conflicts with using other sources that involve patent fees and pesticide sales. Common sense is at times overruled, especially in the case of what has been described as the 'chemical that grows.'[4] Ironically, money is also made of cellulose, and, while it does not grow on trees, it is often made from trees, without which we cannot live.

1. Cross, C.F. Bovan and C. Beadle.*Cellulose.* London, Longman Geon & Co., 1903 [2nd ed.] p. 1
2. *Wall Street Journal*, 30 Nov. 1999
3. Herer, Jack. *The Emperor Wears no Clothes.* Van Nuys, CA. AH HA Pub., 1998 [11th ed.] p. 26
4. Haynes, William. *Cellulose: the Chemical that Grows.* NY, Doubleday, 1953

XXIII. Art and Literature

KENYON GIBSON

While much has been written about hemp on a purely scientific or economic basis, there is also a place for it in the realm of art and culture; no substance could play such a pivotal role in business and be such a part of the environment without making its mark artistically. Aesop in 550 BC writes an amusing tale of birds as follows:

> It happened that a countryman was sowing some hemp seed in a field where a swallow and some other birds were hopping about picking up their food. 'Beware of that man', quoted the swallow, 'Why, what is he doing?' said the others, 'That is hemp seed he is sowing; be careful to pick up every one of the seeds, or else you will repent it.' The birds paid no heed to the Swallow's words, and by and by the hemp grew up and was made into cord, and of the cords, nets were made, and many a bird that had despised the Swallow's advice was caught in nets made of that very hemp. 'What did I tell you?' said the swallow.

In England, Shakespeare makes the following mention:

> What hempen home spuns have we swaggering here,
> So near the cradle of the fairy queen?
> *A Mid-Summer Night's Dream*

John Fletcher and Samuel Butler also allude to hemp, in a macabre way:

> Three merry boys, and three merry boys,
> And three merry boys we are,
> As ever did sing in a hempen string
> Under the gallows tree
> *The Bloody Brothers*

> When less delinquents have been scourg'd
> And hemp on wooden anvils forged
> Which others for cravats have worn
> About their necks and took a turn
> *Hudibras*

227

This last scene, written in the mid-nineteenth century, may have been inspired by the Hogarth engraving of the eighteenth century, pictured below, in which a convict is set to the task of beating hemp.

While these four Englishmen have placed hemp in a common or vulgar place, many other cultures have clothed their priests and kings in hemp. On the continent, the hemp-leaf motif is used in architectural ornament, including ecclesiastical structures. The nineteenth century Polish poet, Adam Mickiewicz, makes frequent mention of hemp:

> Within this crop, so fragrant, green and dense,
> Both man and beast may find a sure defence.
> Surprised among the cabbages the hare
> Leaps in the hemp to find a refuge there.
> The stubborn stalks the greyhound's course prevent,
> The odour puts the foxhound off the scent.
>
> In fight and foray and in confiscation
> Each party struggles hard for occupation
> Of these hemp fields which, since they oft extend
> Up to the manor, while their further end
> Down to the hop-field's boundary runs back,

Give cover for retreat and for attack.
The very odour that the hemp exhaled
Recalled adventures as apparitor,
To which at times the hemp fields witness bore:
Until he fled into the hemp plantation;

Protazy feigned obedience, slowly crept
Towards the window and the hemp-and leapt.

Protazy listens-not a sound-and walks,
Thrusting a cautious hand between the stalks
Of hemp, and as he parts the greenery
Swims like a fisherman beneath the sea.[1]
                                        Pan Tadeusz

In 1900 James Lane Allen writes wistfully of a hemp field in *Reign of Law:
A Tale of the Kentucky Hemp Fields,* in which he writes prosaically of what
was so ubiquitous in that state:

> Some morning when the roar of March winds is no more heard in the
> tossing woods, but along still brown boughs a faint, veil-like greenness runs;
> when every spring, welling out of the soaked earth, trickles through banks
> of sod unbarred by ice; before a bee is abroad under the calling sky; before
> the red of apple-buds becomes a sign in the low orchards, or the high song
> of the thrush is pouring forth far away at wet pale-green sunsets, the earliest
> sower of the hemp, goes forth into the fields.

> What is that uncertain flush low on the ground, that irresistable rush of
> multitudinous green? A fortnight, and the field is brown no longer.
> Overflowing it, burying it out of sight, is the shallow tidal sea of the hemp,
> ever rippling. Green are the woods now with their varied greenness. Green
> are the pastures. Green here and there are the fields; with the bluish green of
> young oats and wheat; with the gray green of young barley and rye; with
> orderly dots of dull dark green in vast array - the hills of Indian maize. But as
> the eye sweeps the whole landscape undulating far and near, from the hues
> of tree, pasture, and corn of every kind, it turns to the color of hemp. With
> that in view, all other shades in nature seem dead and count for nothing.

Sadly, hemp was shortly thereafter vilified, relegating a beautiful, useful plant
to a status lower than that of the convicts whose necks it once encircled.
A recent poem by Art Rey takes a much more upbeat tone:

With roots that reached beyond the depths
of soil, rock and clay
In time of war and peace and death,
a substance here to stay
But some would rather put it down-
sad fools who love a lie